POLLUTION CONTROL AND CONSERVATION

Ellis Horwood books in
Water and Wastewater Treatment

This collection of authoritative works reflects the world awareness of the importance of water, wastewater treatment, and closely-related subjects, to the world. The titles are written and edited by experts from a wide range of countries closely concerned with research and development, monitoring and improving water quality and supplies, and treatment and disposal of wastewater.

Titles published in collaboration with the
Water Research Centre, UK

SEWAGE SLUDGE STABILISATION AND DISINFECTION
Editor: A. M. BRUCE, Water Research Centre
**STABILISATION, DISINFECTION AND ODOUR CONTROL
IN SEWAGE SLUDGE TREATMENT**
Editors: A. M. BRUCE and E. S. CONNOR, Water Research Centre
BULKING OF ACTIVATED SLUDGE
Editors: B. CHAMBERS and E. J. TOMLINSON, Water Research Centre
BIOLOGICAL FLUIDISED BED TREATMENT OF WATER AND WASTEWATER
Editors: P. F. COOPER, Water Research Centre, and B. ATKINSON, University
of Manchester Institute of Science and Technology
**HANDBOOK OF BIOLOGICAL SURVEILLANCE METHODS
FOR MANAGEMENT OF FRESH WATERS**
J. M. HELLAWELL, Severn-Trent Water Authority
WATER RESEARCH TOPICS
Editor: I. M. LAMONT, Water Research Centre
**DESIGN AND OPERATION OF SMALL WATER POLLUTION
CONTROL PLANTS**
E. H. NICOLL, Scottish Development Department, Edinburgh
EFFECTS OF LAND USE ON FRESH WATERS
Editor: J. SOLBE, Water Research Centre
AQUALINE THESAURUS
Editors: G. SMITH, P. J. RUSSELL
RIVER POLLUTION CONTROL
Editor: M. J. STIFF, Water Research Centre

Other books in Water and Wastewater

FISH DISEASES: BACTERIA AS FISH PATHOGENS
B. AUSTIN, Heriot-Watt University, and D. AUSTIN, Fresh Water Biological
Association, East Stoke, Dorset
SOLID-LIQUID SEPARATION
Editor: J. GREGORY, University College, London
POLLUTION CONTROL AND CONSERVATION
Editor: M. KOVACS, Hungarian Academy of Sciences
NATURAL WATER SAMPLING
J. KRAJCA et al.
CHEMICAL PROCESSES IN WASTE WATER TREATMENT
G. MATTOCK, Process Plant and Chemical Ltd, Slough, and W. J. EILBECK,
University College of N. Wales
GROUND WATER PROTECTION
V. PELIKAN, Research Institute of Geological Engineering, Brno, Czechoslovakia
IMPROVING WATER QUALITY
M. RAPINAT, Compagnie Generale des Eaux, France
BIOTECHNOLOGY OF WASTE TREATMENT AND EXPLOITATION
J. M. SIDWICK and R. S. HOLDOM, Watson Hawksley, Buckinghamshire

POLLUTION CONTROL AND CONSERVATION

Editor:

Dr. M. KOVÁCS

Agricultural University, Department of Botany
and Plant Physiology
Gödöllő, Hungary

Translation Editor:
T. WALDMEYER, B.Sc., C.Chem., F.R.S.C., F.I.P.H.E.
formerly Chemical Inspector, Department of the Environment
London, England

ELLIS HORWOOD LIMITED
Publishers · Chichester

Halsted Press: a division of
JOHN WILEY & SONS
New York · Brisbane · Chichester · Toronto

First published in 1985 by
ELLIS HORWOOD LIMITED
Market Cross House, Cooper Street, Chichester, West Sussex, PO19 1 EB, England
and AKADÉMIAI KIADÓ, Budapest

*The publisher's colophon is reproduced from James Gillison's drawing of the ancient
Market Cross, Chichester.*

Distributors:

Australia, New-Zealand, South-east Asia:
Jacaranda-Wiley, Ltd., Jacaranda Press,
JOHN WILEY& SONS INC.,
G.P.O. Box 859, Brisbane, Queensland 4001, Australia

Canada:
JOHN WILEY& SONS LIMITED
22 Worcester Road, Rexdale, Ontario, Canada.

East Europen countries, China, Vietnam, Korean People's Republic, Cuba and Mongolia:
AKADÉMIAI KIADÓ, Budapest

Europe, Africa:
JOHN WILEY& SONS LIMITED
Baffins Lane, Chichester, West Sussex, England.

North and South America and the rest of the world:
Halsted Press: a division of
JOHN WILEY& SONS
605 Third Avenue, New York, N.Y.10158, U.S.A.

© **Akadémiai Kiadó, Budapest 1985**

 **British Library Cataloguing in Publication Data**

Pollution control and conservation. — (Ellis Horwood series in environmental
  science)
  1. Pollution—Congresses 2. Environmental engineering—Congresses
  I. Kovács, M.
  628.5 TD172.5
  ISBN 0—85312—213—X (Ellis Horwood Limited)
  ISBN 0—470—27509—X (Halsted Press)
  LIBRARY OF CONGRESS Card No. 83—23172

Printed in Hungary

Preface

Protection of the human environment has recently become a public matter; governments and international organizations make proposals and pass resolutions and also scientists, writers as well as experts of different fields take up position on this question. It is difficult to survey the problem in its entirety as correct hypotheses and measures often mingle with extreme views.

There are opinions saying that technical and social development will finally lead to catastrophe affecting the whole mankind. Of course, one cannot agree with this view as a mature planning of the social and economic systems can direct both the increase of population and economic development appropriately. On the other hand, there are views which regard all the suggestions and measures in connection with environmental protection as useless efforts made by the governments because no direct danger overhangs the human environment. It is but partially true as several examples have shown that unplanned economic development may upset the natural equilibrium of our environment.

At present the most urgent task is to reveal all the problems and connections of environmental protection and to take proper measures at different levels. Also this book tries to contribute to achieving this objective. It is more important since the biological aspects of the environmental protection are less known for the public than the harmful effects of the artificial environment, in spite of the fact that the majority of the damage caused by the latter can be restored with some financial sacrifice within a definite period of time, while certain kinds of damage are irreversible processes going on in nature. In towns, air pollution caused by heating can be significantly decreased by modernization of heating installations and water pollution can also be reduced to some extent if factories build appropriate filtering systems. However, the decay of certain species of the plant and animal kingdom cannot be stopped any more and this means an irreplace-able loss for mankind.

In Hungary numerous measures have been taken to protect natural and artificial environment. Besides this, however, it is imperative to change the social consciousness since a significant part of damage is caused by the members of society and this can only be overcome with mutual effort.

András Madas

Contents

Chapter 1

The present state and importance
of environmental control

THE DEGRADATION OF THE ENVIRONMENT

During the last decades, parallel with rapidly developing technology, increasing populations and urbanization we are witnessing alarming phenomena all over the world. In almost every country air, water and soil pollution, the decrease in arable land, the danger of radiation, the accumulation of solid wastes, the depletion of energy carriers and of mineral resources, the death of parts of the plant and animal kingdoms have become dominant problems. The problems arising from increasing urbanization include the obsolescence of the infrastructure, the pollution of the city atmosphere, the lack and bad quality of the drinking water, overcrowding and traffic difficulties, the decrease in the areas of greenery, parks and generally, the so-called damage done by civilization.

To illustrate the pollution of the environment the following examples have been selected at random from the Hungarian and the international literature. Both in scientific reviews and in the press, startling examples are quoted of the air pollution of towns and of industrial centres. In the USA, yearly 129 t of dust, smoke, and other contaminants are introduced into the atmosphere. According to data published in West European countries, the permissible amount of contaminants in the air is 150 mg/m³. In the air over North-Rhine-Westphalian towns, contaminants can be detected, frequently, in an amount of 12,000 mg/m³. Clouds of dust and vapour above large towns absorb more than 20% of solar radiation. The vital important ultraviolet rays are absorbed with the result that the human body cannot produce enough vitamin D.

In Hungary, according to the Ministry of Building and Town Planning 45 km west of Budapest, within the residential area of Tatabánya, dust pollution results in a 10–20% loss of ultraviolet radiation.

The National Institute of Hygiene, Budapest has reported that, in the area of Budapest, sulphur and smoke pollution has risen by 50%, as compared with 1930. The damage resulting from it is estimated to cost 2.5 billion Forint. Air pollution and its impacts are today already general problems. Owing to intensive energy consumption, alone in this century approx. 360 billion t of carbon dioxide is introduced into the air, which—according to preliminary estimates—might have an impact also on the energy balance of the world (Bolin 1970). The increasing CO_2 content of the atmosphere causes a more intensive weathering of limestone and dolomite, as carbonates are easily transformed into bicarbonates, thus strengthening karstic processes (the development of e.g. Yorkshire caves and pot holes) (Rjabchikhov 1972). As a result of the growing acidity of ocean-waters, the abundance of phytoplankton increases parallel to the values of the water albedo reflectance (Siemerling 1974).

Increased water consumption caused by urbanization and industrialization leads to the lowering of the underground water-table. For example, in Italy, around Milan, the underground water-table has sunk by 20 m, over a period of 20 years. In 1945, in Bologna, underground water could be found at a depth of 12 m; today it is to be found at 35 m (Dajoz 1971). Industrial effluents and domestic sewage, detergents, pesticides and oil all pollute the rivers, lakes and seas. The death of living organisms in Lake Erie is already known. There are other alarming reports on dying seas (the Baltic), on the damage caused by oil-spills on marine-living organisms, on the Rhine having become a sewer, etc. The pollution of marine waters is a matter for special concern as the sea's phytoplankton and particularly algae are the world's largest oxygen-producing resources. Indications of water pollution have been multiplying in Hungary, too. To mention only a few: the river Sajó has become a lifeless waterway, fish kills occur in Lake Balaton and periodically, polluting substances of smaller or greater quantity emerge in the rivers, bathing is forbidden along the Danube reaches of greater Budapest, etc. Because of the spread of newly established industrial plants, towns, resort-areas, water and gas pipelines, highways and roads, the area of arable land and that of natural plant cover, forests, meadows and marshes has decreased. For example, in the USA the area of arable land shows a yearly decrease of 2 million acres (1 acre=0.7 ha). In the FRG 545,000 ha, 4% of the total agriculturally exploitable land, has been lost between 1949–1966. In Hungary, the cultivated territory has decreased by approx. 500,000 ha since 1945 (Dégen 1971).

As a result of erosion and salinisation, approx. 500 million ha of arable land has become infertile in the world (Láng 1971). One quarter of the arable land in China is eroded and 2.5 billion t of arable land is lost every year. The river Rhine carries 4.6 t of silt into the sea (Klausewitz et al. 1971).

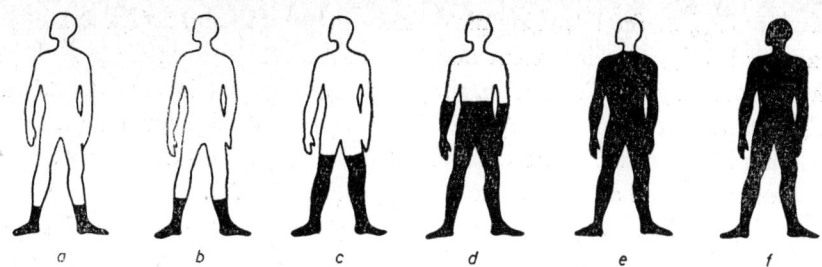

Fig. 1. The mean value of DDT accumulated in the body of the population of different countries (mg/kg fatty tissue) (*a*) England, (*b*) Federal Republic of Germany, (*c*) France, (*d*) United States of America, (*e*) Israel, (*f*) India. (After Klausewitz et al. 1971)

According to a report from the UNO, more than 10 million ha are lost from agricultural cultivation because of secondary salinisation (Szabolcs 1971). In Hungary, 150 million t of fertile soil is carried away by rain-water (Madas 1973).

Different contaminants (pesticides, oil, sewage, faeces, detergents) and excessive use of fertilizers affect both the living organisms of the soil and the vegetation of higher plants. Approximately 700,000 t pesticides are applied yearly. Up to now some 50,000 t DDT has accumulated (Láng 1971). DDT can be detected in the entire living world and can also be found in significant quantities in the human body (Fig. 1).

The growing load of environmental pollution leads to an increase in the number of so-called civilizational damage, that menace the whole of mankind. As a result of the manifold and increased overstressing of the human organism, gastric ulcers, cardiac infarctions, chronic illnesses of the respiratory system, neurosis, etc. occur more frequently. Often different chemicals get into the human organism (Sós 1971). The occasional appearance of certain unidentifiable illnesses, such as the Minamata-disease or the Itai-Itai-disease can also be traced back to the toxicity of chemicals.

The consumer society uses an excessive amount of natural resources, in order to meet its temporary demands. The circulation of consumer goods is becoming quicker and the energy resources of the world are being exploited unreasonably. The burning-up of forests leads to a waste of 2 million t of organic matter.

The accumulation of persistent organic substances means another source of danger for the environment. Apart from this, the quantity of biologically undegradable debris, such as construction rubble, plastics, glass, tins and car wrecks is also increasing. The stress on plants and animals is increasing, as well. In Europe, in the vicinity of large cities and industrial centres, some 6–17% of the flowering plants has disappeared and 50% of the still existing species face imminent destruction. According to investigations in the surroundings of West Berlin, since 1859, urbanization has resulted in the disappearance of some 123 species. In certain plant communities (aquatic communities, forests, shrub communities) the proportion of species which have already perished amounts to 20–25% (Sukopp 1971).

During the last 100 years, more than 100 species have disappeared from the flora of the Budapest conurbation. It may also be shortly expected that a further 80 species will perish (Kovács and Priszter 1975). During the last 300 years, more than 200 mammal and bird species have perished. During the last 100 years some 100 species (an average of one yearly), and out of this number during the last 50 years 76 species (yearly average: 1.5) have disappeared from the fauna. Another 550 mammal and bird species face the danger of imminent death (Dorst 1971; Olschowy 1972). In the zoo of the city of Bronx (New York) one can find a cemetery in which 225 tombs symbolize the number of animal species that have perished owing to the human activity, during the last three hundred years. According to the reports of the Smithsonian Institute (USA), the world almost every day sees an environmental pollution incident of large extent.

Parallel to pollution of the environment and of the living world (air, water, soil) are subject to environmental stresses and a demographic explosion may have to be reckoned with, around the year 2000. According to surveys of the UNO the world population will grow from 3 to 4–6 billion between 1960 and 2000. All these factors point to the danger of the upsetting of the natural environment. Others, on the contrary, express the view that with the appropriate means for the control of population growth in the hands of humanity (Szentágothai 1972) the demographic explosion may be evaded.

THE ENVIRONMENTAL CONTROL PROGRAMME
OF UNESCO

Following the launching of the International Biological Programme (IBP), in 1965, UNESCO—recognising the ever growing danger for human environment—suggested that, within the framework of an international research programme, the rational exploitation of the biosphere and natural resources should be studied.

Biosphere is the common property of the whole of mankind. Only international co-operation, mutually planned and co-ordinated efficient measures can lead to an appropriate environment control and to the solution of existing contradictions. In 1968, on the basis of the inter-governmental conference of experts, in Paris, the 15th General Assembly of UNESCO accepted a resolution and made suggestions for a draft programme dealing with the control of the natural environment, the control and reasonable utilization of natural resources (Máthé 1969; Zólyomi 1972, 1975; Láng 1974). The UNESCO Secretariat has elaborated the international research programme of *Man and the Biosphere* (MAB).

The detailed draft programme of MAB was discussed by the 16th General Assembly of UNESCO. The draft research programme, launched in 1971–72, contained approx. 145 scientific subjects with four main objectives, the latter being: (*i*) The study of natural environments and of those only slightly affected by man, (*ii*) the study of the agricultural environment, (*iii*) the study of the environment as modified by urbanisations and industry, and (*iv*) the problem of pollution. Several international organizations have joined in the work or are interested in the activities of the MAB programme. Such are CEAM, FAO, IUBS, ICSU, IUCN, SCOPE, UNEP, WHO, WMO.

At its session, in 1973, the Co-ordination Council of MAB elaborated the following 13 theme-groups:

1. Ecological impact of human activity on tropical and subtropical forest ecosystems.
2. Ecological impact of different land use and cultivation practices on forest ecosystems of the temperate zone and of the Mediterranean.
3. Impact of human activity and different methods of cultivation on grass-land areas (savannahs, prairie, tundra).
4. Impact of human activity on ecosystem dynamics in the arid and semi-arid zones, with special emphasis on the effect of irrigation.
5. Ecological impact of human activity on the properties and resources of lakes, marshes, rivers, river-deltas and coastal zones.
6. Impact of human activity on mountain ecosystems.
7. Ecology and the rational exploitation of island-ecosystems.
8. Protection of plant and animal populations and the control of genetic variations.
9. Ecological impacts of herbicide and fertilizer usage on terrestrial and aquatic ecosystems.
10. The impact of large landscape-forming engineering works and its environment.
11. Ecological aspects of energy usage in urban and industrial systems.

12. Interrelationship between demographic and genetic development and environmental transformations.
13. Aspects of environmental quality.

The research themes of MAB concern all the countries of the world. The programme emphasizes the necessity of international co-operation in the control of the biosphere, ecosystems and natural resources of the world. At present the number of MAB National Councils exceeds 50. In June 1972, at the International Conference for Environment Control in Stockholm, it was underlined that the landscapes and natural resources of the world should be protected for present and future generations. The slogan of the conference was "Only one Earth".

In its resolution the Conference emphasized, the exploitation of its own natural resources is—in accordance with the United Nations Charter and international law—the sovereign right of each state. It is responsible for the activities carried out under its auspices and control, so that these may not damage the environment of other countries or be a source of impairment in territories outside its national auspices. The programme (Report 1972; Hegel 1972; Wijkman 1972) called for world-wide activity in several fields, e.g.: the irreplaceable resources of the earth to be exploited in such a way, so that they could be utilized for the benefit of the whole of mankind; the control of marine pollution: the conservation of the natural flora and fauna; the limiting of the emission of poisonous substances and of heat energy to such an extent that they do not exceed the absorptive capacity of the environment; the measures taken for environmental control should promote the facilities of developing countries for development; in order to secure efficient environmental control, individual countries should co-ordinate their plans; human settlements and towns should be so planned that their harmful impacts on the environment should be avoided; by preserving basic human rights, appropriate demographic policy should be pursued; environmental research should be developed; the education and popularization of environmental control; international organizations should necessarily play a co-ordinating and efficient role in environmental control.

The United Nations Environment Programme was worked out at a session in Stockholm. At another session in Nairobi, in 1974, its Directorate compiled the following research programmes:

— Human settlements and public health, living space, welfare;
— Earth, water, desertification (also the studies of ecological systems belonging thereto);
— Commerce, economy, technology;

— Marine pollution and the preservation of the marine plant and animal kingdoms;
— Environment control, the protection of genetic resources;
— Energy.

The Economic Commission for Europe of the UNO deals with questions of environmental control in detail. Operations aimed at the surveying of water resources and water protection as well as at the application of fertilizers, herbicides and insecticides and air pollution have been going on for nearly two decades. All these topics belong to the sphere of environmental control. Along with other socialist countries, Hungary also makes attempts to take part in the Environmental Control Programme of the Economic Commission for Europe.

References

Bolin, B. (1970): The carbon cycle. *Sci. Am. Sept.* 125–132.

Dajoz, R. (1971): *Précis d'écologie.* Paris.

Dégen, I. (1971): Contribution to the *Man and the Biosphere* scientific session of the Hungarian Academy of Sciences, 1970 (In Hungarian). *MTA Biol. Tud. Oszt. Közlem.* **14**: 107–110.

Dorst, J. (1971): *Avant que la nature meure.* Neuchâtel.

Hegel, D. (1972): Das ökologische Konzept von Stockholm. *Natur und Landschaft* **47**: 242–244.

Klausewitz, W., Schäfer, W. and Tobias, W. (1971): *Umwelt 2000.* Frankfurt am Main.

Kovács, M. and Priszter, Sz. (1975): Changes in the Hungarian flora and vegetation during the last one hundred years, *Botan. Közlem.* **61**: 185–197.

Láng, I. (1971): Man and the biosphere (In Hungarian). *Magy. Tud.* **16**: 75–82.

Láng, I. (1974): International and national relations of environment control (In Hungarian). Univ. lecture notes, Gödöllő.

Madas, A. (1973): Relations between the natural environment of society and environment control (In Hungarian). *Tud. és Mezőgazd.* **11**: 1–10.

Máthé, I. (1969): Report on some items of the UNESCO conference in Paris 4–13 Sept. 1968 (In Hungarian). *Botan. Közlem.* **56**: 203–205.

Olschowy, G. (1972): Über Belastung und Nutzung der Vegetation. *Natur und Landschaft* **47**: 218–220.

(Rjabchikhov, A. M.) Рябчиков, А. М. (1972): *Структура а динамика геосферы, её естественное развитие и изменение человеком.* Москва.

Siemerling, E. (1974): The negative greenhouse effect and climatic change. Seminar held at the Västbiologiska Institutionen, Uppsala.

Sós, J. (1971): Sanitary requirements and effects of urbanisation (In Hungarian). *MTA Biol. Tud. Oszt. Közlem.* **14**: 131–138.

Sukopp, H. (1971): Über den Rückgang von Farn- und Blütenpflanzen. In: Olschowy, G. (ed.): *Belastete Landschaft–Gefährdete Umwelt*. München.

Szabolcs, I. (1971): Soil as a primary source of nutrients of the living world (In Hungarian). *MTA Biol. Tud. Oszt. Közlem.* **14**: 89–95.

Szentágothai, J. (1972): Man and his environment (In Hungarian). *Magy. Tud.* **17**: 350–357.

Wijkman, P. M. (1972): Second–best solution at Stockholm. *Intereconomics* **9**: 262–265.

Zólyomi, B. (1972): *Man and the biosphere*. Opening lecture at the Session of the Hungarian UNESCO Committee, 25. Feb. 1972 (In Hungarian). Personal communications.

Zólyomi, B. (1975): The international study of the biosphere. Hungary's participation in the international scientific programme on environment control (In Hungarian). *Búvár* **30**: 531–535.

*

The effect of environment on man, the recognition and evaluation of its present state and problems (In Hungarian). Compiled by the "ÉVM" subcommittee for the study of prospective questions concerning human environment. Budapest, 1971. (Repr.)

Report on the Environment Control Conference of the United Nations. Stockholm, 5–16. June 1972 (In Hungarian).

Chapter 2

The biosphere, landscape and natural resources

THE BIOSPHERE

The concept of the biosphere was introduced by Suess in 1909 (cit. in Stugren 1972). Originally it was a geographical concept denoting the cover of the Earth, i.e. that part of the solid crust (lithosphere and its upper part, the pedosphere, respectively), the water cover (hydrosphere) and the atmosphere, in which life is possible (Fig. 2). Man lives in the biosphere in which he exerts his positive or negative activity on the environment.

The troposphere (atmosphere) including also the biosphere constitutes an approx. 8–17 km thick cover around the Earth. The troposphere, with its water-storing ability, plays an important role in the biological circulation of water. Ecosystems are basic functional units of the biosphere.

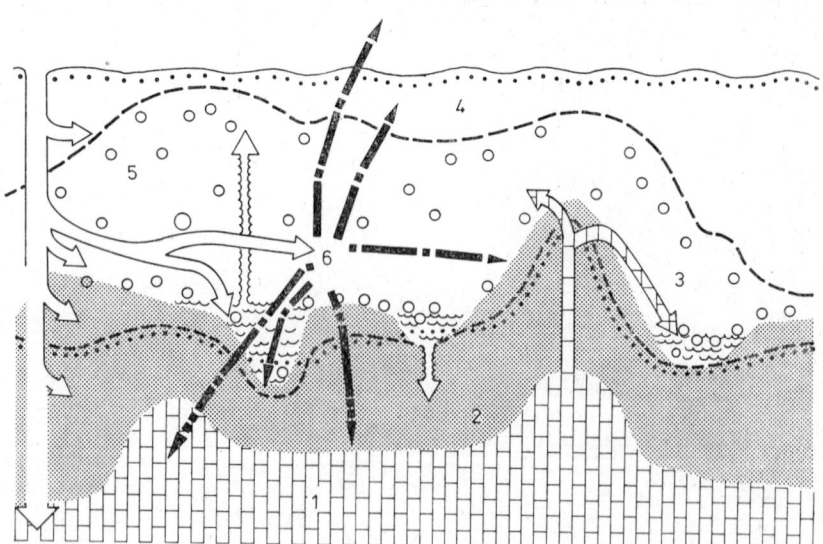

Fig. 2. The different spheres of the Earth. (*1*) pyrosphere, (*2*) lithosphere, (*3*) hydrosphere (*4*) atmosphere, (*5*) biosphere, (*6*) noosphere (Danserau 1966)

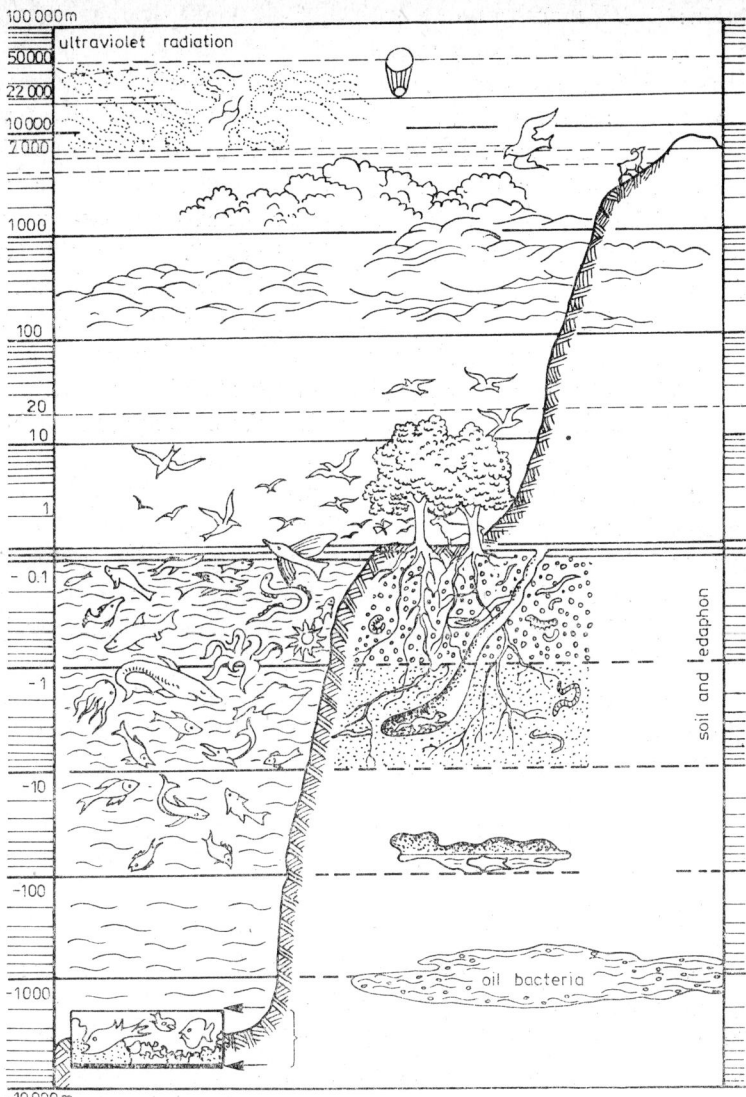

Fig. 3. The distribution of life in the biosphere (Kádár 1965)

According to Zabelin (1959) that part of the earth's crust from which the biosphere has evolved can be called biogenosphere, although Kovalszkij (1963, cit. in Stugren 1972) has called it probiosphere.

All the three inorganic spheres and the living matter are connected with each other by mutual exchange of material. According to Kádár's (1965) definition: "The biosphere is the entity of the constantly developing organic life, having evolved in the geographical cover from the matters of inorganic spheres on the impact of cosmic, mainly solar energy, which it utilizes and transforms. It is a three-dimensional, more or less loose net-like texture in the geographical cover. By way of its life-functions, decomposition products and the activity of its individuals it exerts such an influence on the processes of the geographical cover, that it is an equal component with the inorganic active powers of the geographical cover". Vernadszkij (1967) considers the ecosystem a heterogeneous ecological system consisting of the entire living world and of its habitat. On the basis of this he divides the biosphere into two parts: the first part, consisting of living matter, he calls "geomerida" and the inanimate part, he named the "bioinert-mass".

The vertical extension of the biosphere is limited. Its upper boundary is at approx. 5,000 m (Fig. 3), though in some cases certain spores and bacteria can be detected even in the upper atmosphere (stratosphere). In the sea, living organisms occur down to the depth of 4,000 m. Owing to light conditions the 0–100 m deep level of the sea is the richest in living organisms.

Biosphere is a relatively closed system. The matter and energy exchange takes place within the so-called great-cycle. Vegetation absorbs the energy of the cosmic environment, the radiant energy of the sun and renders it possible to transform it into other kinds of energy (e.g. heat). The vegetation of certain geological ages is capable of storing this energy in the form of coal, oil, lignite, peat, etc. for millions of years.

THE ACCUMULATION AND MIGRATION OF ELEMENTS IN THE BIOSPHERE

Elements to be found in the biosphere, as easily soluble salts, occur also in living organisms, in smaller or greater concentrations.

The living world of the biosphere plays an important part in the chemical composition of the solid crust (lithosphere), water (hydrosphere) and air (atmosphere), in the grouping of elements and the formation of compounds. According to Vinogradov (1949, cit. in Stugren 1972) the major part of the oxygen and carbon dioxide in the air is of organic origin. A number of compounds, such as aluminium silicates and carbonates, are formed only under the influence of living organisms.

The special geochemical functions of the living world are as follows:

Accumulation of elements. Certain plants are capable of accumulating elements, occurring in their environment, selectively. For example, the enrichment of SiO_2 in *Bacillariophyceae* (diatoms) species (3%), in *Cornacuspongiae* (30%) in comparison to the Si content of seawater (0.00005%) means a 60,000- and 600,000-fold enrichment, respectively (Szádeczky–Kardoss 1955).

Certain elements occur in special geochemical deposits in greater amounts, e.g. copper, nickel and zinc. These noble metals can be accumulated in living plants growing in the environment of their habitat, in the biomass. According to preliminary assessments, metal corrosion might lead to the doubling of the soil concentration of ferric oxide by the end of the next century. Similarly, the present lead content might increase tenfold while the increase in mercury could be 100 times the present concentration. Uranium might increase by 200%, and arsenic by 250% (Rjabchikhov 1972).

Migration of elements. Elements are distributed by animals, seeds, spores, etc. in the biosphere. Elements can be found in an irregular distribution in the rocks, in the different forms of water and in the living things. It is the migration of elements that connects the lithosphere, hydrosphere and the atmosphere. Acyclically migrating elements are excluded from the cycle of elements, for a certain period. For example, several elements accumulate in dead plant residues (peat) or in the organic matter that has sunk to the bottom of the sea. In the course of bio-geochemical processes the cyclically migrating elements take part in two cycles, in the ecosystem and in the biosphere. In the ecosystem, within the local circulation systems the elements do not overstep the boundaries of the ecosystem. It is in the ecosystem that they become organic matter or are mineralized, e.g. in a forest. As a result of local circulation the bio-elements may be accumulated in the bottom sediments. The great biological cycle of elements in which hydrogen, oxygen, carbon and nitrogen also take part, takes place in the biosphere.

MAN'S ROLE IN THE BIOSPHERE AND IN
THE NOOSPHERE

The appearance of man, "homo-consumer", in the biosphere is both significant and specific. He is not only a component (a consumer); but parallel with social and economic development he plays an important, frequently negative, role in the biosphere. In order to achieve greater industrial development he intensively exploits the raw material resources, in the meantime strongly polluting his environment. The establishment of towns and industrial plants changes and also decreases the area of the natural landscape. Vernadszkij says (1915) (cit. in Perelman 1973) the noosphere is that part of

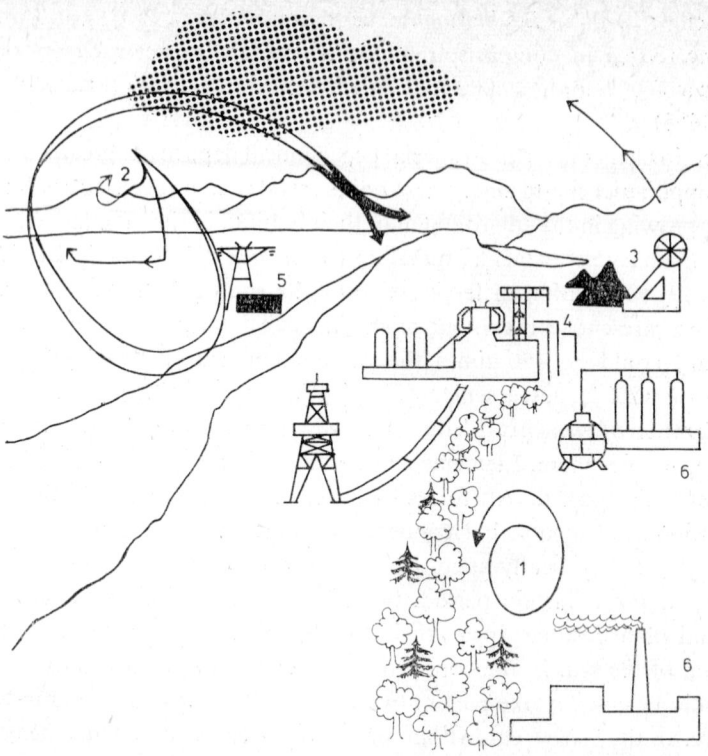

Fig. 4. The geochemistry of the noosphere. Natural processes in the noosphere that form part of the biosphere: (*1*) biological recycling of atoms, (*2*) water circulation, (*3*) dispersion of elements due to the opening up of new resources of raw materials, (*4*) production of metals and other elements at thermodynamic level, (*5*) energy production in nuclear power stations, (*6*) artificial organic matter synthesis outside the biosphere. (Perelman 1973)

the biosphere in which man exerts his activity. The appearance of human society and the technological development extend the boundaries of the noosphere (Mőcsényi 1971), thus a larger part of the biosphere is being transformed into the noosphere. In the noosphere, man makes use of the elements of the lithosphere, hydrosphere and atmosphere. Our forefathers used only 19 elements but, by the 18th century already 28, in the 19th century 50 and at the beginning of the 20th century 60 elements were being used (Vernadszkij 1915, cit. in Perelman 1973).

The noosphere is characterised by the intensive changing, dispersion and concentration of the elements. Owing to the mutual commercial contacts, agricultural and industrial products are transported to all parts of the world. This new pathway for element migration can also be a source of danger for mankind. Thus, in the industrial centres, in large towns, there are already measurable changes in the composition of the atmosphere. Different polluting matters occur already in great quantities (Fig. 4).

LANDSCAPE AND NATURAL RESOURCES

Natural landscape is part of the biosphere. It is a complex taxonomic unit of regionally distributed geographic zones, which consists of the dynamically changing inorganic components of landscape (relief, climate, soil and water) and the living components (plant and animal kingdom) (Bulla 1962; Berninger 1968). The view of a certain landscape and its characteristic features are derived from both the individual landscape elements and from human activity. Each society has a definite connection with the surrounding natural environment. Following the sociological–historical development the specific elements are also changing progressively. The natural plant and animal kingdom is also changing or disappearing.

Danserau (1966) well illustrates the environment-modifying role of man, the changes in a certain natural landscape taking place alongside the economical, industrial and social development (Fig. 5).

In the pre-neolithic ages, man with his gathering and hunting way of living exerted only a minor effect on the natural landscape. Forests, moors and swamps existed in an almost unaffected state. The man in the late-neolithic times acted already as an intensive landscape-former. In order to gain pasture and arable land, he cleared the forests (Buchwald 1971). This surface-modifying activity had created already lasting changes and resulted in the formation of the so-called "cyrogene" relief at several places (Pécsi 1971). Forest clearing had changed certain components of the habitat (nutrient cycle, water-household balance, etc.). At several locations large-scale soil erosion had increased. With the extension of intensive arable land tillage, the natural landscape was being transformed and the nature-true or semi-cultivated agricultural landscape was formed. The natural ecosystems were gradually changing and as a result of forest-management and cultivation of meadows, they were transformed into nature-true and cultural ecosystems.

Landscape elements, i.e. the natural resources, such as air, water, soil and the living world had been only slightly damaged before the start of intensive industrialization. Since the great industrial revolution the natural landscape has been transformed into an unnatural, man-affected and man-managed cultural landscape, the "technogenic" relief (Pécsi 1971, 1974). With in-

30

Fig. 5. Impact of human activity on the landscape (*a*) unaffected natural ecosystem of a forest, (*b*) gathering, (*c*) hunting, (*d*) grazing, (*e*) arable land farming, (*f*) industrialization, (*g*) urbanization (Danserau 1966)

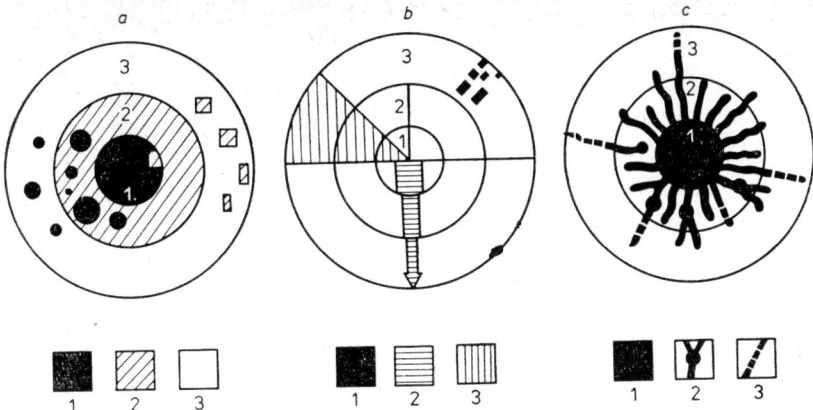

Fig. 6. Zones of human environment. (a) The three main zones of human environment (1) urban–industrial conurbations and centres, (2) zone of intensive production and unproductive activity, (3) natural zone, (b) the scheme of harmful human activity in the three environmental zones, (1) decrease in the intensity of traffic, the zones of noise damage and air pollution, (2) reduction in industrial (and mining) production, the degrading of the landscape, (3) increasing holiday and tourist traffic, (c) the impairment of the environment in the three environmental zones, (1) zone of concentrated destruction, (2) zone of localised sources of impairment and that of their spread, (3) zone of sporadic impairments (Leszczycki 1972)

creasing industrialization and urbanization, industrial plants and towns are consuming an ever increasing area of land. The natural landscape has been confined to an ever decreasing land area and so the pollution of natural resources and their exploitation is going on at an increasing pace. Man prefers to live in an artificial environment where there is increasing overcrowding, traffic difficulties, noise and pollution while the area of verdure and possibilities for recreation are decreasing. According to predictions, in the year 2000, the number of town-dwellers will amount to more than 3 billion. (At present cities of more than 100,000 inhabitants comprise approx. 600 million people.)

Today, in the different parts of the world depending on industrial and social activity, natural landscape and cultural landscape exist side by side.

The designation implies the character and economic functions of the landscape, as well.

In a certain geographical milieu the destruction of the environment occurs in a characteristic spatial distribution (Fig. 6). Leszczycki (1972) distinguishes three zones:

1. Urban–industrial agglomerations have the greatest population density (more than 600 capita/km²). The main cause of environmental pollution and deterioration is the industrial production, which is concentrated in the 1st

and 2nd zones. Here is the greatest noise damage and air pollution. Its polluting matters spread into other zones, too.

2. Zone of intensive productive and non-productive activity. Herein belong areas with a significant population density (more than 100 capita/km^2). Here is the greatest expansion of industrial production, consequently the process of landscape, environment transformation, air, water and soil pollution, degradation of relief, and the devastation of the plant and animal kingdom manifest themselves here the most explicitly.

3. In the zone of the original features and potential reserves of natural environment, the human activity is generally only sporadic (mainly the exploitation of raw materials). Here belong the natural landscapes, resort places and also the seas and oceans. It is primarily tourism that damages nature. The plant and animal kingdom, the natural landscape and its elements can be protected mainly in this zone.

NATURAL RESOURCES UNDER STRESS

Large-scale industrialization and urbanization also increase the load of abiotic and biotic landscape elements. This has a vital effect on the landscape and on the entire biosphere.

The loading of natural resources manifests itself in the following forms (Olschowy et al. 1969, 1974):

Loading of air and its effects. In the vicinity of towns and industrial plants polluting matters (gas, liquid, solid) of different state and composition are introduced into the air. A certain proportion of polluting matters (e.g. CO_2) normally also occur in the so-called pure air, but as a result of human activity they are released to the air in greater concentrations.

Waste gases of different composition (CO, CO_2, SO_2, HF, Cl, NO, N_2O, NO_2) are harmful for man, animal, plant and soil alike. Dust pollution is to be expected mainly in the vicinity of coal separators, quarries and cement-works. According to their origin, the solid air pollutants frequently contain coal dust and elements of Si, Al, Fe, Mn, Ti, Zn, etc.

The exhaust gases of cars mean also a significant source of pollution.

It has been established that motor cars are the main sources of air pollution. The acute damage caused by air pollution (within a radius of 3 km around the source of emission) frequently leads to the complete loss of vegetation, while the permanent air pollution (within a 10–15 km range from the emitting source) results in decreased photosynthesis as well as in the reduction of the size and in the production of the plant's reproductive systems.

The pollution of soil and its effects. It is a world-wide phenomenon that, owing to increasing land utilization (building of towns, industrial plants, roads, the depositing of wastes, etc.) vegetation and agriculturally utilized territory are decreasing. (In Hungary, between 1967–1971, the area of arable land decreased by more than 29,000 ha and the pasture area by approx. 10,000 ha.) As a consequence of the decreased arable land area, a smaller surface remained for the living organisms to decompose organic matters and reintroduce them into the biological cycle of elements. Erosion causes significant soil losses, which also leads to a reduction in the potential production on arable land. Hungary has approx. 520,000 ha of eroded areas.

Growing soil pollution carries an ever increasing danger, which is displayed in the following forms: (*a*) Air polluting matters and their harmful effect on the soil. The sulphur dioxide content of rain-water is of acidic reaction, consequently it increases soil acidity. Parallel with the pH values, the biological activity of soils and the rate of organic matter decomposition also decreases. (*b*) Heavy metals (Cd, Pb, Zn, etc.) which penetrate the soil, also decrease their biological activity and the rate of organic matter decomposition. (*c*) Pesticide pollution appears mainly in agricultural areas which exerts a harmful effect on the microorganisms of the soil. Certain herbicides hinder the decomposition of cellulose and the functioning of nitrifying bacteria. (*d*) Already 0.1% of oil pollution (relating to the percentage of soil weight) significantly damages the bacterial activity in the soil. (*e*) The harmful effect of 'de-icing' salts on arboreous and herbaceous vegetation is displayed mainly along motorways and in towns.

The pollution of water and its effects. Every landscape has a specific water-balance that is greatly influenced by human interference (drainage, river regulation, the building of water reservoirs, etc.) The demand for drinking water and industrial water is growing, which can be met only by upsetting the natural water-balance over a greater area (Lászlóffy 1969). The increasing nitrogen and phosphorus concentrations increase the eutrophication in surface lakes and ponds, and thereby the mass of plankton and aquatic weeds, the primary production and chlorophyll amount.

Surface and ground waters are becoming more polluted mainly in the densely populated and industrially developed countries. Living waters are frequently polluted by acidic, alkali, metallic and toxic industrial sewage, domestic sewage, pesticides, detergents, oil, etc. Within the range of nuclear- and other power-stations the thermal load results in the spread of thermophilic blue algae in waters. Certain species of these can be toxic for both man and animal. The large pollution load kills off the fauna and vegetation in waters. In lakes and rivers, poor in aquatic plants and animals, the biological self-purification is becoming slower and more problematical.

In the case of underground water nitrate accumulation means a very important source of danger for man (methaemoglobinaemia). Pollution, generally, displays itself in a complex form, affecting not only one natural resource. For example, certain air polluting materials affect both the soil and water which should be taken into consideration when implementing landscape regulation or planning projects.

References

Berninger, C. (1968): Die Landschaft und ihre Elemente. In: Buchwald, K. and Engelhardt, W. (eds): *Handbuch für Landschaftspflege und Naturschutz*. I. München–Basel–Wien, 1–72.

Buchwald, K. (1971): Landschaftspflege in einer sich wandelnden Gesellschaft: Aufgaben und Methoden. In: Leibundgut, H. (ed.): *Schutz unseres Lebensraumes*. München–Basel–Wien.

Bulla, B. (1962): *Natural geography of Hungary* (In Hungarian). Budapest.

Danserau, P. (1966): Ecological impact and human ecology. In: Darling, F. F. and Milton, P. J. (eds): *Future environments in North America*. New York.

Kádár, L. (1965): *Biogeography* (In Hungarian). Budapest.

Lászlóffy, W. (1969): Water management aspects in urbanisation (In Hungarian) *Vízügyi Közlem*. **52**: 435–452.

Leszczycki, S. (1972): The participation of geographers in solving problems of the protection of the human environment (In Hungarian). *Földrajzi Közlem*. **20**: 118–126.

Mőcsényi, M. (1971): Man and his environment, the noosphere (In Hungarian). *MTA Biol. Tud. Oszt. Közlem*. **14**: 147–151.

Olschowy, G., Mrass, W., Kullmer, H. J. and Burger, K. (1969): Zur Belastung der Landschaft. *Schriftenreihe f. Landschaftspflege u. Natursch. (Bonn–Bad Godesberg)*, **4**: 5–72.

Olschowy, G., Bürger, K., Zwirner, E. and Weber, D. (1974): Auswertung von Untersuchungen und Forschungsergebnissen zur Belastung der Landschaft und ihres Naturhaushaltes. *Schriftenreihe f. Landschaftspflege u. Natursch. (Bonn–Bad Godesberg)*, **10**: 1–119.

Pécsi, M. (1971): The changing balance of the landscape as a result of the technical-economic activity of man (In Hungarian). *MTA Biol. Tud. Oszt. Közlem*. **14**: 29–37.

Pécsi, M. (1974): Complex environmental studies, and geographical questions. In: Pécsi, M. and Probald, F. (eds): *Man and the environment*. Budapest.

(Perelman, A. M.) Перелман, А. М. (1973): *Геохимия биосферы*. Москва.

(Rjabchikhov, A. M.) Рябчиков, А. М. (1972:) *Структура и динамика геосферы, её естественное развитие и изменение человеком*. Москва.

Stugren, B. (1972): *Grundlagen der allgemeinen Ökologie*. Jena.

Szádeczky–Kardoss, E. (1955): *Geochemistry* (In Hungarian). Budapest.

(Vernadszkij, V. M.) Вернадский, В. М. (1967): *Биосфера*. Москва.

Chapter 3

The role and importance of ecosystems in the biosphere

THE IMPORTANCE OF THE ECOSYSTEM

The ecosystem can be a small or large part of the biosphere. It is the joint functioning and dynamic unit of the biotope (inanimate environment) and biocoenosis (plant and animal kingdom) and has a definite material and energy flow.

Dajoz (1971) defines biocoenosis as a group of living organisms with a definite spatial distribution which is determined by external environmental factors and the interrelationship among the species. Forests, meadows, moors, marshes, lakes, and seas can all be ecosystems. In the following, some examples are given of Central European ecosystems: an Austrian oak-forest (natural ecosystem); onion-couch grassland (semi-cultural ecosystem); wheat or maizeland (cultural ecosystem). In different parts of the world, the biosphere consists of natural ecosystems (tundras, deciduous forests, savannahs, etc.—depending on climatic factors), semi-cultural (meadows and man-affected forests) and cultural ecosystems, which are characterized by a definite flora and fauna and constitute a habitat. It is the existence of ecosystems that serves as a basis for life on the Earth and the survival of mankind.

It is the algae of fresh waters and seas and the higher green plants that possess chloroplasts. Using solar energy, they are capable of synthesizing organic compounds from the carbon dioxide content of the atmosphere. The green plants transfer the radiant energy of the sun into stored (chemical) energy, which, in turn, becomes available for both the animal kingdom and man. At present there is no other significant source of food for man apart from photosynthesis (Balogh 1971).

Green plants stabilize the oxygen and carbon dioxide content of the atmosphere. Nowadays when both the oxygen consumption and the carbon dioxide content of the atmosphere are increasing, this is of primary importance. Although the vegetation of the earth is still able to meet the oxygen demand of living organisms, there are already reports of significant oxygen deficit in certain countries. In Switzerland the estimated annual deficit of oxygen amounts to 4–7 million t (Meyer von Genzenbach 1971). Recent investigations seem to indicate that it is the marine plant organisms (phytoplankton) that produce approx. 80% of the oxygen, therefore, it is of special importance to prevent the further pollution—especially oil pollution—of seas and oceans (Steubing 1972).

Ecosystems play an important role in the preservation of species (for details see Chapter 4). Several species, especially those with a wide ecological amplitude, occur in more than one ecosystem and within the species, numerous biotopes and different ecotypes evolve. The disappearance of natural and semi-cultural ecosystems endanger the genetic and ecological variability of the species. Collections of varieties in botanic gardens can only partly compensate the losses in genetic variability. Pharmaceutical industry demands medicinal plants of natural origin in an ever increasing amount. Demands of this kind can only be met by species with several races (permanent varieties) and ecotypes.

In Hungary the number of ecosystems and biotopes is also decreasing. Due to land reclamation which has been going on since the middle of the last century and also as a result of peat cutting activity, the marshland and swamp vegetations have been greatly damaged. Numerous plant and animal species have permanently disappeared from the Hungarian flora and fauna. Owing to the present intensive reduction of land area, natural and semi-natural ecosystems disappear with their characteristic living organisms. Regrettably, man destroys many ecosystems and habitats without knowing about and being aware of the significance of their life communities (Landolt 1971).

This short introduction may serve as a basis for the statement that the ecosystems of the earth are of vital importance as evidenced by their greatest role in the Programme of Man and the Biosphere. The draft programme of MAB by member-states of the UNO declares: it is an important goal to get to know the main ecosystems of the world. The main sources of oxygen, the environmental factors, their role in biogeochemical cycles, the so-called loadability of ecological factors, the productivity of ecosystems and factors determining production must equally be analysed. Changes in the environmental factors should be measured continuously, with special respect to the degree of accuracy of man-made measures or their expected effects. In order to gain appropriate scientific information, it is necessary to carry out a thorough study of the main basic ecosystems (seas, fresh waters, forests, marshes, meadows, etc.) of the Earth, to make vegetation and soil maps, to determine the basic rules and to establish the probable interaction between man and his environment. In accordance with the objectives of the International Biological Programme and later on, with those of the Programme of Man and his Environment several Hungarian institutes have been carrying out the ecological study of natural, semi-cultural and cultural ecosystems (Zólyomi et al. 1972; Simon and Kovácsné-Láng 1972; Jakucs 1973).

EVOLUTION AND DEVELOPMENT OF ECOSYSTEMS

In addition to its spatial extension (biotope) an ecosystem has its dimension also in time (Ellenberg 1973). In the course of successional development it takes a definite period of time for a certain life community to evolve in a given habitat. Succession is the process of development of vegetation, i.e. the chronological sequence of biocoenoses. Having changed, the biotope appears in the form of a new biocoenosis which, although related to the former one, differs somewhat in several species. By passing through numerous stages (each stage corresponds to an individual biocoenosis and biotope, respectively) the whole process of development (series) reaches the so-called terminal community (climax). The terminal community stands in equilibrium with the climatic conditions. It is stable and relatively constant. Under our climatic conditions, the forest is this terminal community.

The well-known example is the ageing and silting up of lakes. The vegetation appearing in the eutrophic lake (aquatic weed, reed, rush, etc.) produces organic matter in an ever growing quantity and as a consequence the sediment at the bottom of the lake thickens and the water depth and area of the water surface decrease. In the course of silting up reeds are followed by stands of *Carex acutiformis* and *C. gracilis* (moor-meadows) and then *Alnetea glutinosae* marshes as the terminal community. The colonization of forests on the steppe of the calciferous sandy soils of Hungary can also be mentioned. On the steppe of sandy soils, parallel with the increasing humus content of the soil, mosses and lichens are followed by the open (dominating species: *Festuca vaginata*) and the closed grassland of sandy soils (dominating species: *Festuca sulcata*), then as terminal community the oak forest of the sandy soils (*Festuco sulcatae-Quercetum*).

The natural ecosystems are the result of a longlasting development. The main features of successional development are the following (Margalef 1963; Whittaker 1971; Odum 1972):

1. The changing of life communities and biocoenoses is a regular, directed and predictable process.

2. The composition of the species changes and the number of species increases.

3. The quantity of dead organic matter increases.

4. In the course of succession the total amount of biomass increases.

5. The quantity of chlorophyll increases.

6. The structural variety of the ecosystem is growing, the number of vertical levels is increasing.

7. The net production of biocoenoses in the initial stage is great, while that of the climax ecosystems is small, practically equal to nil. The small net production of climax communities is due to the fact that a large proportion of the production is consumed by respiration, however, owing to their role in the oxygen–carbon dioxide equilibrium, climax communities are very important in nature and in the biosphere.

Being in dynamic equilibrium with their environment, the climax communities are more resistant to detrimental environmental impacts. For example, in contrast to an open or closed grassland growing on a sandy steppe, the oak forest growing on sandy soil is rather stable, therefore, its capacity for self-regulation is also greater. Owing to the relatively greater humus content of their soils, terminal communities are capable of absorbing, e.g. the waste gases of the air (Ellenberg 1972). In view of the stability of the biosphere it is very important that on the Earth, the territory of the so-called climax communities be as large as possible. In the different areas, ecosystems of varying successional stages and net production should be maintained in a proper proportion (arable land, meadow, forest). To man, farmlands with a large net production are of importance, though the maintenance of the stability of the biosphere also requires the maintenance of the climax (forest) communities.

The destruction of climax forest ecosystems—with the aim of gaining arable land or of building towns and industrial plants—would lead to the changing of the Earth's biosphere and the upsetting of its equilibrium. When working out the proper measures for nature conservation and protection of the environment, it is of vital importance to be aware of the successional development of ecosystems. Recognition of the rules of successional changes makes it possible to determine, in advance, the prospective impact of drainage, grazing and forest clearing. The knowledge of the development of ecosystems is also important in the preservation of nature reserves. In order to preserve a given ecosystem in a proper stage of development, frequently regular human interference is needed, for example, a moorland meadow rich in rare species can be saved from the invasion of the forest by regular mowing.

COMPONENTS OF THE ECOSYSTEM

The functioning of a terrestrial or aquatic ecosystem is based on the following four components (Figs 7, 8 and 9) (Duvigneaud 1967, Odum 1971, 1972; Ellenberg, 1973):

1. Abiotic environment (biotope), which is the complex of ecological factors (air, water and soil).

2. Producers (autotrophic components) comprise green plants with chloroplasts (trees, bushes, herbaceous plants, agricultural crops, marine and fresh water algae) that transfer solar energy into chemical energy. They

Fig. 7. Components of an oak forest with Austrian oak (*Quercetum petraeae-cerris*) and meadow (*Danthonia provincialis*) ecosystems (with contribution by I. Loksa) (*1*) Clay-washed brown forest soil, (*2*) producers in the field layer *Poa nemoralis*, in the shrub layer *Acer tataricum*, in the tree canopy *Quercus petraea, Q. cerris*, in the meadow *Danthonia provincialis*, (*3a*) herbivorous consumers in the field layer *Sus crofa* in the tree canopy the caterpillar of *Erannis defoliaria*, (*3b*) indirect consumers in the litter of forests *Chromatoiulus projectus*, in the soil *Lumbricus rubellus*, in meadow soil *Octodrilus transpadanus*, (*3c*) carnivorous consumers *Calosoma sycophanta, Parus major*, which feed on the caterpillars of *Erannis defoliaria*, (*4*) decomposers, different species of fungi and bacteria

Fig. 8. Beech-forest (*Melico-Fagetum*), mountain meadow (*Cynosuro-Festucetum rubrae*) and cultural ecosystem (a potato-field) in the Hungarian Central Mountains (with contribution by I. Loksa). (*1*) clay-washed brown forest soil, (*2*) producers: plants of the forest, meadow and cultivated territory, (*3a*) primary consumers (herbivores) in the forest *Cervus elaphus, Lymantria dispar*, in the meadow the cattle *Stenobothrus lineatus*, in the potato-field *Leptinotarsa decemlineata*, (*3b*) indirect consumers are the different species of millipedes and worms in the forest *Leptophyllum nanum, Dendrobaena octaedra*, in the meadow *Octolasium lacteum*, in the soil of potato-fields *Allobophora rosea*, (*3c*) carnivorous consumers are in the forest, *Cuculus canorus* decomposers are the different fungi and species of bacteria

produce organic matter from inorganic matter by accumulating it in the form of carbohydrate, protein and fat. It is only in the presence of an appropriate number of autotrophic organisms, i.e. green plants, that an ecosystem can be regarded as "complete". A large area of the earth is at present covered by autotrophic ecosystems (cf. Ellenberg 1973). Producers are the starting point in the food chain; the existence of all living things (including man) depends on the existence of producers. The total rate of assimilation of producers is called the gross primary production. Gross primary production involves the total amount of organic matter including the amount of organic matter that the plant consumes in its life processes (vital processes). The organic matter accumulated in the plant tissues in the course of vital processes, is called the net primary production. This quantity is available to consumers.

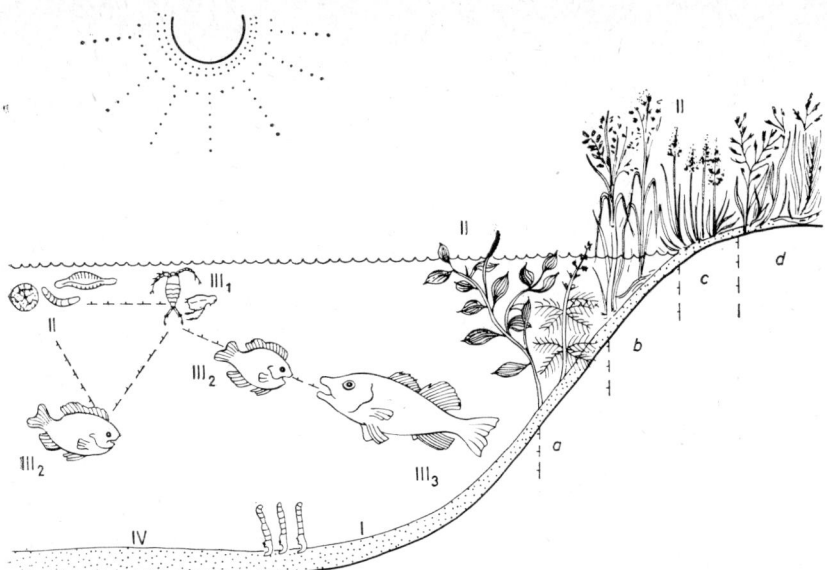

Fig. 9. A lake ecosystem illustrated by the example of Lake Balaton (with contribution by J. Ponyi and J. Tóth). Components: (I) biotope is the calcium bicarbonate-type water of the lake and the bottom deposit of the lake; (II) producers are the reed bank of the shoreline, different sedge species, the aquatic weed (*Potamogeton perfoliatus*) and aquatic species of algae (*Cyclotella bodanica, C. ocellata, Ceratium hirundinella*); (III$_1$) primary consumers are the zooplanktons (*Eudiaptomus gracilis, Daphnia cucullata, Diapha nosoma brachyurum*), the consuming plankton *Abramis brama* (common bream); (III$_2$) zooplankton eater *Alburnus alburnus;* (III$_3$) carnivorous fish *Lucioperca lucioperca;* (IV) decomposers are the different species of bacteria (*Bacillus aquaticus communis, B. megatherium, B. saccharobutyricus, B. subtilis, Micrococcus candidus, M. sulfureus*), (*a*) macrophyl colonies (*Myriophyllo-Potametum*), (*b*) reeds (*Scirpo-Phragmitetum*), (*c*) high-sedge community (*Caricetum gracilis*), (*d*) marsh-meadow (*Festucetum pratensis*)

3. Consumers (macro- and microscopic consumers, heterotrophic components) constitute another large group of the following components;

(a) The first group of consumers is formed by green plant-eating (herbivora) animals. They are direct or primary consumers. Here belong, e.g. the cattle grazing upon the plants of a meadow, the field mice on arable land and in waters, the zooplankton. Primary consumers utilize carbohydrates, proteins and fats accumulated in green plants and by decomposing them, they make the potential energy resource of plants available for animals with other feeding processes.

(b) Indirect consumers or detritus-eaters comprise invertebrate animals in soils and waters.

(c) Carnivores form the "top" of consumers. They can be either herbivorous predators (secondary consumers) or carnivorous feeding upon carnivores (tertiary consumers). In a terrestrial ecosystem, such are the birds of prey and flesh-eating mammals in waters (predatory fish).

Where herbivores are replaced by carnivores, which in turn are eaten by other animals, this kind of transition of food energy is called a food chain. Since a given ecosystem is capable of maintaining only a definite amount of consumers, a given production means a limited amount of food sufficient to maintain a population with a definite number of individuals.

The existence of consumers is not indispensable for an ecosystem. In an arable land ecosystem (e.g. wheatfield) herbivores occur in the form of pests. Their activity can be somewhat reduced by integrated plant protection. In this case the consumer of primary production is man himself.

4. Decay organisms (micro-consumers, biological reductors, biological reducers, destructive, decomposing, mineralizing organisms) comprise different microscopic organisms, bacteria and fungi. In natural ecosystems, such as forests and lakes, larger quantities of organic matter accumulate (litter, fallen branches, felled trunks, dead herbs, plants and animals sinking to the bottom of a lake, etc.). In cultural ecosystems the accumulation of organic matter is rather small (stubs, roots, etc.). Indirect consumers and microorganisms play a very important role in natural ecosystems. Their task is to return the dead organic matter into the food-cycle. Decomposers are essential components of natural, semi-cultural and cultural ecosystems.

The heterotrophic organisms are classed as secondary producers.

Each ecosystem has a definite structure. The structure of a forest ecosystem (see Fig. 8) is determined by the tree, field, ground layers as well as by the different soil levels. In a meadow ecosystem, depending on the physiognomy of the dominating grass species, upper and lower field and ground layers can be distinguished. In these layers, the light, temperature and microclimatic conditions differ. In a forest the autotrophic food exchange of producers takes place in the tree canopy, shrub or ground layers. Heterotrophic consumers also occur in these layers.

In the tree canopy of the oak forests, in Hungary, (*Quercetum petraeae-cerris*) *Erannis defoliaria* and in the field layer the deer (*Capreolus capreolus*), the red-deer (*Cervus elaphus*) and the wild-hog (*Sus crofa*) are primary consumers. Decomposers, fungi and bacteria can be found in the upper level of the soil (Balogh 1953).

It is the decomposers that prevent the accumulation of greater quantities of organic matter and refuse in nature. However, a dangerous situation should be faced as there are certain kinds of refuse (e.g. plastics), which are undegradable or poisonous for the biological reducers (Steubing 1972). Furthermore the amount of elements lost from the food cycle is increasing.

ECOSYSTEM TYPES AND THEIR CLASSIFICATION

As a basis for classification, three main types of ecosystem can be distinguished (Balogh 1971):

1. Natural ecosystems or self-maintaining, self-controlling ecosystems. These include the ecosystems in which relative stability is maintained by changes taking place within the ecosystem. For example, in a jungle, old trees die off, younger ones grow up, thus the food chain, the energy flow and nutrient recycling are undisturbed in the ecosystem. Only normal amounts of foreign substances or biogenic elements have access to the ecosystem and within certain limits, the ratio of herbivores and carnivores is fixed. For both producers and consumers the composition of the species is varied and consequently, the food chain is relatively long.

Depending on environmental factors, the plant and animal populations of the ecosystem vary to a greater or smaller extent, within certain limits. A regulating mechanism controls the number of individuals in a given population, in which—apart from the abiotic environment which is devoid of life—competing species with specific interrelationships, the capacity of individuals for reproduction and adaptation and their mortality, play an important role. The abundance of a population in a species (e.g. in the case of an animal population), therefore, reacts to the amount of food and the number of individuals taking part in the food chain. The genetical and ecological factors produce either a favourable or an unfavourable impact on the population in question. These two antagonistic effects, achieve a relative equilibrium within the ecosystem. Plant and animal species taking part in the food chain, regulate the number and quantitative proportion of their individuals.

In an ecosystem, self-regulation is very important for maintaining a species, and by adapting itself to the living and inanimate environment the species fluctuates within definite quantitative limits. Ecological buffering systems (self-regulation, inner-regulation) are primarily characteristic of relatively stable ecosystems. Owing to the varied composition of species, the adaptability and relative stability of the entire biocoenosis is greater. Nowadays, self-regulating ecosystems occur only rarely. Even the seemingly undisturbed equilibrium of these is disappearing. Such are the ecosystems of the nature reserves.

2. The degraded ecosystems (meadows, pastures) where the self-controlling equilibrium has almost ceased. It is characteristic of these that their phytomass and productivity have also decreased. In contrast to the number of herbivorous and carnivorous consumers, the number of their individuals

increases. The ecosystem is less varied and both the diversity of species and the relative stability of the ecosystem declines, the food chain becoming shorter.

3. In the third group of cultural ecosystems, the self-controlling equilibrium has entirely ceased. The whole ecosystem is maintained by human activity and man who—by various methods—tries to reduce the number of herbivorous pests, is the only consumer of the increased production.

ENVIRONMENTAL FACTORS, BIOTOPE
AND BIOLOGICAL INDICATORS

Each ecosystem and each species constituting the ecosystem exist under definite environmental conditions maintaining an interrelationship with the inorganic environment. Terrestrial and aquatic ecosystems can exist and function in proper species composition only by complex interaction of the inorganic environmental factors (light, air, water, soil, relief).

Altitude, exposure and the slope of the land influence both the micro- and mesoclimates, soil conditions and by the latter, the occurrence and species composition in ecosystems.

The CO_2 content of the air is a basic pre-condition for the existence of vegetation while light and solar energy represent the most important and only source of energy of the ecosystem. A certain proportion of the radiant energy affects living things in the form of heat (temperature) and can limit the distribution of species and ecosystems.

Living organisms cannot exist without water, necessary for the osmotic conditions within the cell protoplasm. It is the medium of nutrient transport. As a medium of transpiration it regulates the temperature of the organisms. Water, as an environmental factor, limits the existence of aquatic ecosystems.

Every organism needs a number of inorganic substances to be able to build up its body. Producers of terrestrial ecosystems take up these substances from the soil, while green plants in aquatic ecosystems—depending on their life forms—take them from water or sediment. Plants utilize numerous biogenic elements, from which they build up their body. In addition to the already mentioned carbon, hydrogen, and oxygen they utilize also nitrogen, phosphorus, sulphur, calcium, magnesium, potassium, iron, etc. and the so-called trace or microelements (manganese, strontium, zinc, copper, etc.) are also important.

The biotope is the entity of the environmental factors. Every biocoenosis requires a well-defined habitat. Naturally, the requirements of habitat differ in the case of a lichen community from those in a forest ecosystem. An ecosystem exists in the presence of the appropriate number of ecological factors, which undergo periodical changes. Every biotope (desert, river, isolated lake, forest soils, etc.) has a definite biocoenosis, the living creatures of which are in a definite interrelationship with each other.

The occurrence of several rare plant and animal species is connected with a definite biotope and its biocoenosis. Laws, passed for the protection of animal species, generally, do not take into account the fact that, e.g. a certain bird species' nests in a definite biocoenosis and its food supply are connected with a definite biotope. The species is protected in itself, without taking into consideration the fact that it is restricted to a certain biotope and biocoenosis.

With the environmental factors slowly changing, new species and new individuals appear in accordance with the rate of change, e.g. in the course of gradual silting up of a lake. With sudden changes in the environmental factors (e.g. drainage) or the large-scale pollution of ecological sites, there is not necessarily an adaptation of the species so it may lead to the destruction of living organisms.

Biological indicators used in bioassays are organisms, the presence — occasionally their large-scale reproduction (positive indicators) — or absence (decrease in the number of species; negative indicators) of which indicates the properties of the environment and the degree of the pollution of air, soil and water. Positive indicators, e.g. different nitrophilous weeds, become numerous where there is a higher nitrogen content in the soil (e.g. through the deposition of refuse). Such are certain aquatic-weed species (Láng 1968; Carbiener 1969) and also algae—especially blue algae— (Felföldy 1972) which are the best indicators of the eutrophication of lakes and waters. In the case of negative indicators, e.g. lichens, it is the decrease in their species and individuals or even their death which indicates the pollution (especially that of SO_2) of towns and industrial districts.

Recognising the importance of biological indicators, one of the goals of the MAB Programme is their identification as they may indicate the stress of different environmental factors, furthermore, the limits of their capacity for stress. The MAB programme declares that in the study of ecosystems, it is necessary to use biological indicators independently of the physical and chemical analyses. Species reacting sensitively to the changes in the ecosystem and which are able to indicate the changes taking place in ecological factors, should be determined. Studies, that are based on chemical analyses are generally, circumstantial and consequently, the required measures of protection cannot be introduced in due course. According to the MAB programme, the application of biological indicators has the following advantages: (*i*) They indicate the impact of all the individual environmental factors and of the entire environment. (*ii*) The provisional assessment of biological impacts, by means of physical and chemical analyses, becomes unnecessary. (*iii*) They indicate those sites within the biological system, where toxic and polluting matters accumulate.

PRIMARY AND SECONDARY PRODUCTION

Energy flow, production, nutrient cycles and internal regulation are functional properties of ecosystems. The green plants of the ecosystem utilize 1–5% of the radiant energy of the sun, reaching the surface of the earth, by means of photosynthesis. The rate of light utilization of plants, in the temperate zone, is 1%, while that of tropical plants amounts to 4–5%. Radiant energy is absorbed in the form of chemical energy in the organism. Plants consume a certain proportion of this energy in their vital processes, which is lost from the organism in the course of respiration and exothermic processes. In photosynthesis, producers (green plants) accumulate the radiant energy in the form of organic matter and this process is called primary production. At any given time, there is a definite quantity of living organisms present in the ecosystem called the biomass. The quantity of biomass can be expressed by the number of individuals, their weight and by their energy content. The rate of biomass accumulation is named production. By secondary production we mean the biomass accumulated by consumers and biological reducers (Duvigneaud 1974) and also that amount of organic matter, which is produced by heterotrophic organisms. According to Duvigneaud (1974) plants on dry lands and oceans produce 6×10^9 t of organic matter annually.

Because of increasing human population, it is important to assess the production of the vegetational units of different climatic zones, their ecosystems (forests, meadows, farmlands, lakes and seas). One of the main objectives of the International Biological Programme launched in 1964, was to determine the production of the Earth's vegetation. Estimates of regional production are summarized after Lieth (1972) (Fig. 10). While, according to assessments, forests (especially tropical forests) have the highest phytomass, deserts produce the least. In Table 1 production data of the main vegetational zones of the Earth are given after Rodin and Bazilevich (1965–66, 1968), Ovington (1965) and Précsényi (1971). In 1960 the yearly

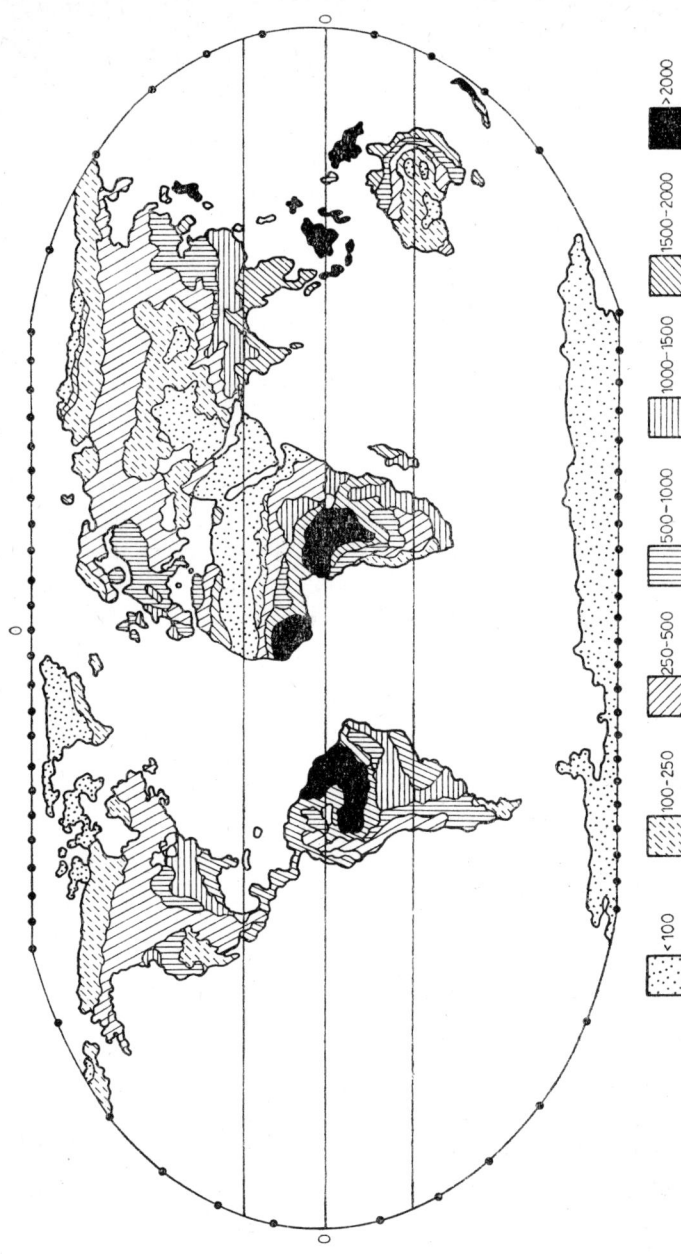

Fig. 10. Map of the primary production of the Earth (g/m²/year). Prepared with the help of a computer on the basis of Lieth's map. (Lieth 1972)

Table 1

Phytomass and net production of the ecosystems of the world

	Tropical	Sub-tropical	Moist temperate	Coniferous
	forests			
Phytomass t/ha	500	400	370–400	100–300
Net production t/ha/yr	32.5	24.5	9–13	4.5–8.5
	(24–70)		(9–16)	(4–30)
	savannah	desert	steppe	tundra
Phytomass t/ha	26–27	4–12	10–25	5–28
Net production t/ha/yr	7–12	0.5–1(–9)	4–11	1–2.5
	(7–25)	(0.4–9)	(0.5–15)	

demand for calories of the world amounted to 2.7×10^{15} Kcal. From the overall production of the biosphere 2.4×10^{15} Kcal/year can be used for human nutrition (Zólyomi 1973). Generally speaking, this quantity meets the demands of the world's population. But, when taking into account the expected increase in world population by the year 2000, it should be stressed that increasing the productivity of ecosystems and their more intensive exploitation is an urgent task. According to Nichiporovits (cit. in Máthé 1971) 16% of the dry land surface (2,500 millions ha) is under cultivation. This area, however cannot be increased to a large extent, for it would not be economical. Therefore, the more intensive exploitation of already cultivated areas and increased productivity of cultural ecosystems have become crucial issues. The protection of the oceans is also of vital importance, as they contain huge amounts of food resources (Máthé 1971).

FOOD CHAINS, TROPHIC LEVELS, FOOD PYRAMID AND ENERGY FLOW

The transformation of food energy from green plants via animal organisms—through multiple consumptions—is already known.

An example of a short food chain is the following:

green plant (seeds)→ field vole→ fox
(producer)   primary   secondary
                        consumer

Decomposers (biological reducers) constitute the end of the food chain. According to Duvigneaud (1974) three types of food chains are known: (*a*) The chain of predators, leading from herbivores via carnivores to the decomposers. (*b*) The chain of predators, which leads from large-bodied organisms towards organisms of smaller size. This is just the opposite of the previous chain. (*c*) The chain of saprophytes starts from dead organic matter and leads in the direction of microscopic organisms.

On the basis of food consumption, members of an ecosystem can belong to different groups and according to the components, different trophic (food) levels can be distinguished: (*i*) In the level of the producers, there are various herbivores. (*ii*) Predators feeding upon herbivores belong to the level of primary consumers. (*iii*) The level of secondary consumers contains carnivore-eating carnivores. (*iv*) Consumers of the secondary consumers belong to the tertiary level of consumers.

A particular population of a definite species can occur in one or more trophic levels. Energy transmittance from one level to the other takes place in the form of thermal energy. The shorter the food chain—i.e. the nearer the individual organisms are to the starting point of the chain—the larger the available food energy is. The energy flow decreases in subsequent trophic levels.

In a given area, in a definite ecosystem, numerous green plants (producers) can be found. These can feed a definite number of herbivores and carnivores. If the number of individuals in the subsequent food levels are written above each other (or illustrated in a graph) a steeply declining column of figures or graph takes shape. This aspect of the food chain is called a food pyramid (Elton-pyramid). The number of individuals of the subsequent links in the chain regularly decreases.

The accumulated chemical energy in the food chain, following a number of transmittances (consumptions) will be stored in the form of chemical energy in the body of consumers (Fig. 11). A definite amount of energy is stored in the bodies of living organisms at a given trophic level. In the course of multiple consumptions and transition from one level to the other (energy flow), the amount of chemical energy decreases in accordance with the principles of thermodynamics. This loss of energy is due to the following factors: (*i*) A certain proportion of organic matter leaving the food chain is consumed by saprophytes. (*ii*) Another proportion of the assimilated food is burnt in respiration. (*iii*) A certain proportion of organic matter is incorporated into the body of the members of the following trophic level.

In the ecosystem, chemical elements participate in the recycling of both living and dead matter. Energy utilized by one or more organisms is,

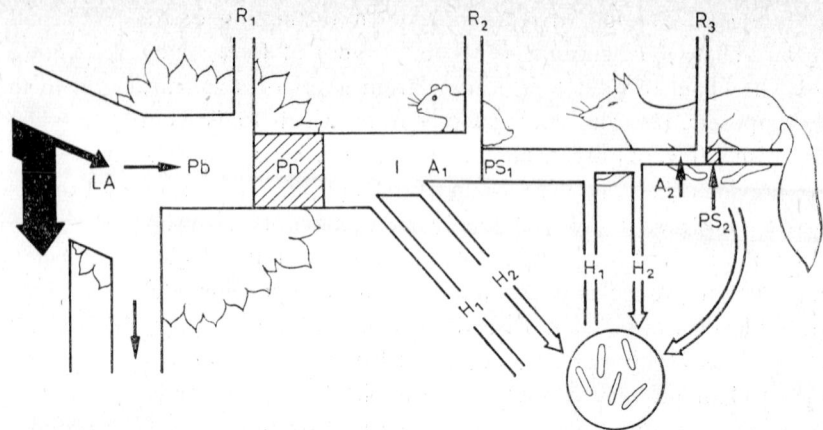

Fig. 11. Energy flow at three levels of a simple food chain. (LA) absorbed light, (P_b) gross production, (P_n) net production, (A_1, A_2) assimilated energy, (PS_1, PS_2) secondary production, (R_1, R_2, R_3) respiration, (H_1) non-absorbed matter, (H_2) waste and refuse matter. (Duvigneaud 1974)

however, transformed into heat which leaves the ecosystem. When studying natural and cultural ecosystems all of the members in the food chain should be taken into consideration. Drastic measures taken by man, may lead to the loss of certain links (e.g. an animal species) in the food chain. Owing to this, the next member in the food chain—because of the lack of food—will be poorer in individuals or else, it will perish. When applying chemical weed, insect or pest control in a forest, meadow or arable land, one has to consider the ecosystem in its entirety and assess the expected impact of chemicals both on producers and consumers. The total extinction of certain insect species may bring about also the loss of other species in the biocoenosis. Modern integrated plant protection (Ubrizsy 1968) emphasizes the need to know the components of the ecosystem and to be aware of the role of these species in the food chain. Plant protection is not aimed at the total extinction of pests, but at keeping their number below the danger limit, for the food chain must not be disrupted.

As far as nature conservation is concerned, one should consider that the incorporation of certain elements (e.g. mercury), radioactive matters (strontium 90) and plant protective agents (pesticides) by the members of the food chain may lead to the death of animal species and may have a detrimental effect on man, as well.

A classical example of the incorporation of pesticides in food chain took place in Clear Lake, California. DDT applied against mosquitoes (0.02 ppm) drifted into the water and accumulated in the plant plankton living there

(5 ppm). Fish, feeding upon plankton, contained 40–300 ppm DDT, while in predacious fishes eating them, the concentration of DDT and of its decomposition products increased to 2,500 ppm. In the eggs of the birds of prey feeding on fish such a large amount of DDT had already accumulated that it was toxic for the embryos. As a result of this several bird species had become exterminated within a few years (Ubrizsy 1969; Dorst 1971; Woodwell 1971).

Between 1953–60, the inhabitants of the Minamata-bay area, in Japan, had been suffering from a mysterious illness. Its symptoms were muscle weakening, impairment of vision and mental retardation followed shortly by death. The illness was caused by the mercury content of the effluent, which the bay had received from a local chemical (PVC) factory. The mercury had accumulated in the body of fish and shellfish in dangerous concentrations.

As a result of human activity, large amounts of radioactive elements frequently escape into the atmosphere where they accumulate over a certain period of time. It is generally assumed that most radioactive elements can be carcinogenic and are harmful to the human body causing genetic damage. Small amounts of radioactive elements can also make a strong biological impact by causing changes in the tissues of living organisms. Strontium 90 is especially harmful. As a result of pollution from nuclear tests it has spread all over the world maintaining its radioactive effect for a long time (half period: 28 years). According to Kulp (1961), in 1960, the biosphere of the Earth contained 4 million curies of strontium 90. Strontium 90 especially penetrates the human organism very quickly. It accumulates in vegetables, fruit and via the food chain—hay-cattle-milk—it is introduced into the human body. Strontium 90 accumulates in the bone-marrow of man and animal alike.

THE BIO GEOCHEMICAL CYCLE AND THE NUTRIENT CYCLES

The biogeochemical cycle is a more or less circular (or spiralform) pathway of elements in the biosphere and ecosystem which leads from the inorganic environment to the living organisms and back again. These elements take part in the kind of cycles which are involved in the weathering of rocks, soil formation, plant growth, the synthesis of organic matter, material exchange and decay and the uptake of these elements in a water-soluble form. These elements can migrate, accumulate, leave an ecosystem or ap-

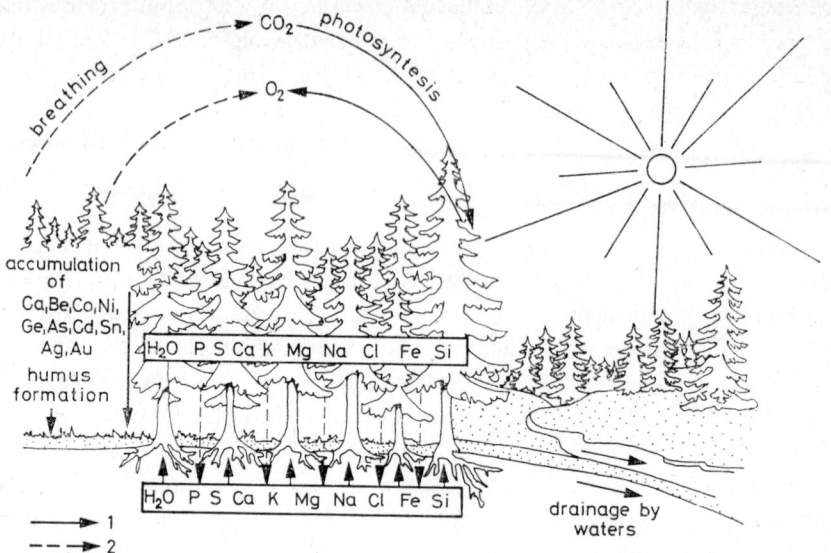

Fig. 12. Local material flow in a forest ecosystem. (*1*) accumulation of biogenes, (*2*) mineralization. (after Perelman 1961)

pear in another one. As the cycles frequently have resting stages, they are not always regular. On such occasions, for instance, a large proportion of the organic matter may accumulate (peat building in the course of the silting up of eutrophic lakes) thus bringing about a temporary or a fixed period of immobilization of some elements.

Under tropical climate basic elements are leached out and this can lead to their total absence; in the continental or arid climatic regions, the concentration of certain elements may reach the level of toxicity (salinization). In biogeochemical cycles biogenic elements are derived mainly from soil and also, to a lesser extent, from rainfall. In these processes, elements take part in two cycles: in the ecosystem (Fig. 12) and in the biosphere. In the ecosystem, herbivores utilize the organic matter stored by the producers. These, in turn, serve as food for the secondary and tertiary consumers. Each consumer oxidizes a proportion of the food and releases CO_2. Consumers utilize only a minor proportion of food for the construction of their body (secondary production).

Plant and animal detritus, such as animal carcasses are decomposed by microorganisms (decay organisms) living in the soil. As a result of this activity, inorganic compounds are produced from organic ones and are made available for the producers. The so-called mineralization dynamics are dependent on the number of plant and animal organisms living in the soil and also on both the physical and the chemical properties of the soil. Depending on environmental factors and a definite biological activity, a certain proportion of organic matter deposited on the soil accumulates in the form of humus. In the presence of favourable ecological conditions, an adequate amount of organic matter is degraded annually, thereby securing an adequate supply of nutrients. The most important elements to flow along the biogeochemical cycle or ecosystem are: hydrogen, oxygen, carbon, nitrogen and phosphorus. From among the elements of the biogeochemical cycle, nitrogen, and carbon are stored in the atmosphere (vapour cycle) while phosphorus is stored in the sediment (sedimentary cycle).

Water circulation

It is known that water is the source of oxygen and hydrogen. It is also one of the basic components of living organisms.

The circulation of water on the Earth is illustrated in Fig. 13. Under the impact of solar energy, surface waters evaporate and get into the air in the form of vapour, which condenses in the atmosphere. The cooling down of clouds leads to precipitation in the form of rain. Rainwater reaching the surface of the earth either penetrates the soil or runs off the surface and eventually, flows into open water surfaces (river and sea).

On the impact of civilization, however, certain disturbing factors manifest themselves in the individual phases of the water cycle (Giessler 1972). Thus, contaminating substances which get into the air in the course of water evaporation and condensation, may result in the formation of an industrial fog or smog effect, over the land surface. The point of precipitation may also be shifted in the atmosphere. Polluting substances change both the chemical reaction (pH) and the composition of the rainwater. For example, in the vicinity of polluting sources the sulphur content (SO_3) of rainwater can be so high that it is strongly acidic, having an impact similar to that of a diluted sulphuric acid solution (Mészáros 1973). Such a high degree of pollution causes great damage to living organisms, monuments (stone corrosion), power lines, etc. In certain industrial districts an amount as high as 20–30 kg sulphur can be deposited on 1 ha of land surface annually (Kozák and Mészáros 1971a).

The increasing acidity of the environment in North America, in North and Central Europe has caused the nitrogen mineralization in soils to be decreased, and lake and river ecosystems have changed. Forests are seriously damaged by acid rains originating from remote industrial areas (Oden

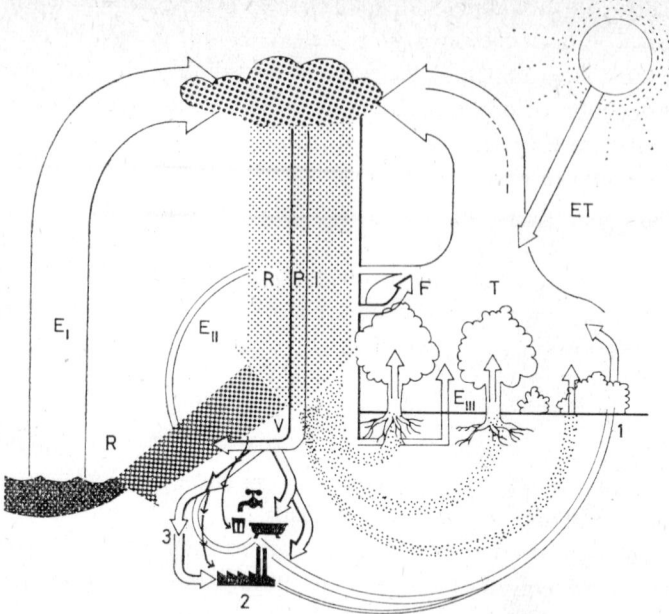

Fig. 13. Water circulation. (CS) run-off waterflow, (I) infiltration, (P) percolation, (T) transpiration, (E_I) evaporation from the sea, (E_{II}) evaporation from open water surfaces, (E_{III}) evaporation from the soil surface, (ET) evapotranspiration, (F) catching of rainwater by vegetation, (V) ground-water level, (*1*) human water consumption, (*2*) domestic and industrial water demand, (*3*) wastewater. (Clodius-Kellner 1951; Duvigneaud 1974)

1976; Hutchinson and Havas 1980; Ulrich et al. 1980; Meiwes and Khanna 1981).

It has been generally observed that the nitrogen content of rainwater has increased. According to data from Italy (Nucciotti-Rossi 1968, op. cit. Kozák and Mészáros 1971*b*) a deposit of 40 kg nitrogen is estimated to fall on an area of 1 ha annually in industrial districts. In Hungary, 14.6 kg nitrogen falls on an area of 1 ha yearly in the form of rain. According to some investigations (Szabó and Csortos 1975) this annual quantity already exceeds 20 kg/ha. Rain-borne nitrogen has a great impact on the nutrient enrichment of soils and waters (eutrophication). In Western Europe the amount of nitrogen reaching the soil already gives ground for concern in the preservation of certain nature reserves—oligotrophic marshes and heath vegetation.

The development of urbanization accelerates the pollution of both surface and underground waters. In the water cycle, three types of purification mechanisms can be distinguished: (*i*) Evaporation in the atmospheric phase, (*ii*) physical, chemical and biological self-purification in the soil phase, (*iii*) physical, chemical and biological self-purification in open seas.

In the present stage of urbanization, air, soil and water pollution slow down or hamper the above-mentioned processes of self-purification.

In an ecosystem, the circulation of water takes place in the following phases: the collection of rainwater, its evapotranspiration and infiltration into the soil and drainage. Vegetation plays an important part in controlling the amount of rainwater reaching the soil. In forests a certain proportion of rainwater, caught by the tree canopy, evaporates from the leaves. The rest penetrates through the leaves or flows down along the trunks and then infiltrates the soil. In areas free of forests, rainwater runs off, generally destroying the surface (erosion). Penetrating into the soil, a certain proportion of water returns into surface waters by way of underground waters, the rest is retained in the soil, in a form available for plants. Approximately 1% of rainwater is taken up by the biomass of the ecosystems (Duvigneaud 1974). Plants of the ecosystem introduce a certain amount of water by transpiration and evaporation (evaporation of the soil and water surface) into the atmosphere.

Carbon cycle

The carbon content of air is absorbed by plants and transformed into sugars, protein, fat, etc. by the process of photosynthesis. This organic matter constitutes the food for man and herbivores. Living organisms give off carbon dioxide in the process of respiration. Biological reducers also release carbon dioxide in the course of the decay of dead organic matter (Fig. 14). Because of the accumulation of organic matter, the carbon cycle process may slow down. Organic matter buried in the depth of the Earth is stored in the form of coal or oil. The accumulation of peat, the increment in the biomass of forests, the thick humus layer of acidophil forests (acidic mull: mor) means the inactivation of the carbon cycle. In aquatic ecosystems, biological lime excretions can indicate the locking-up of carbon dioxide.

Man, by heating or other industrial applications, liberates carbon stored both underground (coal, oil, methane) and above ground (peat and wood). Heating and industrial activity introduce a great volume of carbon dioxide into the air. Between 1957–1975, the CO_2 content of the atmosphere, measured at different locations, had increased by 5% (Breuer 1977). In contrast to this, the area of carbon dioxide-absorbing natural forest ecosystems (especially

58

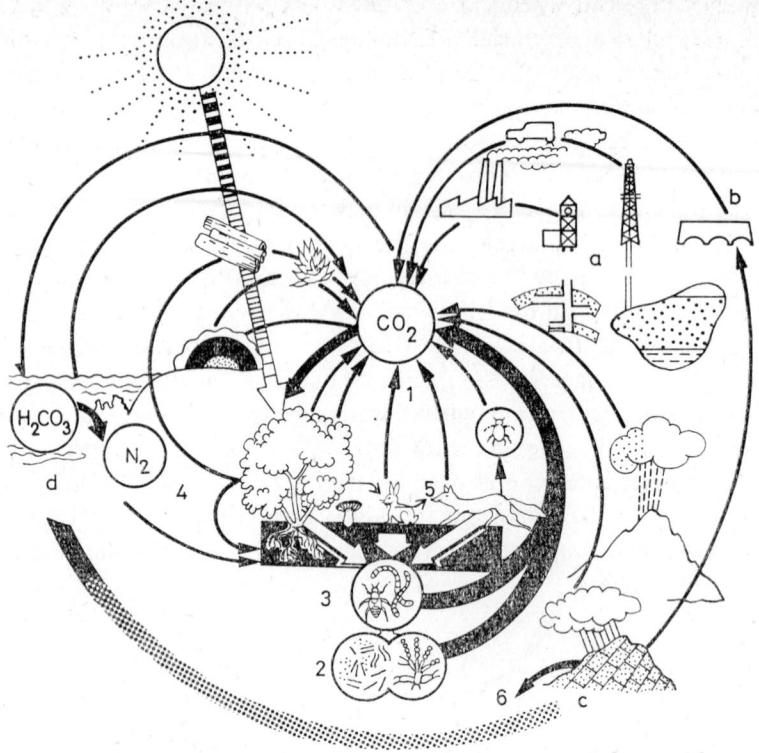

Fig. 14. Carbon cycle. (*a*) coal-fields, (*b*) lime, (*c*) limestone, (*d*) coral-reef, (*1*) respiration, (*2*) decomposition, (*3*) mineralization, (*4*) protein, (*5*) humus, (*6*) solution. (Duvigneaud 1967)

the tropical jungles) is receding. While the biomass of one m^2 of forest area stores 10–20 kg CO_2, that of the cultivated land, which has replaced the forest, amounts to merely 0.5 kg (Woodwell 1976 cit. in Breuer 1977).

Nitrogen cycle

Because of its 80% nitrogen content, air is considered to be a significant store of nitrogen. There are several ways of introducing nitrogen into ecosystems: (*a*) from the air, on the occasion of electric discharges and thunderstorms, (*b*) by nitrogen-fixing microbes and bacteria (*Rhizobium, Azotobacter, Croococcum agile, Clostridium butyricum*) and by a few species of algae, (*c*) by bacteria transforming the proteins of dead organisms into ammonia, nitrite and nitrate which, after penetrating into the soil, become

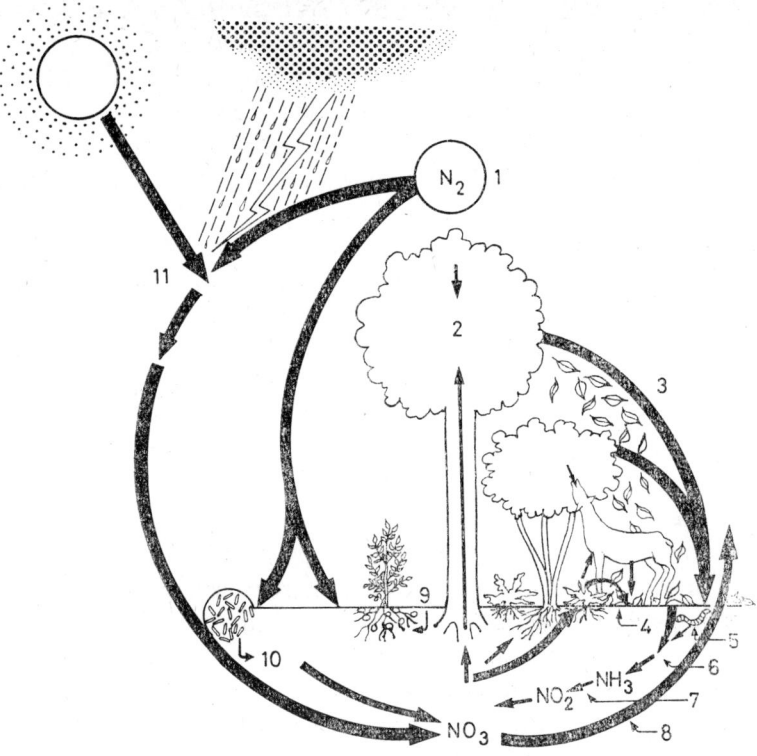

Fig. 15. Nitrogen cycle. (*1*) N_2-content of air, (*2*) photosynthesis and protein synthesis (*3*) fall of leaves, (*4*) decomposition by bacteria and fungi, (*5*) worms, (*6*) ammonifica tion, (*7*) nitrification, (*8*) denitrification, (*9*) Papilionaceae and root nodules, (*10* absorption of atmospheric nitrogen, (*11*) electrochemical and photochemical absorption (Duvigneaud 1974)

available for plants in the form of nitrate–nitrogen (Fig. 15). A certain proportion of the nitrogen thus mineralized returns to the air in the form of gas. The decomposition of organic nitrogen-containing compounds (protein) into ammonia is called ammonification. Several species of fungi (*Actynomyces*) and bacteria (*B. mycoides, B. mesentericus, B. subtilis*) take part in the process of ammonification. In the course of nitrification, ammonia is oxidized to nitrites and nitrates. While the mineralization to nitrites is carried out by species of *Nitrosomonas, Nitrosococcus, Nitrosospira* and others in the oxidation to nitrate, species of *Nitrobacter* and *Nitrocystis* are involved. In the reverse process to nitrification, denitrification, in the final step of reduction, gaseous nitrogen is released into the air, which leaves the ecosystem. This process takes place mainly under anaerobic conditions.

From the continental cycle 10×10^6 t of nitrite–nitrogen and 20×10^6 t of organic nitrogen are lost which, being leached from the soil, returns to the oceans together with the water of rivers (Duvigneaud 1974). The rising water-table and the increasing nitrate content of surface waters, owing to the large-scale use of nitrogen-containing fertilizers, may mean a growing danger (Kumm 1976; Shuval and Gruener 1976). When the NO_3 content of drinking water exceeds the value of 45 mg/l, it can cause methaemoglobinaemia in infants. The accumulation of nitrogen in vegetables e.g. spinach, may prove to be similarly dangerous or harmful. Under certain circumstances, either in food or in the digestive system of man, nitrites and nitrates can be transformed into secondary or tertiary amines. Nitrosamines thus formed may have carcinogenic, teratogenic or mutagenic effects.

Phosphorus cycle

As a result of the weathering of rocks, phosphorus is made available for plants in the form of adsorbable phosphorus and it is used in the synthesis of organic matter (Fig. 16). None of the processes of energy transformation can take place in the absence of phosphorus. It is phosphorus that distinguishes living protoplasm from dead systems. Bacteria participating in the decomposition of deposited litter, plant parts and carcasses, liberate phosphorus from organic compounds and repeatedly make it available for plants. In the decomposition of phosphorus-containing organic compounds (nucleoproteids, lecithin, parathion, etc.) different species of bacteria and *Actynomyces* participate. Being discharged into the seas, a certain proportion of phosphorus is incorporated in the body of phytoplankton. By sinking to the sediments of deep seas, part of this phosphorus is removed from circulation, while the remainder returns to the continent along the following food chain: phytoplankton–fish–bird of prey. According to Duvigneaud (1974), although a yearly amount of 60,000 t of phosphorus is being thus returned to dry land, nevertheless, 2 million t is lost yearly, which is washed off or drains away.

The lack of phosphorus means an ever increasing menace (Walter 1975). While the phosphorus resources of the continents are gradually being depleted, the accumulation of phosphorus in running waters is increasing, thus phosphorus is lost. However, it is of primary importance for the agricultural production to possess adequate phosphorus resources as the ever increasing population should be supplied with more and more produce

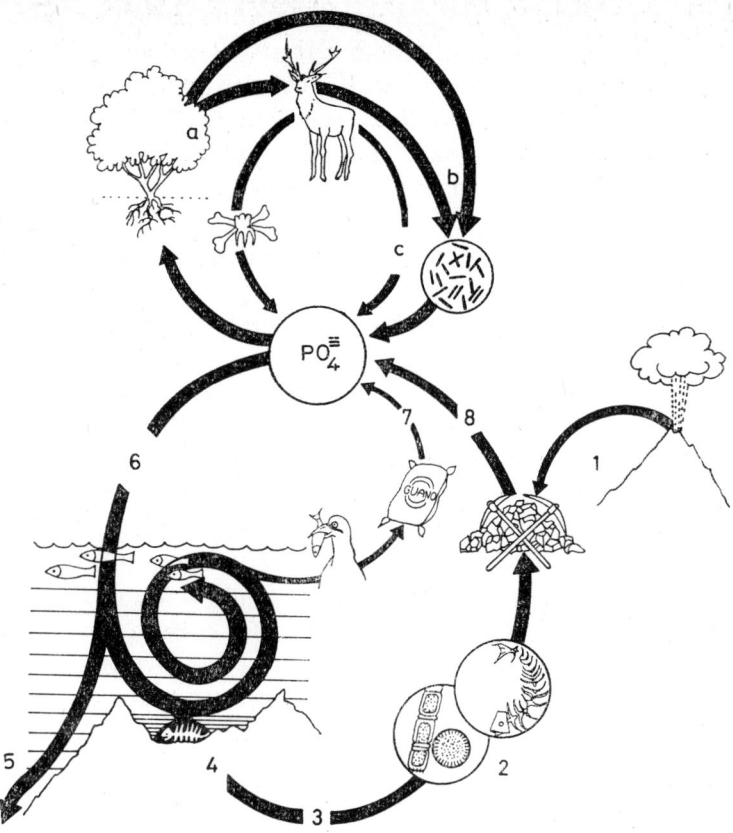

Fig. 16. Phosphorus cycle. (*a*) cycling of organic phosphorus, (*b*) mineralization of organic phosphorus, (*c*) excreta, (*1*) volcanic apatite, (*2*) epigenesis of diatoms, (*3*) fossilization, (*4*) shallow water sediment, (*5*) deep-water sediment, (*6*) phosphorus content of oceanic water, (*7*) use of guano as fertilizer, (*8*) use of fertilizers based on phosphate rock derivatives (superphosphate). (Duvigneaud 1974)

of plant origin. Phosphorus introduced into running waters and lakes, plays an important part in the eutrophication of waters, the occurrence of algal blooms and in the mass spread of certain aquatic weed species.

CHANGES IN THE FOOD CYCLE BROUGHT ABOUT BY ANTHROPOGENIC IMPACTS

Man plays an important role in the biochemical cycles in the following ways: extraction of elements (crop production, mowing, deforestation, etc.), the return of elements (use of fertilizers), the modification of the hydrological cycle (drainage, irrigation and dam construction), the introduction of new elements into the biosphere. Both agricultural and industrial activities modify to a large extent the normal circulation of biological elements. It is of fundamental importance to know the biogeochemical cycles of elements, which makes it possible to assess the impact of human interference and to achieve the most reasonable and practical exploitation of ecosystems and of other natural resources.

Man has been exerting his impact on the biosphere and ecosystem for thousands of years. It was his first major activity to deforest territories in order to gain meadows and arable land. This has resulted in the disruption of local food cycles.

In forests, it is the litter covering the soil that ensures the supply of nutrients. Depending on the chemical composition of the litter, this means that large amounts of calcium, potassium and phosphorus are deposited on the soil surface (Fig. 17). According to measurements carried out in the North-Eastern Central Mountains in Hungary (Kovács 1975), elements that have accumulated in the plant cover (especially K and P) of meadows replacing cleared beech forests, on brown soils, are regularly removed by mowing and grazing. Parallel with the loss of elements from the ecosystem, the content of potassium and phosphorus in the soil of meadows is also decreasing. Variations in the circulation system affect several soil characteristics

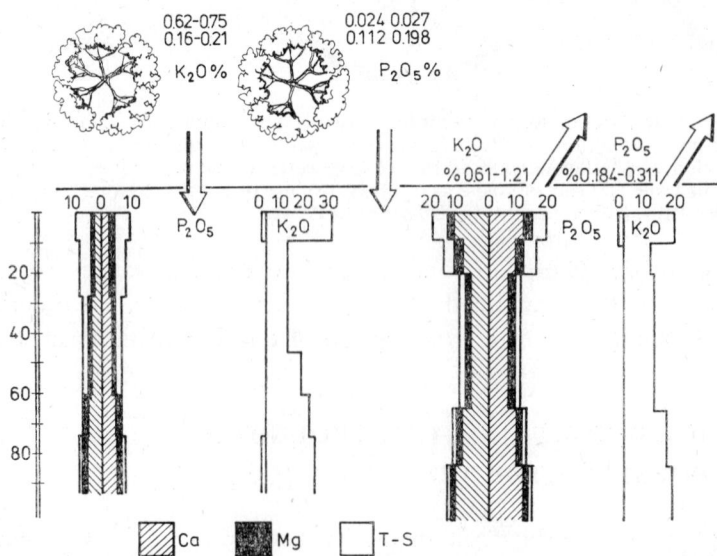

Fig, 17. The effect of woodland (*Melico-Fagetum*) and herbaceous (*Cynosuro-Festucetum rubrae*) vegetation on clay-washed brown forest soil. (Kovács 1975)

such as the water- and anionic-exchange capacity, the ammonia and nitrate content, the already mentioned amount of phosphorus and potassium as well as changes in the adsorption capacity and in the quantity of adsorbed cations.

The grazing of forests or the gathering of litter also extracts large amounts of biological (biogenic) elements from the ecosystem. This results in a decrease in nutrients and later on, in the weakening of the biocoenoses. In cultivated land ecosystems, the natural food cycle is also interrupted. In this case man is regarded as a consumer. Man can replace the missing links in the disrupted food chain by composting agricultural wastes and using manure and fertilizers, which result in the returning of nutrients to the soil.

Due to human activity and environmental pollution, certain biogenic elements such as C, N and S might be introduced into the biogeochemical cycle in amounts greater than normal. The concentration of heavy metals (Pb, Hg, Cd, As) has increased and this may mean an increased danger for man.

References

Balogh, J. (1953): *The principles of zoocoenology* (in Hungarian). Budapest.

Balogh, J. (1971): The principles of biosphere-research (in Hungarian). *MTA Biol. Tud. Oszt. Közlem.* **14**: 13–22.

Breuer, G. (1977): Wird die Welt-Biomasse grösser oder kleiner? *Naturwiss. Rundschau* **30**: 281–286.

Carbiener, R. (1969): Aperçu sur quelques effects de la pollution des eaux douces de la zone tempérée sur les biocenoses aquatiques. *Bull. de la Section de Géographie* **80**: 45–132.

Dajoz, R. (1971): *Précis d'écologie*. Paris.

Dorst, J. (1971): *Avant que la nature meure*. Paris.

Duvigneaud, P. (1974): *L'ècologie, science moderne de synthèse. Écosystèmes et biosphère*. 2nd ed. Paris.

Dylla, K. and Krätzner, G. (1972): *Das biologische Gleichgewicht*. Heidelberg.

Ellenberg, H. (1972): Belastung und Belastbarkeit von Ökosystemen. In: *Belastung und Belastbarkeit von Ökosystemen*. Tagungsbericht der Gesellschaft für Ökologie, Tagung Giessen 1972. 19–26.

Ellenberg, H. (1973): *Ökosystemforschung*. Berlin–Heidelberg–New York.

Felföldy, L. (1972): Taxonomic key of the blue algae (Cyanophyta) (in Hungarian). *Vízügyi Hidrobiológia* Budapest.

Giessler, A. (1972): Wasserkreislauf und Umweltschutz. *Wasser und Boden.* **24**: 31–34.

Hutchinson, T. C. and Havas, U. (eds) (1980): *Effects of acid precipitation on terrestrial ecosystems*. New York.

Jakucs, P. (1973): "Síkfőkút Project". The environment-biological study of an oak forest ecosystem within the framework of the biosphere-program (in Hungarian). *MTA Biol. Tud. Oszt. Közlem.* **16**: 11–25.

Kovács, M. (1975): *Beziehung zwischen Vegetation und Boden*. Budapest.

Kozák, M. and Mészáros, M. (1971a): The role of the chemical composition of rainwater precipitation in the study of air pollution (in Hungarian). *Agrártud. Közlem.* **30**: 395–401.

Kozák, M. and Mészáros, E. (1971b): Chemical composition of rainwater in Hungary and its agricultural importance (in Hungarian). *Agrokém. és Talajt.* **20**: 329–352.

Kulp, J. L. (1961): Radionuclides in man from nuclear tests. *J. Agric. Food Chem.* **9**: 122–126.

Kumm, K. I. (1976): An economic analysis of nitrogen leaching caused by agricultural activities. In: Svenson, B. H. and Söderlund, R. (eds): Nitrogen, phosphorus and sulphur global cycles. SCOPE Report 7. *Ecol. Bull.* **22**: 169–183.

Landolt, E. (1971): Bedeutung und Pflege von Biotopen. In: Leibundgut, H. (ed.): Schutz unseres Lebensraumes. München–Bern–Wien.

Láng, G. (1968): Vegetationsänderung am Bodenseeufer in den letzten hundert Jahren. *Schrift, d. Vereins f. Geschichte des Bodensees u. seiner Umgebung* **86**: 295–319.

Lieth, H. (1972): Modelling of primary productivity of the Earth (in Hungarian). *MTA Biol. Tud. Oszt. Közlem.* **15**: 341–348.

Margalef, R. (1963): Successions of populations. *Adv. Front. Plant Sci.* **2**: 137–188.

Máthé, I. (1971): The role of plant production in the biosphere (in Hungarian). *MTA Biol. Tud. Oszt. Közlem.* **14**: 97–102.

Meiwes, K. J. and Khanna, P. K. (1981): Distribution and cycling of sulphur in the vegetation of two forest ecosystems in an acid rain environment. *Plant and Soil* **60**: 369–375.

Mészáros, E. (1973): Chemical composition of rainfall in Central Europe (in Hungarian). *Időjárás* **74**: 35–47.

Meyer von Genzenbach, R. (1971): Die Beanspruchung der Umwelt durch die Besiedlung. In: Leibundgut, H. (ed.): *Schutz unseres Lebensraumes*. München–Bern–Wien.

Oden, S. (1976): The acidity problem—an outline of concepts. *Water, Air and Soil Pollution* **6**: 137–166.

Odum, E. P. (1971): *Fundamentals of Ecology*. 3. ed. Philadelphia–London–Toronto.

Odum, E. P. (1972): *Ökologie*. München–Basel–Wien.

Odum, E. P. (1980): *Grundlagen der Ökologie I–II*. Stuttgart–New York.

Ovington, J. D. (1965): Organic production, turnover and mineral cycling in woodlands. *Biol. Rev. Cambridge Phil. Soc.* **40**: 295–336.

Précsényi, I. (1971): *The primary production of natural terrestrial ecosystems* (in Hungarian). Dissertation.

Rodin, L. E. and Bazilevich, N. J. (1965-66): *Production and mineral cycling in terrestrial vegetation*. Edinburgh.

Rodin, L. E. and Bazilevich, N. J. (1968): *World distribution of plant biomass*. Unesco Copenhagen Symp. Paris. 45-52.

Shuval, H. I. and Gruener. N. (1976): Infant methaemoglobinaemia and other health effects of nitrates in drinking water. In: Dobolyi, E. (ed.): The role and importance of nitrogen in the water ecosystem. (in Hungarian). *Vízügyi Műszaki Gazdasági Tájékoztató.* 74: 33-34.

Simon, T. and Kovácsné-Láng, E. (1972): Production—biological investigations at the IBP model area of Csévharaszt (in Hungarian). *MTA Biol. Tud. Oszt. Közlem.* 15: 61-69.

Steubing, L. (1972): Ökologie als Wissenschaftliche Grundlage des Umweltschutzes. *Funkuniversität RIAS Vortragsfolg. Mscr.* 70: 1-14.

Szabó, M. and Csortos, Cs. (1975): A study of the nutrient content of the canopy throughfall in an oak forest (*Quercetum petraeae-cerris*) measured for one year. *Acta Bot. Acad. Sci. Hung.* 21: 419-432.

Ubrizsy, G. (ed.) (1968): *Encyclopedia of plant protection I-II*. (in Hungarian). Budapest.

Ubrizsy, G. (1969): Pesticides—a blessing and a curse (in Hungarian). *Korunk Tudománya*. Budapest.

Ulrich, B., Mayer, R. and Khanna, P. K. (1980): Chemical changes due to acid precipitation in a loess-derived soil in Central Europe. *Soil Science* 130: 193-199.

Walter, H. (1975): Besonderheiten des Stoffkreislaufes einiger terrestrischen Ökosysteme. *Flora* 164: 169-183.

Whittaker, R. H. (1971): *Communities and ecosystems*. London.

Woodwell, G. M. (1970): The energy cycle of the biosphere. *Sci. Amer.* 64-74.

Woodwell, G. M. (1971): Toxic substances and ecological cycles. In: Ehrlich, P. R., Holdren, J. P. and Holm, R. W. (eds): *Man and the ecosphere*. San Francisco.

Zólyomi, B. (1973): Environment control aspects of the material and energy flow in the biosphere (in Hungarian). *Tud. és Mezőgazd.* 11: 15-17.

Zólyomi, B., Máthé, I., Précsényi, I. and Szőcs, Z. (1972): Investigations into the productivity of vegetation at the IBP model area of Újszentmargita (in Hungarian). *MTA Biol. Tud. Oszt. Közlem.* 15: 31-43.

Chapter 4

Genetic principles of environmental control and population biology

---

THE IMPORTANCE OF THE GENETIC STUDY OF POPULATIONS

The living components of each ecosystem are made up of systems of living organisms, including plant and animal communities and large numbers of microorganisms. Each of these communities, forming the entire living world of the particular habitat, is divided into numerous populations. Generally each population with a separate density comprises a number of individuals belonging to the same biological species. These individuals are more or less closely related and descended from a common stock thus—in respect of several generations—they are frequently members of the same breeding community. The populations interact with one another and with other components (in short with the environment) and they are either active or passive participants in the energy and mass flow of the ecosystem. They fulfil this function by adapting themselves to the environmental conditions. A successful adaptation means the following: (*a*) Its members possess those inheritable biological characters that are essential for their biotic and reproductive potential; (*b*) The characters of the population, as a unit of a multi-individual organization (e.g. its size, i.e. the number of its individuals, the rate of increase, the distribution of individuals according to their age and their genetic composition) are compatible with the structure of the given ecosystem both in space and time.

Populations are confronted in different ecosystems with more or less variable environmental conditions, changing continuously not only in space but also in time and they either steadily adapt themselves to the changing environment or will be annihilated. Therefore, the fate of a given population depends, on one hand, on the rate and amplitude of the environmental changes and on the other, on its potential adaptability. More or less serious environmental disruptions always result in the inability of some populations to adapt themselves to changing environments (overdrying or overhumidification or other microclimatic changes, changing light conditions or soil structure, accumulation of poisonous substances, starvation) consequently they are sooner or later eliminated. Therefore, in order to protect the living world, it is very important to know, at least approximately, the tolerance of certain populations, that is to say, those limits beyond which populations are eliminated, or deteriorate to such a degree, that the productivity, energy utilization and balance of the whole ecosystem are also reduced.

The degradation or extinction of individual populations may also have other unfavourable consequences. Natural populations are specific genetic resources similar to the unexploited sources of raw materials, from which developments in scientific and technological innovations can lead to increasing benefits in different branches of applied biology (plant and animal breeding, medical sciences) and related branches of industry. New methods using the techniques of molecular biology, are already taking shape. By means of these, genes or series of genes of systematically distantly related species can be built into the genotype of a domestic animal or cultivated plant, with the aim of increasing the productivity of the organism or of a variety in a favourable direction or of eliminating the transmission of deleterious characters. It can be stated that the fate and future of mankind largely depend on the quantity of genetic resources, wasted almost irrecoverably through the deterioration or annihilation of natural populations. The adaptability of a given population—its loadability—depends on its genetic structure and genetic variability. Therefore the following sections survey present knowledge of the genetic structure, variability and of the genetic mechanism of adaptation. The results of the process of adaptation—the main factors of fitness or adaptability—will also be analysed. Knowing them, we can outline the genetic parameters of the population upon which its loadability also depends.

GENETIC STRUCTURE OF POPULATIONS

The behaviour pattern of a population, i.e. the genetic standards (norms) of reaction manifesting themselves under given environmental conditions, is determined by the composition of the gene pool of all the individuals. The allele structure of this gene pool is, in all cases, characteristic of the population and more or less different from that of other populations. By allele structure, in this context, we mean the relative frequency of alleles belonging to the same gene loci. Thus, for example, where the relative frequencies of the alleles of a certain gene (A_1 and A_2) are p and q respectively, then $p+q=1$ and $p=1-q$ or $q=1-p$.

In populations of haploid organisms (in the case of several mosses and single-celled algae) the allele frequency equals that of the genotype. In diploid populations, the frequency of the genotypes, i.e. the ratio of homozygous (A_1A_1 and A_2A_2) and heterozygous (A_1A_2) genotypes, deduced from the Mendelian rules of inheritance, are as follows:

alleles:	A_1		A_2
their frequency:	p		q
genotypes:	A_1A_1	A_1A_2	A_2A_2
their symbols:	P	H	Q
their frequency:	p^2	2pq	q^2

Supposing, that the population is large enough and the mating is free and random (panmixis) and there is no genetic mutation or selection, then allele and genotype frequencies assume an equilibrium value, which is sustained from one generation to the next (Hardy–Weinberg equilibrium). The quantitative relation between allele and genotype frequencies is illustrated in Fig. 18.

The Hardy–Weinberg equilibrium can also be extended to three or more alleles at one locus. If three alleles belong to the gene locus in the population studied (A_1, A_2 and A_3) and their frequencies are p, q, r, and $p+q+r=1$,

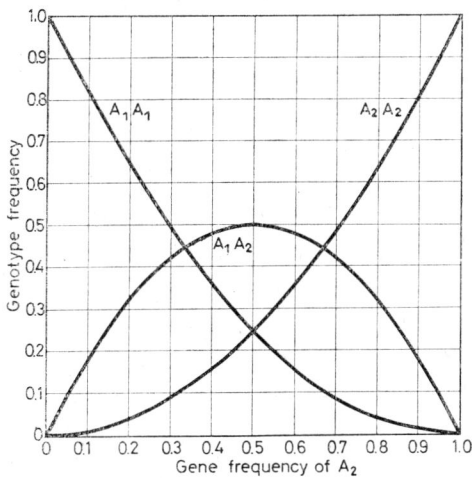

Fig. 18. Relationship between genotype frequencies and gene frequency for two alleles in a population in Hardy–Weinberg equilibrium. (Falconer 1960)

then the frequency of the six possible genotypes (allele combinations) will be as follows:

$$A_1A_1 \quad A_1A_2 \quad A_1A_3 \quad A_2A_2 \quad A_2A_3 \quad A_3A_3$$
$$p^2: \quad 2pq: \quad 2pr: \quad q^2: \quad 2pr: \quad r^2$$

External factors or internal changes can cause changes in the allele frequency; in the case of certain genotypes, the mortality of homozygous recessive individuals exceeds the average; the reproductive fitness of certain heterozygous combinations is above the average; the migration of individuals of different genotypes in large numbers from outer populations; the destruction of the major part of the population; in the latter case the new equilibrium frequency of the genotypes re-establishes itself through one generation of free, random mating in the diploid part of the population. In the case of two gene loci (two allele pairs), situated on separate chromosomes, the difference from the equilibrium value (disequilibrium) will be halved in each subsequent generation; if they were sited on the same chromosome as linked loci, the situation is different from the case where only one locus was involved. As the disequilibrium is reduced by linkage value in each generation in polyploidic populations the equilibrium state establishes itself more slowly. Should random, free mating be limited, the ratio of the genotypic frequencies will be modified even in the case of unaltered allele frequencies, while the number of homozygotes increases, that of the heterozygotes decreases. The equilibrium of allele and genotype frequencies is consequently in a state of dynamic balance (equilibrium) within the population. Even free, random mating is nothing but a statistical probability characterised by a certain dispersion.

Considering the fact that the genotype of individuals composing the population may comprise numerous combinations of several gene loci and alleles, it is obvious that there can be many phenotypes. A major part of the phenotypic variability (differences deriving from the modifying effects and their interactions within a given environment) is determined, in most cases, by the genetic or genotypic diversity. The biometric index for the phenotypic diversity of the population is the phenotypic variance (square of the standard deviation: s^2). Generally, genetic variance plays a much smaller part, being a proportion of phenotypic variance which is caused by differences in genetic make-up of the genotypes of individuals in the population. Most genotypic variations, however, do not manifest themselves through the phenotype. Thus, there is no phenotypic difference between the dominant homozygotes and heterozygotes in the presence of total dominance. Such hidden genotypic differences constitute the potential or hidden genetic variance that might be transformed into free genetic variance in future generations. To give an idea of the size of the potential genetic variance and of the infinite variability resources deriving from it, one should try to assess the cumulative capacity of both the individual and of the population, i.e. the amount of information that can be stored in the genetic stock and germ plasm of the population. As far as we know, this genetic material is, in most cases, the deoxyribonucleic acid (DNA). Geneticists have already detected up to about 50 to 100 genes in the DNA of some virus particles. The circular chromosomes of bacterial cells may contain 500 to 1000 genes. One of the sex chromosomes of *Drosophyla melanogaster* (the X chromosome) contains approx. 1,000 genes and its total chromosome set, almost 5,000 genes. The number of genes in vertebrates, including man, may vary between 10,000–100,000 (Dobzhansky 1970). Naturally, the number of gene alleles is greater than the number of genes: although several dozens of alleles are known to exist in certain genes, the entire allele complement may be substantially larger. The number of possible allele combinations is:

$$V = \frac{r(r+1)^n}{2}$$

in which r signifies the number of alleles belonging to the same locus and n is the number of genes. According to this, 1,000 genes—each with 10 alleles—can give 55^{1000} combinations, genotypes. This is more than the number of all the electrons in the universe.

GENETIC VARIABILITY OF POPULATIONS

From the large number of the possible allele combinations mentioned above one should conclude that the majority of possible genotypes could not have been realised during the millennia of previous geological ages. In other words, only a fragment of the potential genetic variance has yet been realised in true populations. The explanation for this lies with the linkage of several loci on chromosomes. The genotypes are, namely, the possible combinations neither of the genes nor of their alleles, but of their linked groups. Thus, assuming complete linkage, the value of n—in the previous formula—will be equal to the number of the linked groups, i.e. the haploid chromosome number, e.g. if n=10, then $V = 55^{10}$; which is already 55^{990} times less than the previous number. However, it is a relatively high number with 18 decimal digits.

Since the size (number of individuals) of populations is not large enough, it is obvious that so many genotypes cannot exist in the populations of higher organisms at the same time. On the other hand, the number of alleles belonging to the same locus is often less than 10, i.e. sometimes not more than 1 or 2. It is only in very large populations, or in a whole biological species that all the possible genotypes might occur. Consequently, in a population of average size (the number of individuals being a few thousands or a few millions) only a small percentage of the entire potential genetic variation of the species can be manifested. The question therefore arises: what is the source of new variants and what factors influence their frequency and future fate. According to our present knowledge, the sources of genetic variation are (*i*) genetic recombination, (*ii*) gene flow and (*iii*) mutation. In all three mechanisms, chance plays an important part, therefore, the probability of the events is a statistical one. The other mechanism, limiting the genetic variability, the drift or random fixation is similar in character (see later in this chapter).

Recombination

The essence of genetic recombination is the following: in some of the offsprings, or all of them, the allele pairs of parents carrying distinguishing characters are found in different combinations from the parents. The classical Mendelian crosses are well known examples of this. Thus, e.g. in the second (F_2) generation from parents with wrinkled green and smooth yellow seed coats, recombinational variations of yellow, wrinkled and green and smooth seeds also appeared. The cytological basis for this mechanism is to be found in the reductional nuclear division (meiosis) followed by fertilization.

As already seen, the number of recombinant types is, basically, the function of linkage groups, i.e. that of the number of gametic chromosomes. Of course, it is not so simple. This would only be true, if the composition of the linkage groups never changed. In this example one of the two linkage groups should reappear exactly in the second chromosome of each maize plant, representing one of these groups, e.g. as ABCDEFG... and other as abcdefg.... In the course of meiosis, however, the mating homologous chromosomes cross over during chiasma formation and reciprocal exchange of genes takes place. One of the possible results of such an exchange, using the above example, could give ABCdefg... and abcDEFG... as allele-sequence in a certain percentage of the resulting gametes. Therefore, concerning the second chromosome, merely one crossing over results in not only two but four types of gametes from the meiosis. These, then, following self-fertilization, will give instead of three, nine genotype combinations.

The frequency of crossing over varies greatly. Cytological studies of meiosis and the determination of chiasma frequencies furnish some useful quantitative data here. That is why the product of the multiplication of the chromosome number and chiasma frequency, the recombination index, gives useful data on the probable frequency of new combinations (Darlington 1958). Consequently, the number of genetic variants increases in proportion to the degree of polyploidy, as the chromosome number grows parallel with the values of the recombination index. The frequency of recombination in the population is also regulated by further factors. These jointly constitute the genetic system of the population or species, i.e. a regulating system, which tries to maintain the appearance of new genotypic combinations between certain limits, at an optimal or nearly optimal level.

The reproduction or breeding system is a very important component of the genetic system. In a population reproducing merely asexually (through parthenogenesis or vegetatively) genetic recombination is limited in the absence of reductional nuclear division. The genetic variance of the resulting offspring generation is near to zero. In a stable environment, this kind of breeding system may favour the quick, explosive spread of a well-established genotype, but gives only little opportunity for the continuous adaptation to the spatial and temporal changes of the environment.

In the course of evolution, several mechanisms and devices have been formed, which partly or completely eliminate self-fertilization. By means of this, the decrease in frequency of heterozygous genotypes is slowed down in the population. In the simplest case, either the formation of male and female gametes in a plant is not simultaneous or the flower structure is an obstacle to self-pollination. The different kinds of self-sterility are sometimes as effective in eliminating autogamy as in dioecious plants (where the sex organs are on different plants). There are numerous transition forms between these two extreme types.

Another component of the genetic system connected with reproduction is the way and effective range of the spreading and transmission of gametes. In the living world one may find an immense variability in this field, too. For example, the pollen-cloud of wind-pollinated plants often reaches to a great distance and in this way, contributes to the formation of the gene-pool of the next generation in remote populations. In other cases some gamete transmission mechanisms function as limiting factors. It is interesting that certain pollinating insects visit flowers of only the same colour, thus reducing genetic variability in a given population. In the animal world frequently the assortative mating takes place, i.e. the distribution of pair selection does not fit the curve of the random distribution. These few examples well illustrate that those factors of genetic system which favour or limit the genetic recombination are in a continuous interaction with each other in order to keep the genetic variance of the population at a nearly optimal level.

The life span of the individuals and especially the length of the reproductive, fertile phase constitutes another essential element of the genetic system. In the case of long-living individuals producing several broods of numerous offsprings, a much greater percentage of the genetic variability is manifested in their progeny as in that of the short-lived species reproducing only once and producing only a few offsprings.

The genetic variability very frequently manifests itself only with delay. For example, only a tiny percentage of the seeds of steppe or desert plants germinate immediately. Their majority remains dormant for many—sometimes up to 5–10—years. In this way, the variability of the populations is preserved in a resting state for a long time, therefore their survival depends on extreme environmental factors much less than if all seeds germinated immediately.

Gene flow

The regular or repeated migration of individuals or groups of individuals into a certain population may also contribute to the enrichment of its gene pool with new alleles. In the case where generative organs (seeds, spores, rootstocks) or gametes (pollen, eggs of fishes or frogs) get into the population and promote the formation of the genetic pool in the next generation, the result will be the same. The intensity of migration and, in general, that of the gene flow may be so intense that the existence of certain populations can be due to them. Gene flow can be hindered by certain factors of isolation, such as mountain ranges, basins, rivers, lakes, seas, huge forests or marsh land, deserts. Internal factors like cytological, physiological, aetiological, reproductive, in short, genetic factors can also often hinder the gene flow, sometimes even among related populations.

Introgressive hybridisation is an extreme example of gene flow. This means a single hybridisation of populations belonging to different species and the back-crossing of the species hybrids with the individuals of the recipient population. As a result, the alleles of the donor population enrich

the gene pool of the recipient population. This process is called gene introgression. This results in a widening of genetic variability in the recipient
population and sometimes the merger of a donor population of only a few
individuals into a large recipient population; decrease of the hybrid sterility caused by the weakening of the isolating factor between the two species;
morphological and/or ecological separation of the recipient population from
other populations of the same species; increase of chromosome homolo-
gy between the genomes of the donor and the recipient populations (Anderson 1949). Introgressive hybridisation has been detected in many cases.
The increasing amount of data available also indicates that it may happen
between populations of differing ploidy level (e.g. between diploid and
tetraploid *Dactylis* species; Stebbins and Zohary 1959).

Mutations

While in the case of recombination it is the available allele pool of the population that increases the genetic variability of the population, in terms
of gene flow the same result is reached by the inclusion of foreign alleles.
The appearance of mutations has the same consequence. Owing to less
well-known external and internal factors, different alleles of genes can be
altered through the changing of the internal molecular structure of DNA
(exchange of nucleotides, their duplication, deletion). The result is called
mutation. It can be detected only by the obvious morphological or functiona
changes. Its frequency in each generation is very low (approx. 10^{-5}–10^{-6}
but, considering the size of the entire gene pool of a population, it can be
assumed that the number of mutant alleles might be quite substantial, even
in only a single generation. The majority of mutations are, however, recessive, they manifest themselves only in homozygotes. Therefore, considering
the low frequency, the formation of homozygous mutant recombinations is
also strictly limited. In the gene pool of larger populations numerous
damaging mutations can accumulate (genetic load). However, in extreme
cases, in certain allele combinations (genetic background) even damaging
alleles may have a beneficial influence.

Genetic drift

Recombination, gene flow and mutations are partly responsible for maintenance of the variability and manifoldness of the population. The incorporation of new alleles and allele combinations, however, increases its genetic

variability although, in the life of a population, some events may also happen that can reduce both the free and the potential genetic variability. Should a major part of the population be destroyed suddenly, e.g. as a result of a disaster or destruction of the environment, this can lead to the permanent loss of several allele combinations or alleles from the gene pool. The remaining fraction of the gene pool of the original population, contains only a "random sample" of its genes, as it is too small a sample to give a reliable representation of the original gene pool. This mechanism is called genetic drift (random sampling, Sewall–Wright effect). In the fragmented population, owing to the error of sampling, the genotype and allele frequencies differ greatly from those of the original population. The variance of the allele frequencies in the changing generations is inversely proportional to the number of individuals, N, in the population:

$$s_{\Delta q}^2 = \frac{p_0 q_0}{2N}$$

Should the number of individuals be low, the change of allele frequencies, calculated for one generation, will then be high, i.e. the frequency of many alleles will be reduced to nil, while that of the others will reach 1 (random fixation). Consequently, in small populations, those alleles can remain as well which occur in the large populations only with small frequencies. Therefore, large differences could evolve between genetic constitutions of different splinter populations. This might have far-reaching ecological, genetic and evolutionary consequences.

THE GENETIC MECHANISMS OF ADAPTATION

In the previous sections of this chapter, it has been shown that the sources of genetic variability in the population are infinite. Recombination, gene flow, mutation and genetic drift are, on the whole, free, random and unregulated events. If the allele and genotype frequency in the population depended only on these factors, there would never be permanent differences and therefore no evolution among populations. Within the population itself, the genotypes of the majority of individuals would be loaded by a multitude of damaging mutations. Their number and quality would vary within wide limits and—depending on it—viability as well as fertility would show a wide individual variation from the mean. Only selection will transform this merely random and unregulated variation into an orderly state. The effect of selection implies the classification of different genotypes according to their adaptive values, as a result of which they become dominant or recede into the background during the life of the population.

The adaptive value (fitness)

The adaptive value expresses the degree of viability and reproductive capability of a certain genotype, in comparison with other genotypes, within a given environment. The higher adaptive values—the more successful adaptations—can have several genotypically determined components. Such are faster growth, greater or smaller size and fertility, life span and competitive abilities, climatic resistance and resistance to certain diseases. The adaptive value depends more or less on the whole genotype. It is not merely the sum of the "reaction norms" of certain alleles, but the result of the action and interaction of all the alleles constituting the genotype. As, in certain cases, similar or identical phenotypes can belong to different genotypes, it is relevant to note that there will be no substantial difference between their adaptive values. On the other hand, under different environmental conditions, the same genotype has different adaptive values. The adaptive value is, therefore, only a relative basis for comparisons. This relativity is even more important when comparing different populations, the average adaptive value being reflected in the growth rate of the population, which however, varies also according to the degree of saturation of the ecosystem, that is to say, the degree of population density, which depends on the diverse genotypic structure of the populations. Consequently, the mean value of adaptation (adaptive value) varies not only within, but also among populations.

Fitness of the population and flexibility

In a constantly changing environment there are two possible conditions when the adaptive value may remain constant. Firstly, the individuals should be capable of phenotypic adaptation, when the extent of environmental changes does not exceed the limits of the genotypic reaction norms (phenotypic flexibility). Secondly, recombination could transform the hidden, potential genetic variance of the population into free variation (genotypic flexibility). Where the rate of environmental change results in a longer time for adaptation than one reproductional cycle, then this would allow for the effective operation of genotypic flexibility. While the phenotypic flexibility of heterozygotes is generally low, their genotypic flexibility is always greater than those of the homozygotes. In exceptional cases, under extreme environmental conditions or in the case of colonizing species, it is not flexibility but genetic stability that increases the adaptive value of the population, the genotypic constitution of which remains nearly unchanged under widely varying environmental factors. This is brought about by the different mechanisms of the genetic system: structural hetero-zygosity, obligate autogamy and the high degree of homozygosity resulting from it, permanent hybridity and preferential pairing, apomixis and parthe-nogenesis, certain types of polyploidy. Generally, such populations are to be found at the boundaries of the area of a particular species.

Coadaptation and super-genes

The adaptive value consists of several factors. Each of these factors, as fertility, drought and cold resistance, is a multiple compound of genetic features controlled by several genes. The more closely these genes are linked, the less likely it is that their alleles would recombine into genotypes differing from their parents (their crossing over frequency is low). This means, in other words, that these gene loci are situated in the same chromosome, next to each other and that in this chromosome segment, the formation of chiasmata is very rare in meiosis. The very closely linked alleles are in-herited as though they were only one allele. Since they also complement each other functionally, they can substantially increase the adaptive value of a given genotype. The units of such coadapted alleles are the super-genes (Darlington and Mather 1949). The mechanism of genetic coherence indicates the frequent formation of coadaptations and super-genes. This is the strong correlation of certain phenotypic characters and their joint in-heritance in the crossings of different races, sub-species, that is also evident under widely varying environmental conditions (Clausen and Hiesey 1958).

Polymorphism

It has already been mentioned that, in the same environment, the adaptive value of individuals with different genotypes can be the same. In such cases their frequencies, compared with each other, presumably remain the same. However, many examples indicate that the frequencies of two or more mutually dependent genotypes affect each other. A well-known example of this, the ratio of male and female individuals in the populations of sexually differentiated organisms, is based on the structural dimorphism of sex chromosomes. The distribution of human blood types, amongst the inhabitants of different continents, is also related to the adaptive value of certain genotypic characters. The heterozygous forms of the human sickle-cell anaemia is always present in populations where malaria is endemic. A further example is that in a certain percentage of cross-fertilizing (allogamic) plants, the frequency of alleles responsible for the self-incompatibility is generally constant, even in a changing environment. Thus, a well-balanced polymorphism can be looked upon as the consequence of the generally greater adaptive value of heterozygotes. But polymorphism can also result from the negative correlation between the adaptive value of one of the genotypes and its own frequency in the population (frequency- or density-dependent polymorphism). The polymorphism of structural and enzyme proteins, studied at the molecular level, has proved to be unexpectedly high (Scandalios 1969). Generally speaking, genetic polymorphism significantly increases the adaptive value of the population and thus weakens the damaging effect of environmental changes on the survival of the population.

Selection

From the previous facts it follows that, according to the adaptive value, i.e. principally as a result of natural selection, a classification on the basis of viability and fertility, the genotype and allele frequencies are modified, while the rate of genotypes with higher adaptive values increases, the proportion of those with lower values decreases. This process goes on until a balance is established between the genetic gain due to mutation and gene flow and by selection elimination. In a given environment, the result of selection can vary depending on the identity of genotypes of the highest adaptive value within the most frequently occurring genotypes of the population. Following from this, three main types can be distinguished:

1. Stabilizing or normalizing selection. The genotypes with the most frequent and the highest adaptive value remain nearly the same. Thus, genotypes differing from the average in any direction (the rarest genotypes) are eliminated and variability decreases in the population.

2. Directional selection. Where the environment is progressively changing in one direction (or the population migrates into another environment), genotypes with the highest adaptive values do not remain identical with

the most frequent genotypes, but belong to one of the positive or negative variant classes. Thus, selection results in the increase of the positive or negative variant class while the rate of handicapped variants decreases. In other words, the peak of the distribution curve will be shifted either in a positive or negative direction.

3. Disruptive or diversifying selection. Similar to the previous example, it is possible for the adaptive value of both positive and negative variants to be higher than that of the most frequent genotypes. Consequently, this type of selection results in two peaks on the distribution curve and is most frequent in the heterogeneous, mosaic-like environments.

The quantitative measure of selection intensity is the selection coefficient. It is the extent to which the gametes of the genotype under study—compared with the gametes of the genotype with the highest adaptive value—contribute to the gene pool of the next generation. The other quantitative measure of selection is the selection pressure, the rate at which the allelic frequencies change per generation. For a given community, selection results in the dominance of populations which have adaptive values higher than others. To put it simply, the higher adaptive value can become apparent in greater reproductivity and in a higher capacity to exploit spatial and energy sources. It depends on the environment which of the factors determining the adaptive value is more favourable. In an unsaturated (underpopulated) habitat (e.g. a newly colonized island in the wake of a disaster, an abandoned mine, a burnt-out or cleared forest) those populations will become dominant which have a high net growth rate (r) (i.e. the difference between the birth (s_0) and death rate (h_0) is high):

$$r_0 = s_0 - h_0$$

Consequently, these populations are capable of rapid reproduction. In saturated (overpopulated) ecosystems, however, those populations will have higher adaptive values which can best utilize the available material and energy sources, i.e. selection results in the increase of the carrying capacity (K) of the habitat. The former are called r-strategist, the latter K-strategist populations.

EXAMPLES OF THE ADAPTIVE TRANSFORMATION OF NATURAL POPULATIONS

Investigations into the adaptive transformation of natural or artificially synthesised populations clearly demonstrate the role of adaptive factors and their interactions. Thus, in the well-known Park Grass Experiment, at

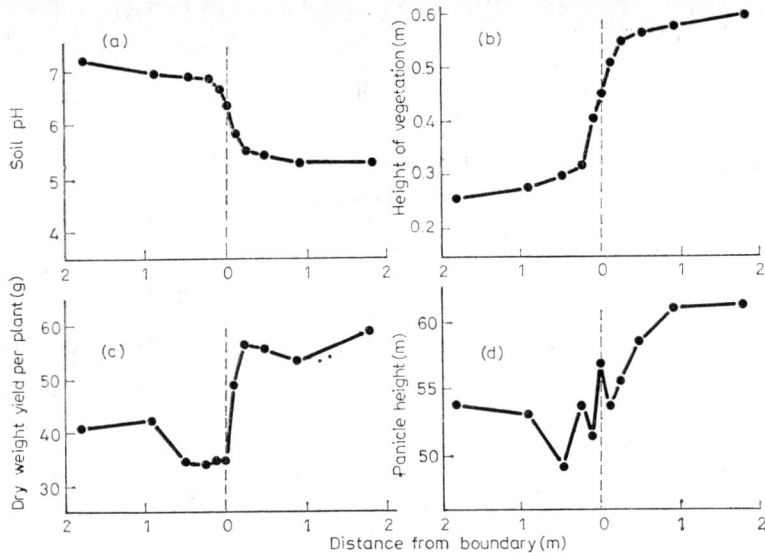

Fig. 19. Spatial changes in environmental conditions at the boundary between two plots
of the Park Grass Experiment at Rothamsted (*a* and *b*), and associated morphological
differences between populations of *Anthoxanthum odoratum* L. collected at the boundary
(*c* and *d*). (*a*) Soil pH., (*b*) height of vegetation, (*c*) dry matter yield of *A. odoratum* plants
in a spaced plant trial, (*d*) panicle height of *A. odoratum* in a spaced plant trial. (Snaydon
1973)

Rothamsted, under the same environmental conditions, the genetic variance
of ten morphological characters was studied in limed and unlimed plots, in
each fourth year, since 1903 (Snaydon and Davies 1972). Towards the edges
of the plots—within a few decimetres—an immediate change of the soil pH
(between 4.0–7.0) was observed. In strong correlation with this, several
morphological features of the population had changed. There were substantial differences in the yield, the height of panicle, etc. (Fig. 19). In this
example, in a closed grass community, K-selection resulted in a diverging
evolution. Continuous or abrupt changes of the environment are followed
by similarly continuous or sudden changes of the genotypic constitution of
the population, e.g. *Agrostis stolonifera* stands on the sea-shore. The short-
stoloned genotype grows in grass patches on the top and at the bottom, of
the approx. 30 m high cliffs. The long-stoloned genotype, which is characteristic of the species, can be found in the continuous grass cover above the
cliffs whilst, on the slope, ascending from below, the increase of stolone
length can be observed. Its genetic determination has been shown by
comparisons in the experimental field (Aston and Bradshaw 1966), (Fig. 20).

82

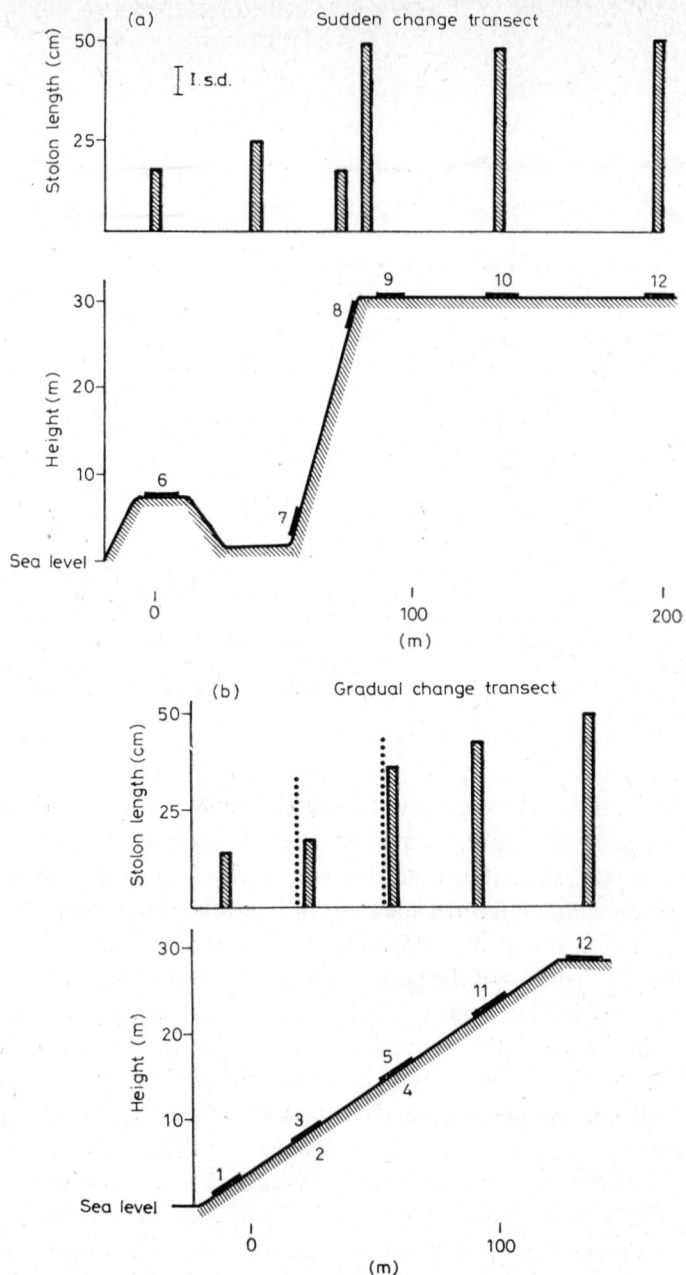

Fig. 20. The pattern of population differentiation in a creeping bent grass (*Agrostis stolonifera*) in a small area of exposed sea cliffs. (*a*) The pattern of differentiation in six populations in a transect across a sharp environmental boundary. (*b*) The pattern of differentiation on five populations in a transect across a nearby gradual environmental change, and in two populations (shown by dots) in a stream two metres away from the transect. (Bradshaw 1975)

In this example, strong selection pressure hindered the manifestation of the genotype structure, modifying the effect of gene flow.

In grass populations, the interaction of selection and gene flow has frequently been studied on the basis of the spatial distribution of heavy metal tolerance. For example, in North Wales, there is a small (100 × 300 m) waste heap from an abandoned copper mine which worked from the 13th century until the beginning of the 20th century. In the valley the prevailing wind generally blows from the west. At the western side of the mine, along a transect which is perpendicular to the wind direction, the available copper content of the soil abruptly decreases at the edge of the mine. In strong correlation with this, the copper tolerance of plants of a common grass (*Agrostis tenuis*) decreases. Another transect, on the eastern side of the mine, lies in an east-west direction. The copper tolerance index values of plants collected in- and outside the mine were higher than at the northern end of the first transect. The copper tolerance index values of seeds, from plants of the first transect, was smaller, than those of the second transect and was higher than that of the mother plants. This can be ascribed to the effect of gene flow. In both cases the alleles of copper tolerance were present in pollen carried by the wind.

In certain populations, due to selection, heavy metal tolerant genotypes can accumulate over a period as short as a few decades. In the vicinity of Liverpool, a copper mill was established in 1900. In its surroundings, all plants died off with the exception of *Agrostis stolonifera*. Over a period of 70 years, the values of the tolerance index exceeded 50. Even in the latest grass plantings this value had exceeded 30, during 8 years, while after 14 years it is above 40. This can obviously be considered to be the combined effect of both gene flow and selection (Wu and Bradshaw 1972), (Fig. 21). There are several other studies, similar to the above examples, which all confirm the basic role of selection in the development of differences in the adaptive values of populations. Gene flow, however, frequently works against selection. The size and speed of the differentiation of populations depends on a dynamic equilibrium of these two processes. These interrelations and the role of other beneficial and limiting factors are outlined in Fig. 22.

84

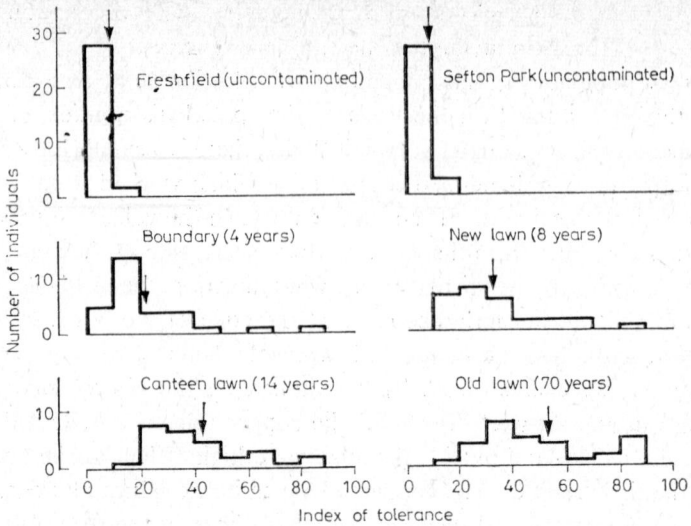

Fig. 21. Distribution of copper tolerance in populations of creeping bent grass (*Agrostis stolonifera*) which have recently become subject to copper pollution. (Bradshaw 1975)

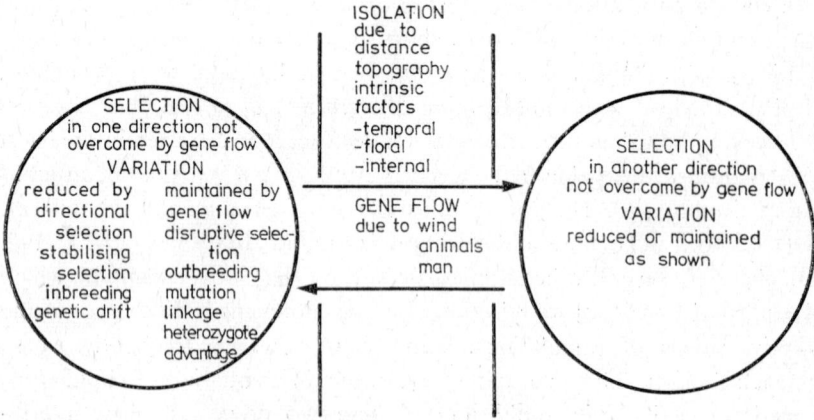

Fig. 22. A more complex and more realistic model of the interplay of gene flow, selection, and other factors, indicating that evolutionary divergence of neighbouring populations under the influence of natural selection can occur. (Bradshaw 1975)

GENETIC PARAMETERS OF ADAPTABILITY
AND GENETIC LOADING

By its disruption, the environment generally suffers rapid and fundamental changes. Even a relatively slight lowering of the soil water level, the building of a new road or power line, the laying of a pipeline—where their tracks do not run along the borders of natural ecosystems—can start the degradation of a meadow or forest ecosystem. Microclimatic relations change and generally, r-strategic species advance into the closed forest or meadow environment along a road or pipeline. These are then followed by their accompanying parasitic and other consumer species and thus the inner equilibrium of the ecosystem will be modified. Increasing soil and air pollution also help to bring about environmental changes. The populations of the original community are generally very susceptible to these factors as, in the course of their evolution, they have not been subject to these pollutions, therefore they either do not or only rarely contain resistant or tolerant genotypes. In such cases, selection pressure suddenly increases in the population. The ability of the population to oppose this pressure and to adapt itself to environmental changes, depends on its genetic structure, the constitution of its gene pool and on its adaptation mechanisms.

A road or railway line, even a pipeline, can form an isolating barrier and divide the population. In these cases the free gene flow is hindered. Therefore, by reducing the size of the population below the critical value, the preconditions for the start of genetic drift are already present. Both the above-mentioned causes and other similar environmental disruptions may lead to a rapid decrease of populations. Consequently, the reproduction rate of the obligatory allogamic populations decreases further and this brings about the speeding up of the random drift.

As seen, environmental disruption results not only in the increase of selection pressure, loading the population, but also in the involvement of feedback mechanisms which reduce the reproduction rate and lead to the evolution of the population into an impasse. Obviously, the fate of a population depends either on the amount of loading, which results from the environmental disruption or on its loadability. On the basis of the previous sections, one might survey those genetic features of the populations which, by helping or hindering adaptation, also influence their loadability. The most important of these features is the mean genetic variance of the population. Its value can be derived—in a sample of adequate size—from the phenotypic variability manifesting itself under the same environmental circumstances. The higher its value, the more probable that the genotypes—which, owing to their high adaptability, are capable of escaping selection in the changed, new environment—are already present in the population or they may be formed by recombination. In large cross-breeding populations there are, generally, more heterozygotes and the potential genetic variance is, generally, much greater than in both smaller self-fertilizing or apomictic populations in which the variability has decreased due to genetic drift. Therefore, the disruption of the environment primarily endangers the survival of the small endemic, relict populations.

As already seen, the liberation of potential genetic variability and the speed with which the new variant genotypes are formed, greatly depend on the genetic system. Should the environmental changes be faster than the formation of recombinants with the required adaptive value, the population will degrade or dissolve. High values of the recombination index and of the rate of reproduction, free mating and large mutation frequencies are factors improving the loadability and adaptation potential in the population. As gene flow does not supply the small, isolated populations with new alleles of greater adaptive value, which the formation of appropriate genotypes would require in the changed environment, their loadability is rather small. The rebuilding of coadapted gene complexes and the exchange of their specific alleles is a slow process. Gene introgression and cross-breeding may also assist the reconstruction of such super-genes, whose constitution is inadequate in the new environment, and their substitution by appropriate allele combinations.

A balanced genetic polymorphism gives a special advantage to the population. The gene combinations, capable of living more successfully in the new environment, are—occasionally only with a small frequency—present in most cases in polymorphic populations. Thus even the lack of recombination does not result in the total loss of the population. Even if the population survived the disruption of the environment, gene-erosion is inevitable. A lot of the alleles which were present in the original population with great frequency, will be absent from the gene pool of the remaining population fragments and of the regenerating populations. In any case, the variability of the population will be smaller, the development of isolated fragment populations will be hindered or else they will make no further progress. Most of them will—sooner or later—be absorbed in other populations or else they will disappear from the ecosystem. This danger overshadows not only the populations, but also some very precious species of the Earth's living world. According to experts of the 85,000 plant species of the temperate zone approximately 4,500 species face the danger of extinction. In the tropics, the situation is even worse. Some experts are of the opinion that one third of plant species, the number of which totals 150,000, will perish by the turn of the millennium! (Raven 1976).

It must be stressed that in artificial ecosystems (arable land and other plantations) established in the wake of disrupted natural ecosystems, genetic diversity is reduced to only a tiny proportion of the original one (less than 1%). To illustrate the size of the problem, it suffices to say that, according to expert estimates, 90% of the total genetic diversity of the biosphere has already been disrupted within historical times. This has been brought about only partly by the extinction of certain species, genetic erosion having played an even more important role (Vida 1978). Erosion is still going on at an ever increasing rate. Unless we succeed in stopping it, it will menace the whole biosphere and with it also humanity.

PLANS FOR WAYS AND MEANS OF PREVENTING GENE EROSION

The importance of the conservation of native populations and of the gene pool stored in them in the most practicable way has only become a matter of interest during the last decade. It is recognised that the gene store concealed in the biosphere is similar to arable land, minerals, pure water energy resources, the entity of production equipment, etc., being part of national wealth. While these resources are generally limited, the evolutionary potential of the genetic stock is infinitely large (Frankel 1974). It is, however, this potential for development that is endangered by the above-mentioned size and rate of decrease of inter- and infra-specific diversity. In other words, the basic ability of the living world to regenerate itself is threatened.

There had already been made attempts earlier to try to preserve the genetic stock. Nevertheless, partly due to the lack of the awareness of biological concepts required, the action taken so far has proved to be far less effective than expected.

Before considering the real prospects for the more effective preservation of genetic stock the most important factor that could menace the biosphere of our planet should be mentioned, this being starvation resulting from the rapid increase in human population in large areas of the world. In the present situation, the cutting-down of tropical rain forests and ploughing of the territories thus gained and the agricultural development of virgin territories, are means by which agricultural production can be increased with much less investment than by the intensification of agricultural production in long-established cultivated areas. According to FAO, approx.

10 million ha are being deforested in the tropics, purely for temporary economic reasons. It is important that a reasonable compromise should be found between short-range interests and the long-term preservation of the stock of genes. The search for a solution should be launched in two directions. The first one is to make an attempt to preserve the populations in their native environment, save them from genetic erosion and provide conditions suitable for further evolution (conservation). The second way is to store samples, large enough to represent the genetic pool of the population in an unchanged, preserved form (preservation). These measures of nature protection, aiming at the conservation of populations, are more or less capable of slowing down the genetic erosion of native populations. The preservation of endangered species, as a first step, is only effective if the necessary regulations can be enforced. Preservation, however, is often hindered by external temporary economic interests.

The establishment and maintenance of nature reserves and national parks—under expert direction—may achieve more practical results. The hope for the survival of genetically intact populations, of adequate size, is especially good in national parks covering a large area. In these, the inner processes of the ecosystem and its equilibrium, are only slightly or slowly modified by unforeseen or neglected effects arising from economic development. It should be remembered however, that the living organisms in national parks are also continuously changing and developing; it is not sufficient just to observe this development but—in the case of emergency—controlling measures should also be taken. Genetically impoverished, disappearing populations, in which the number of individuals is greatly reduced or scarce, can be enriched by the inset of population samples from other areas. This method, which increases genetic variance and therefore the adaptation potential of the population, reduces the degeneration caused by inbreeding. The method has become well established and it is used in game husbandry today.

It is also possible that conservation measures, result in aggressive species settling in or becoming dominant, thus altering competitive conditions to such a degree that certain more sensitive, less competitive species or populations become eroded. Several such cases are known. In the mountainous areas of the Tahitian islands, for example, the introduction of some non-indigenous vertebrate species for the sake of hunting has given rise to a situation where the new species is threatening to kill off thousands of plant species (Raven 1976). Domestication of moufflon (*Ovis Musimon*) in Hungary has also caused similar problems.

Because of the above-mentioned problems, when establishing national parks and especially smaller reserves, basic principles of population biology must be taken into account. The most important precondition is that the population to be protected should be dense enough to prevent genetic drift. In other words, the protected territory should be of such an extent that the most important species of the biological community are represented by large well-knit populations. In this respect, a coherent territory is much more favourable than reserves made up of several smaller units. Within the protected area gene flow should be unhindered and should not result in an increase of selection pressure, nor should this be reduced to a damagingly low level. In both cases there could be an imminent danger of degradation. This precondition is most difficult to achieve, primarily because of our limited knowledge of regulating mechanisms within the population, i.e. the biology of native populations and of biological communities.

Should economic, administrative or other reasons make it impossible to form a coherent and large protected area, the stepping-stone model (MacArthur and Wilson 1967) should be followed. According to this theory, by establishing numerous protected locations, one has to protect the gene flow between the national park or reserve and the nearest populations with a similar biological community. The organization of international gene bank networks helps to preserve the gene pools of some cultivated plants and domestic animal species with an unchanged composition. This organization was initiated by FAO in order to meet the demands of breeders and a close co-operation developed among FAO, ICSU and IBP (Frankel and Bennett 1970; Frankel and Hawkes 1975). It was proposed that ten large gene banks should constitute the backbone of the network. Each of these would be situated in one of the Vavilovian gene centres. Their main task would primarily be to collect and preserve adequately large samples from the gene pools of primitive varieties, geographic varieties and their related wild species in the area of the gene centre. Each sample (seed, bulbs, tubers, etc.) should be large enough to contain at least 95% of the entire genetic variability of the population, to eliminate genetic drift. Peripheral or isolated populations should be collected using special precautions. These contain higher frequencies of precious resistance alleles or alleles for earliness, dwarfism or nutritional characters than the improved localised varieties or, in case of wild species, than the populations living in the centre of the area. Seed samples should be stored under controlled environmental condition (cooled room and pre-set humidity). From time to time (at 5–10 yearly intervals) the seeds should be sown and refreshed by recultivation, thus eliminating the danger of their being lost or mixed up.

In fact, the preservation of gene pools under artificial conditions has been carried out by botanical gardens and zoos for centuries. In some instances they have achieved outstanding successes: several species have thus been saved from total extinction. Botanical gardens and zoos can, however, raise or propagate only a small number of certain species or populations so that the wider preservation of the gene pool of a particular population—under those conditions—remains out of the question. Existing exchange (arrangements between various zoos, etc.) may mean a slight improvement in this field, though the danger that co-adapted genotypes might perish through spontaneous crossings is imminent. Consequently, though the collections of botanical gardens and zoos can be interesting, they do not meet the criteria required for either conservation or preservation. The greatest problem is that it is very expensive to maintain the most endangered species of tropical biological communities in the zoos or botanical gardens of the temperate climate zone, therefore they can be bred and propagated only in limited numbers. In the tropics, however, there are no botanical gardens or zoos that would be capable of carrying out these tasks. In order to preserve and save endangered species, the main task of the above-mentioned living collections would be to collect and preserve those species, belonging to their own regional flora and fauna, which are the closest to complete deterioration. Here they should be preserved until they could in the wake of environmental conservation measures, be replanted in their original habitats or introduced into newly formed habitats. There are already examples where this has been done (Simmons et al. 1976).

The aims for conservation and preservation can, eventually, best be realised by the systematic and possibly rapid construction of a world-wide network of reserves, national parks and well-equipped gene banks of great capacity. The rapid spread of modern agricultural methods, factory production systems and high yielding varieties, characteristic also of the developing countries, has made urgent the organization of gene banks. As the gene stock of both primitive and geographical varieties and also that of related wild populations contains alleles, which are totally absent in modern varieties, first priority should be given to preserving them in the gene banks. In Hungary, the Research Institute for Agricultural Botany has been commissioned to establish a gene bank, the scope of which extends to the Carpathian basin.

References

Anderson, E. (1949): *Introgressive hybridisation*. New York–London.

Aston, R. W. and Bradshaw, A. D. (1966): Evolution in closely adjacent plant populations. II. Agrostis stolonifera in maritime habitats. *Heredity* **21:** 649—664.

Bradshaw, A. D. (1975): Population structure and the effects of isolation and selection. In: Frankel, O. H. and Hawkes, J. G. (eds): *Crop genetic resources for today and tomorrow*. Cambridge Univ. Press., Cambridge.

Clausen, J. and Hiesey, W. M. (1958): *Experimental studies on the nature of species*. IV. Genetic structure of ecological races. Carnegie Institute of Washington Publication 615. Washington, D. C.

Creed, R. (ed.) (1971): *Ecological genetics and evolution*. Oxford and Edinburgh.

Darlington, C. D. (1958): *Evolution of genetic systems*. Edinburgh — London, Oliver and Boyd.

Darlington, C. D. (1963): *Chromosome botany and the origin of cultivated plants*. Revised second edition. London.

Darlington, C. D. and Mather, K. (1949): *The elements of genetics*. London.

Dobzhansky, T. (1970): *Genetics of the evolutionary process*. New York and London.

Falconer, D. S. (1960): *Introduction to quantitative genetics*. Edinburgh and London.

Ford, E. B. (1965): *Genetic polymorphism*. London.

Ford, E. B. (1971): *Ecological genetics*. Third edition. London.

Frankel, O. H. (1974): Genetic conservation: our evolutionary responsibility. *Genetics* **78:** 53–65.

Frankel, O. H. and Bennett, E. (eds) (1970): *Genetic resources in plants—their exploration and conservation*. IBP Handbook No. 11. Oxford and Edinburgh.

Frankel, O. H. and Hawkes, J. G. (1975): Genetic resources—the past ten years and the next. In: Frankel, O. H. and Hawkes, J. G. (eds): *Crop genetic resources for today and tomorrow*. Cambridge Univ. Press Cambridge.

Gadgil, M. and Solbrig, O. T. (1972): The concept of r- and K-selection: evidence from wild flowers and some theoretical considerations. *American Naturalist* **106**: 14–31.

Grant, V. (1963): *The origin of adaptions*. New York and London.

Grant, V. (1971): *Plant speciation*. New York and London.

Jones, D. A. and Wilkins, D. A. (1971): *Variation and adaptation in plant species*. London.

Juhász–Nagy, P. and Vida, G. (1978): Supra individual organization. In: Csaba, Gy. (ed): *The biological control* (in Hungarian). Budapest,

Lewontin, R. (ed.) (1968): *Population biology and evolution*. New York.

Lewontin, R. C. (1974): *The genetic basis of evolutionary change*. New York and London.

Mac Arthur, R. H. and Wilson, E. O. (1967): *Island biogeography*. Princeton.

Mayr, E. (1970): *Populations, species and evolution*. Cambridge, Mass.

McNeilly, T. (1968): Evolution in closely adjacent plant populations. III. Agrostis tenuis on a small copper mine. *Heredity* **23**: 99–108.

Mettler, L. E. and Gregg, T. G. (1969): *Population genetics and evolution*. Prentice-Hall, Englewood Cliffs.

Murray, J. (1972): *Genetic diversity and natural selection*. Edinburgh.

Owen, O. S. (1971): *Natural resource conservation. An ecological approach*. New York.

Raven, P. H. (1976): Ethics and attitudes. In: Simmons et al. *Conservation of threatened plants* New York, 155–179.

Savage, J. M. (1977): *Evolution*. Third edition. New York.

Scandalios, J. G. (1969): Genetic control of multiple molecular forms enzymes in plants: a review. *Biochem. Genetics* **3**: 37–79.

Simmons, J. B., Beyer, R. I., Brandham, P. E., Lucas, G. Ll. and Parry, V. T. H. (eds) (1976): *Conservation of threatened plants*. New York.

Szinszkaja, E. N. (Синская, Е. Н.) (1948): *Динамика вида*. Москва.

Snaydon, R. W. (1970): Rapid population differentiation in a mosaic environment. I. The response of Anthoxanthum odoratum populations to soils. *Evolution* **24**: 257–269.

Snaydon, R. W. (1973): Ecological factors, genetic variation and speciation in plants. In: Heywood, V. H.: *Taxonomy and ecology*. London and New York, 1–29.

Snaydon, R. W. and Davies, M. S. (1972): Rapid population differentiation in a mosaic environment. II. Morphological variation in Anthoxanthum odoratum. *Evolution* **26**: 390–405.

Stebbins, G. L. (1966): *Processes in organic evolution*. Prentice-Hall, Englewood Cliffs.

Stebbins, G. L. and Zohary, D. (1959): Cytogenetic and evolutionary studies in the genus Dactylis. Univ. of California Publications in Botany **31**: 1–40.

Terborg, J. (1974): Preservation of natural diversity: the problem of extinction prone species. *Bioscience* **24**: 715–722.

Vavilov, N. I. (1951): The origin, variation immunity and breeding of cultivated plants. *Chronica Botanica* **13**.

Vida, G. (1978): Genetic diversity and environmental future. *Environmental Conservation* **5**: 127–132.

Wu-Lin and Bradshaw, A. D. (1972): Aerial pollution and the rapid evolution of copper tolerance. *Nature* **238**: 167–169.

Zohary, D. and Nur, U. (1959): Natural triploids in the orchard grass, Dactylis glomerata L., polyploid complex and their significance for gene flow from diploid to tetraploid levels. *Evolution* **16**: 311–317.

Chapter 5

Air pollution

THE ATMOSPHERE AND ATMOSPHERIC POLLUTION

"As the atmosphere has a capacity for dispersion and dilution, it is used as if it were a giant channel"—wrote Munn and Bolin (1971). At present with the amount of pollutants introduced into the air this channel has proved to be restricted and its diluting capacity small. Only a decade ago, experts regarded the air pollution (smog) of industrial districts as the main problem. Recent studies have called attention to the harm arising from air pollution, which menaces both the physical and chemical conditions of the whole atmosphere and indirectly the biological equilibrium of the entire Earth.

Pure air

From the point of view of colloid chemistry, atmospheric air belongs to the group of incoherent, coarse dispersal systems. More exactly, it is a system of colloidal particles dispersed in gas, in which solid and liquid components can be found in a mixture of gases. It is frequently called an aerosol.

The term "pure air" is chemically not properly defined. Stern (1962–1968) describes the composition of the "homosphere", the air to be found near the soil level (Table 2). Natural pure air is composed of various amounts of substances additional to its constant components. Actually, these additional components form the objects of studies on air pollution. "Pure air" has never existed on the Earth, whereas natural pollutants, such as cosmic dust, dust deriving from land surfaces, combustion products of forest fires, gases of volcanic eruptions have existed from the very beginning. Air-borne microorganisms, pollen and spores, i.e. the multiplicity of floating organisms can also be grouped into this category. It is also useless to talk about pure

Table 2

Components of air

Gaseous component	Volume ppm	Weight ppm
Nitrogen	780,900	755,100
Oxygen	209,500	231,500
Argon	9,300	12,800
Carbon dioxide	300	400
Neon	18	12.5
Helium	5.2	0.72
Methane	2.2	1.2
Krypton	1	2.9
Nitrogen oxides	1	1.5
Hydrogen	0.5	0.03
Xenon	0.08	0.36

air in a historical context, as the chemical composition of the atmosphere has undergone radical changes. The concept of pure air can, nevertheless, be defined from the viewpoint of biology and hygiene. Unless the amount of pollutants exceeds the experimentally determined limit, the air can be regarded as pure. This also implies that it does not exert—either in the short or in the long run—a detrimental impact on plants, animals or man.

Sources of pollution

A large proportion of air contaminants is of natural origin. The hydrosphere, which constitutes the larger part of the Earth's surface, produces a significant quantity of aerosols. Drops of water which get into the air in the course of wave motion of the sea, evaporate, thus producing Na, Ca, K, chloride, sulphate, etc. ions or simple compounds of these. Air masses of marine origin are characterized by relatively high concentrations of these elements.

Marine plants and animals, the most significant factors in the world from the biological point of view, produce a large volume of gaseous materials. These, depending on the partial pressure and temperature, are dissolved in water or introduced from there into the atmosphere. Carbon dioxide is the most important of these.

Solid state pollutants originate, mainly, from the surface of the lithosphere. Desert and sea-sand (SiO_2), depending on weather, may frequently occur in the atmosphere in high concentrations. Soil dust also contains organic components, though it is composed mainly of the dust of minerals, carbonates, sulphates and oxides ($CaCO_3$, $CaSO_4$, $MgCO_3$, Al_2O_3, ZnO,

SiO_2, etc.). Volcanic activity also introduces dust, fumes, and gases (H_2S, SO_2, HCl, CO, CO_2) into the air. Combustion products of steppe bush or forest fires carry, besides carbon dioxide, soot and carcinogenic carbon and also their hydrates.

Decomposition products of plant and animal origin, especially those containing sulphur, have frequently an offensive odour (ammonia, hydrogen sulphide and mercaptans, indole and skatole, etc.).

The plant and animal kingdoms play the main role in the maintenance of atmospheric equilibrium.

Vegetation primarily and fauna secondarily affect the natural balance of oxygen and carbon in the atmosphere. Simple hydrocarbons of small atomic number are emitted into the air either by discharges of gas or in the form of organic decomposition products. Among them methane, a component of the carbon cycle, is stable. It can be detected in low concentrations: 1.2 ppm.

Floating microorganisms of the air can be divided into the following groups: viruses, bacteria, fungi, algae, pollens. Agricultural activity also introduces substances into the air which can be found under natural conditions. The dust of fertilizers may also be mentioned as a source of air pollution. With the increased use of chemicals in agriculture numerous new substances are introduced into farming practice. All these may exert harmful effects on the natural equilibrium. In most cases, insecticides, herbicides, fungicides contain chlorinated hydrocarbons, organic phosphate-esters, dithio-carbonates or hormones which are biologically active substances. They are frequently introduced into air, in the form of dust or spray, especially by aircraft used in large-scale agricultural production. While only a few years ago agriculture was only a minor source of atmospheric pollution, mainly of local importance, it has become one of the most menacing sources of pollution, endangering biological equilibrium.

It is known that the major part of air pollution of artificial origin is derived from the combustion products of industry, traffic, households concentrated in urban areas. Certain changes have been observed recently in the relative distribution of these components. While a few decades ago traffic did not play an important role in this respect, today it is the main contaminant in developed industrial countries. Pollution from other sources is static or decreasing in these countries. This can be ascribed to three reasons: (i) the number of vehicles has multipled, (ii) industrial sources of pollution have been controlled, (iii) individual households have been converted to central heating, or else, the use of oil, gas and electric heating has gained ground.

Formerly, the degree of air pollution was generally proportional to the industrial development of the country in question. The further development is characterized by the growing proportion of contamination arising from the use of motor vehicles. In fact, the polluting impact of modern industry is decreasing. This trend is going to persist until a practical solution has been developed which will make it possible to put an end to the pollution impact of the combustion-engine.

In Fig. 23 the directions of pollution are marked by black arrows. The thickness of arrows represents only proportions. They do not concern individual countries but the entire biosphere. These proportions are, naturally, only shown as a guide. It cannot be our aim to give a detailed survey of the manifold polluting impact of industry. The most important and most frequently occurring pollutants—grouped according to their physical state—are summarized in Table 3.

Primary sources of pollution produce and introduce contaminants into the air. As a result of the activity of so-called secondary sources of pollution, material which had already been extracted from air or arising from production processes may re-introduce such contaminants into the atmosphere.

Such are lagoons of fly-ash, pit heaps or the dust of cement works that is deposited on roads, soil or buildings and which is blown about by wind.

Table 3

Main pollutants

Solid phase	dust	cement dust
	soot	textile dust
	fly-ash	organic dusts
	mineral dust	toxic dusts
	metallic dust	
Liquid phase (smog, spray)		
	H_2SO_3	HCl
	H_2SO_4	C_nH_m
Gaseous and vapour, phase		
	SO_2	C_nH_m polycyclic and aromatic hydrocarbons
	H_2S	Cl_2
	CS_2	HCl
	CO	HF
	CO_2	F_2
	NO	O_3
	NO_2	metallic fumes
	N_xO_y	solvent vapours

98

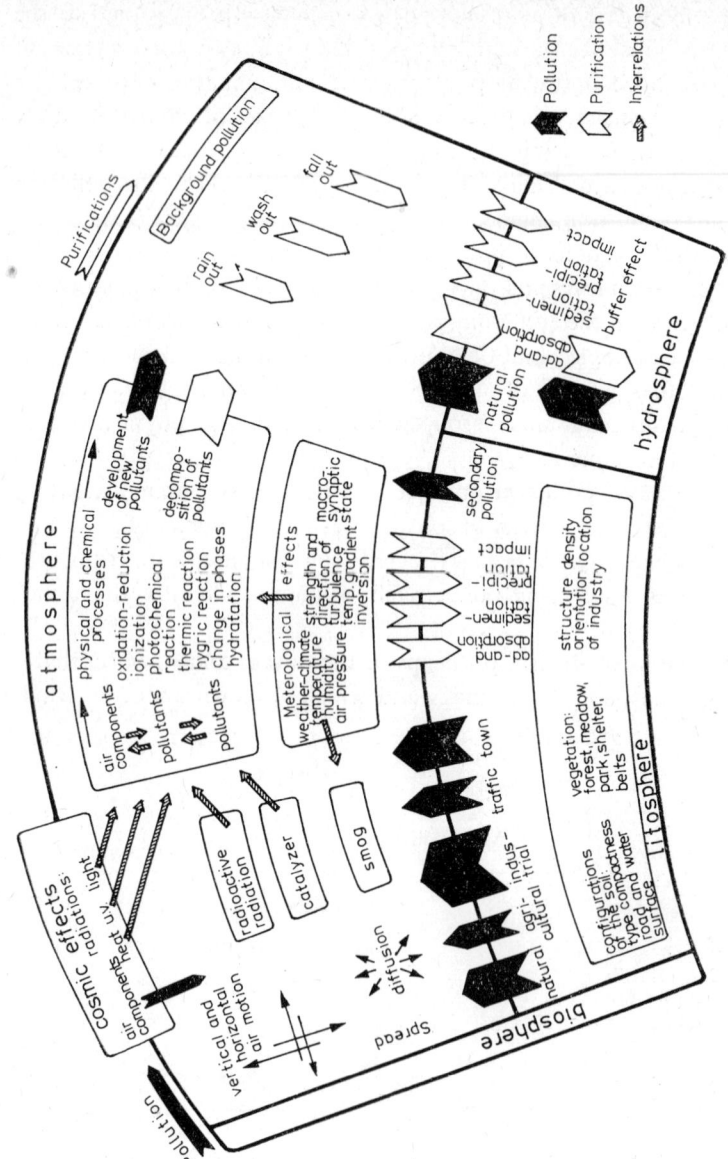

Fig. 23. The balance of pollutants in the atmosphere

Refuse tips, sewage sludges are other examples. From these, the vapour of absorbed gases or detergents may diffuse or percolate out.

In general, traffic introduces dust, soot, carbon dioxide and their derivatives, sulphur dioxide, carbon oxides (CO, CO_2) into the air. From among the combustion engines, Diesel-engines emit an exhaust gas into the air which, owing to the combustion taking place at high pressure, is rich in nitrogen oxides (NO, NO_2 N_xO_y). The sulphur content of Diesel oil reappears in the form of SO_2 in exhaust gases.

Exhaust gases of petrol engines contain carbon monoxide, petrol vapour, aldehydes, straight-chained and polycyclic hydrocarbons and lead, which is derived from the lead-containing tetraethyl additive. An increasing number of papers report on the intense air polluting effect of aeroplanes, mainly of those equipped with turbo and jet engines. This phenomenon manifests itself especially in the vicinity of airports. The introduction of vapour condensation nuclei into the higher atmospheric layers is also not to be neglected. Their contaminants are: aldehydes, carbon oxides and soot.

The polluting effect of household heating can be clearly explained by inefficient heating. Being burnt in small heating-units, a unit quantity of fuel is more polluting than when used in modern industrial boilers. The use of coal produces the largest amount of pollutants. Oil heating is much more favourable. Gas heating produces, practically, no particulate contaminants.

Purification processes

If the foreign matter content of the air persisted in an unchanged form, it would change the composition of the atmosphere to such a degree that, within a relatively short period of time, air would become unsuitable both for man and other living creatures. Fortunately, air—similarly to water—has its processes of self-purification. As the study of these processes has started only recently, we do not yet understand them properly. In Fig. 23 white arrows mark the processes of purification.

According to the suitability of purification processes, three main groups can be distinguished: (*i*) the pollutant leaves the atmosphere, (*ii*) the pollutant is transformed into inactive matter, (*iii*) the concentration of contaminant decreases, i.e. it is diluted.

The first group may comprise the following possibilities:

Sedimentation. The coarse fraction of solid or liquid pollutants are removed from air in this way. In general, particles with a diameter larger than 10 μ are called sediment forming dust. Their rate of sedimentation differs depending on the weight, shape, size of the particle and the flow conditions (Fig. 24).

Impingement and precipitation mean the removal of pollutants by means of collision, friction and adhesion. This process takes place in the course of air drift (in the case of coarser particles) or in that of diffusion and Brownian motion. In the process of thermal precipitation particles deposit on surfaces cooler than themselves. Electrical precipitation means the deposit of particles on surfaces oppositely charged. These processes take place, mainly, in air layers at the boundary of the surface of earth and sea, though they can be brought about also on the surface of atmospheric particles or on drops of water.

Adsorption and absorption are of basic importance in the case of gaseous pollutants. Gas molecules can be adsorbed either by inorganic matters or living organisms. For this, especially, the vast surfaces of seas have to be considered. In Fig. 23 two opposite arrows illustrate the huge buffering capacity which seas represent in the case of gaseous pollutants. Depending on air-pressure, temperature and the partial pressure of gases, water either absorbs or desorbs gases. This process can take place either on wet surfaces

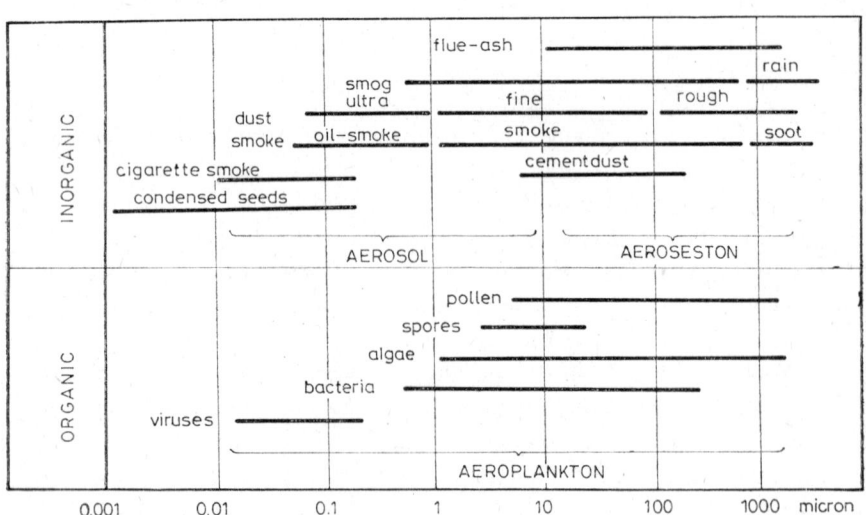

Fig. 24. Different air-borne particles

or on the surface of atmospheric water particles. As a carrier of large numbers of microorganisms, the gas adsorbing capacity of soils is important. Living organisms play an especially essential role in the adsorption of polluting gases. Unfortunately, the respiratory systems of vertebrates including man, almost entirely adsorb it. The gas-adsorbing capacity of plants is especially great.

Condensation, rain out. Polluting materials serve as condensation nuclei in the process of cloud and precipitation formation. As a result of the actual rainfall, they themselves are also extracted from the air.

Wash-out. In the course of its fall to Earth, rainwater washes out several air layers. The surface of raindrops, especially that of snow flakes, not only adsorb, absorb or dissolve large amounts of polluting materials, but they also carry them to the surface of the Earth.

The different types of processes of purification cannot be defined precisely. For example, the impingement and dissolution of an aerosol particle can take place on the surface of a raindrop. This also corresponds to a wash-out. Wash-out particles reach the surface of Earth also in the process of sedimentation: dry and wet wash-out processes can be distinguished. The other group comprises those possibilities of purification in which pollutants are transformed into inactive matter. In general, these are chemical processes of decomposition.

Another group, representing the possibilities of dilution, is based on meteorological phenomena. In this case the effect of winds and of turbulence in the lower layers of the troposphere is well known. As the absolute amount of pollutants does not change and only its concentration decreases, this is the least effective group of possibilities by which pollution can be eliminated. Though it is favourable for the local environment of the emitting source, it has no effect on larger regions or on the atmosphere.

Atmospheric interactions and processes

Pollutants introduced into air are subject to numerous impacts. This implies that they are brought into contact both with air components and other pollutants. Reactions between pollutants and air take place more frequently than between pollutants themselves.

Cosmic impacts manifest themselves in the form of radiation: heat, light, UV-radiation and partly, man-made radioactive radiation. Cations to be found everywhere act as catalyzers. Atmospheric water plays an active role in several processes, either in the form of molecules or in that of microdrops: the water content of the atmosphere amounts to 1–3% by volume. Oxidizing–reducing materials, ions of high affinity also have an impact on pollutants.

As described above, pollutants take part in physical and chemical processes like oxidation–reduction, photochemical reactions, thermal reactions, hydrolytic reactions, hydration, ionization, and phase-change.

The energy requirement of atmospheric reactions is supplied, mainly, by light, heat and UV-radiation. Photochemical reactions are induced chiefly by high energy UV-radiation. Ozone formation is one example of this:

$$O_2 + h = O^{--} + O^{--}$$
$$O^{--} + O_2 = O_3$$

This is the principle of the formation of photochemical smog.
A classical example of a light-catalyzed reaction is the following:

$$Cl_2 + H_2 + h = 2\ HCl$$

Thermic reactions take place partly under the influence of thermal radiation. Increasing temperature is known to accelerate endothermic processes. In aqueous reactions it is the water content of air that enters into reaction with pollutants. For example:

$$SO_3 + H_2O = H_2SO_4$$

Oxidation is a process in which, for example, nitrogen oxide is transformed into nitrogen dioxide:

$$2\ NO + O_2 = 2\ NO_2$$

Should the molecules of pollutant be of dipolar character, they undergo a hydration reaction with atmospheric water. Hydration increases the particle size and where the substance is water-soluble, it is dissolved. Simultaneously it acts as a nucleus for condensation in fog formation. Apart from the above-mentioned modifications of physical state, phase-changes can be brought about by desiccation, evaporation of liquid drops or by the sublimation of solid pollutants. In the course of these processes decomposition predominates. It has, however, been established that simple pollutants can become more complex: the changes taking place in the atmosphere, in several cases, intensify the harmfulness of pollutants. The reaction of ozone with free-radicals (alkyl, acyl, etc.) is a good example of this.

Polluted air can be regarded as a dispersed colloid reaction mixture in which most of the decompositions and syntheses take place.

Meteorological effects. From among factors belonging to this field, the role of radiations, temperature, vapour content has already been mentioned. Air pressure plays an especially important role in the adsorption and absorption reactions of gases; among the meteorological factors the movement of air masses affects air pollution in the most conspicuous way. The intensive dispersion effect of wind has been established in air layers near the ground. The character of winds must, however, not be neglected. While turbulent winds exert a great diluting effect, laminar winds can, in certain cases, even hinder air dispersion.

Depending on wind direction and local conditions, wind can transport either polluted or pure air to a given area. Concerning the continents, it has been shown that large amounts of polluted air can be transported by wind. It is also known, that vertical air motions play an important part in the dispersion of polluted air layers near the ground. The inversion of a thermal gradient exerts an effect on the accumulation of pollution. The thickness of the mixing layer and its stability are further very important factors.

In addition to the above-mentioned factors, climate exerts its impact on the formation of air pollution. Two basic types of smog can be mentioned as examples. In temperate climates, the reducing type of smog (the old London type) predominates. It can be characterized by the dominance of reducing substances, mainly, SO_2. The oxidizing, or Los Angeles type of smog, is frequently called photochemical smog. In regions subjected to strong radiation, ozone, nitrogen oxides, etc. are produced and accumulated in the air, bringing about the predominance of oxidants.

A specialized field of meteorology, diffusion-climatology deals with the spread of pollution.

Topographic factors. The role of topographic conditions has been known for a long time: the history of industrial cities situated in valleys has already witnessed several smog catastrophes. Due to ground elevations and depressions, local drifts, inversions or on the contrary, stagnancy can be brought about; consequently they play an important part in the dispersion or accumulation of pollutants. The effect of soils and water surfaces has already been mentioned. Effects connected with urbanisation can be considered as inanimate factors. Buildings exert a significant modifying effect on air turbulence, the warming up of surfaces and also, due to this, on vertical currents.

The effect of both development and planning of the location of industrial and residential areas within a given urban area is a very important factor in respect of air pollution. The plant and animal kingdoms also play a very important role in this context. It has been shown that afforested areas, parks and shelter belts have beneficial effects.

The balance of pollutants in the atmosphere

Oxygen, nitrogen, carbon and water cycles in nature are well-known processes. Besides these several other substances, among them air pollutants, also take part in similar global cycles, between the lithosphere, hydrosphere and atmosphere, which also affect the plant and animal kingdoms. We have already some knowledge as to the balance of ozone, nitrogen oxides, carbon and carbon oxides.

The amount of sulphur introduced into the air annually has already been estimated by several authors. According to Robinson et al. (1970) artificial sources emit $73 \cdot 10^6$ t sulphur into the air. 93% of the sources of emission is situated in the northern hemisphere. Sulphur emission of natural origin amounts to $43 \cdot 10^6$ t/year. This amount of sulphur has to be eliminated by processes of dilution or dispersion, so that the sulphur balance of the atmosphere remains undisturbed. If the rate of elimination of sulphuric compounds does not reach the rate of emission, it may have harmful consequences. It will manifest itself in the increase of global emission (the background pollution comprising the entire Earth). Certain signs of this have already manifested themselves (Fig. 25).

In the USA and several other countries, too, the present rate of emission exceeds that of decomposition (elimination). Atmospheric sulphur can be found in three forms: sulphate (SO_4)-ion, hydrogen sulphide (H_2S) and gaseous sulphur dioxide (SO_2). The balance of carbon dioxide is at present a current topic of interest and debate.

The carbon dioxide content of the atmosphere, which amounted to 285 ppm at the end of the last century, had reached the value of 300 ppm by 1930. Today it amounts to some 330 ppm. Should this long-term trend continue further, the value of 350 ppm will be reached by the year 2000. This will give rise to the so-called "glass-house" effect which will warm up the climate of the Earth, thus upsetting several meteorological and biological states of equilibrium. Other authors try to prove by experiments that, during the last 80 years, atmospheric temperature has not risen, but rather slightly fallen. According to Peterson (1969) increasing CO_2 concentration may bring about the modification of the carbon cycle in living organisms.

In general, we talk about the disturbance of atmospheric equilibrium

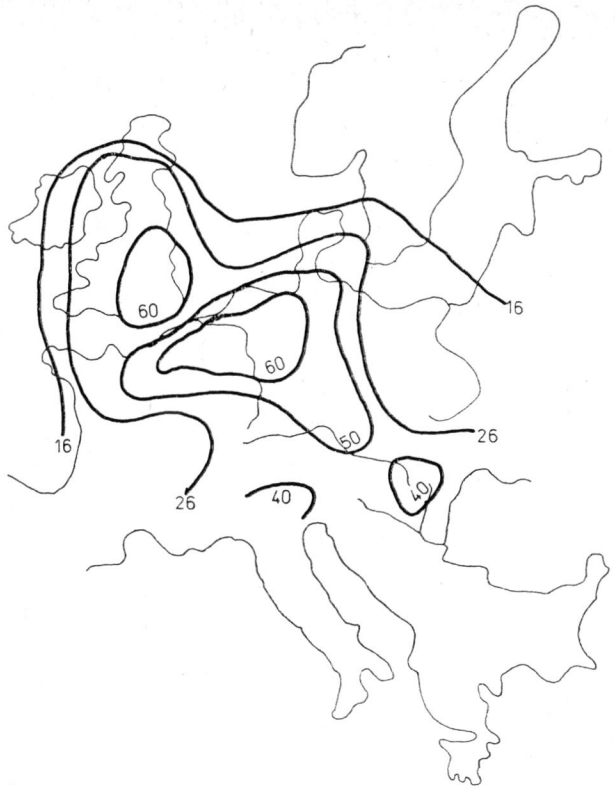

Fig. 25. Sulphur dioxide background pollution in Europe, in winter, $\mu g/m^3$ (based on data by Garber 1967 and by Várkonyi 1972)

when trying to express the extent of the damage caused by pollution. Nevertheless, it is worth considering that, in a chemical sense, atmospheric equilibrium will not be upset by the emission of pollutants by a given amount. It is relevant that a new state of equilibrium will come into being, in which the content of pollutants will be somewhat higher than previously. Nevertheless, it is questionable, whether the plant and animal kingdoms and man will be capable of adapting themselves to the new equilibrium and its atmosphere. Over a period of a few generations, really radical changes are not to be expected from large variations in the level of pollution. The really great problem of air pollution lies in its latent character, i.e. its long-term harmfulness.

EFFECT OF AIR POLLUTION ON LIVING ORGANISMS

Effect on the plant and animal kingdoms

Every living creature is strongly bound to its environment and forms a biological unit with it. Plants, animals and man (with the exception of living aquatic organisms, a few spores and parasites) are most closely bound with the atmosphere. Living organisms with an intensive metabolism and higher living beings can only live without air or oxygen for a very short period of time.

During their development, lasting for millions of years, living organisms have adapted themselves to the changing physical and chemical circumstances, in the formation of which they themselves had also played an active role. For a long time man's appearance had almost no effect on the state of the atmosphere. Since the second half of the last century, the situation has changed. As a result of growing industrialization ever increasing amounts of foreign substances have been introduced into the air, thus changing its composition and properties over vast areas. Living organisms are not able to adapt themselves to—from philogenetical point of view—immediate changes without suffering damage. In view of the fact that initially, the impact of air pollution was observed in the closest surroundings of sources of pollution, firstly its impacts on man had been observed in the industrial towns and in industrial plants and so it was these symptoms which had been first studied and remedied.

In the last few decades, the history of air pollution entered into a new phase. With the amount of polluting substances increasing by several orders of magnitude, with concentration of industry in certain regions and with the development of motor travel, air pollution has grown out of its local surroundings and has become a regional phenomenon; the eastern coastline of the USA or the Ruhr-region are characteristic examples.

Since polluted air reaches not only industrial and residential areas but also agricultural regions, in addition to man, its impacts on plants and animals are also beginning to manifest themselves. It has been observed that plants are far more sensitive to pollution than animals or man. Therefore, plants, among them algae, are also used as indicators. The effect of different pollutants on plants should be first surveyed. Particulate pollutants exert their detrimental effect by settling on the surface of leaves, decreasing the active surface and consequently, their assimilative capacity. Colloidal dusts, e.g. cement dust, block the stomata of plants and toxic dusts exert

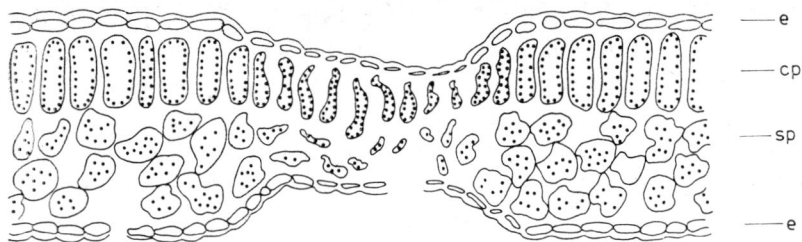

Fig. 26. The impact of sulphurdioxide on leaf tissue, e: epidermis, cp: columnar parenchima, sp: spongy parenchima

their harmful effect by interfering with the metabolic processes of plants. Gaseous pollutants penetrate into the intercellular tissues via the stomata. They may be fixed on the surface of cells, enter into reactions with water or take part in the metabolism. On the other hand, gases may also enter into reaction with chlorophyll, thus inhibiting photosynthesis (Fig. 26).

The epidermis of the leaf is most resistant to these impacts. However, spongy parenchyma and columnar cells, the main places of assimilation, are very sensitive. Cells are capable of decomposing and neutralizing low concentrations of pollutants. Beyond a certain limit, however, loss of water, plasmolysis, occurs followed by death. More severe damage results in visible injuries. The tissues of the leaf will shrink, shrivel and wilt in places. The symptoms of chlorophyll and chromoplast decay are changes in colour and chlorosis: yellow, brown or red spots can be observed on the leaf. Similar symptoms appear also on the petals. Marginal necrosis, the dying off of the edges of leaves and petals are very characteristic symptoms. Naturally, other factors can also result in similar symptoms: draught-impairments, damage done by insects, bacteria, etc. Still, the individual types of symptoms are characteristic of certain pollutants. Sulphur dioxide affects mainly the spongy parenchyma. In the middle of the leaf, mainly in the areas between the nerves, dry, transparent or light-coloured spots appear. Ozone exerts its effect on the columnar cells, the leaves are sporadically blotched. The symptoms of fluorine damage are well-defined marginal necroses.

It should be mentioned that since plants do not transfer fluorine absorbed from air to the soil, they are good indicators of fluorine pollution. They are not capable of taking up more than 5 mg fluorine/100 g dry weight, from the soil. Should their content of fluorine exceed this value, the surplus must have been absorbed from the air. Naturally, smog can also have harmful effects on plants. The oxidizing and reducing types of smog cause characteristic symptoms.

The particular stage of development of the plant is also a factor in determining the effect of pollutants. Young, still dividing tissues, though being more sensitive, regenerate well, if the effect is not a lasting one. Older tissues, generally, suffer irrevocable damage. Concerning their sensitivity to pollution, even plants can differ from one another. For example, clover, barley, cotton, wheat and apple, in that order, are the most sensitive to sulphur dioxide. Gladiolus, peach, plum and pines are the least resistant to fluorine. Tomato, tobacco, bean, spinach and potato are sensitive to ozone, while other species may be resistant to it. Examples of this, in the case of sulphur dioxide, are: potato, onion, oats. Clover, rose, tobacco, tomato, cotton are resistant to fluorine. Pelargonium, gladiolus and pepper are resistant to ozone.

It emerges from the foregoing lists that it is mainly cultivated plants that have been studied in this respect, because of the financial implications. In contrast to this, there are only a few data available relating to the natural plant cover. Nevertheless, it is known that lichens, considered to be plants with the smallest nutritional requirements, are very sensitive. Therefore, in the neighbourhood of towns with polluted air, there are vast areas which are devoid of lichens.

As a result of long-lasting or regularly recurring impacts, vegetation is retarded in growth and plants will have fewer leaves and these will be of smaller size. Plant size, flower numbers and yield will also decrease. By covering the useful surface of fruits and leaves dusts of different origin reduce their value. Products with a strong offensive smell, emitted by chemical factories, are absorbed on the edible parts of plants thus spoiling their quality. Both the viability and reproductivity of plants affected are reduced. Resistant, mainly, less valuable species, will proliferate. The composition of populations and communities will be changed (Fig. 27). In contrast to this, vegetation also influences the development of air pollution zones as it filters and purifies air. The beneficial role of shelter belts of trees, in the control of air pollution, is known and has been demonstrated.

Passing over to questions related to the animal kingdom, the impact of air pollutants on certain animal species is well known, as they are used in experiments aimed at elucidating this problem. Guinea pigs, rats, rabbits and dogs are most frequently used in laboratory experiments. Air pollutants penetrate into the organism primarily through the respiratory system where they exert their effect. As animals can live without air only for a short period of time, they are not capable of selecting air in the way they do in the case of quality of food or drinking water. In the animal kingdom the organ of detoxication (pancreas and liver) which effectively prevents noxious

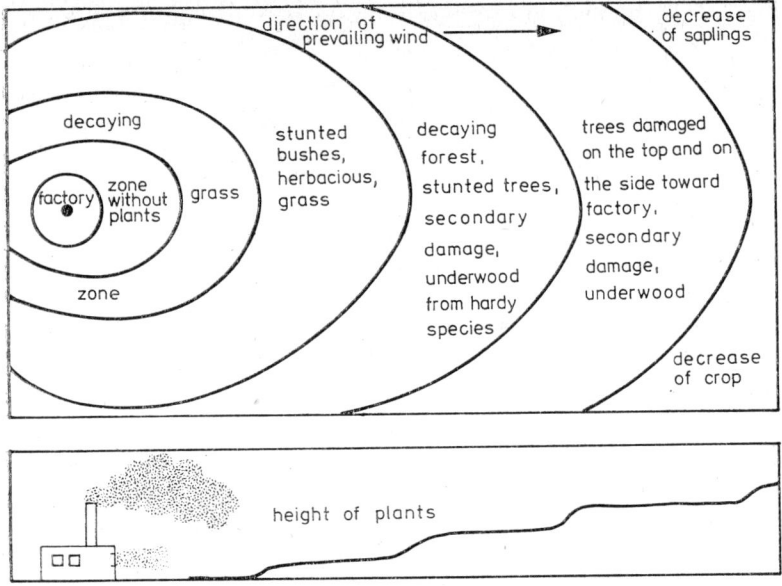

Fig. 27. Deteriorating zones of vegetation around a polluting factory

materials from entering into the metabolism by way of the alimentary tract, appeared already in the primitive branches. The protection of the respiratory system is, however, not so perfect. Inhaled air is partly filtered from pollutants of larger size by the hairs of the nostrils. It warms up and becomes saturated with vapour. In the respiratory tract, it is the ciliated pyramidal epithelium and salivation of subepithelial stratum that carries out the function of purification. All particles larger than 5 μ are filtered in the respiratory tracts, similarly to the action of an aerosol-filter.

When pollutants are inhaled, as a result of the protective reaction, salivation increases and ciliary motion is initiated. The adsorbed solid and gas particles dissolved in the mucus are driven in the direction of the mouth at a speed of several cm/min. The perfect functioning of the ciliated epithelium can prevent particles adsorbed in the upper part of respiratory tracts from penetrating into the lungs. This does not happen with the non-adsorbed particles.

High concentrations of polluting gases (e.g. sulphur dioxide) can cause coughing, cramp of the respiratory tracts and suffocation, while others, such as carbon monoxide, nitrogen oxides, organic solvent vapours, paralyse breathing and stop metabolic processes. These high concentrations, however, seldom occur in the open air. Macrophages belonging to the immunological system (RES) constitute the last stage of control. These try to neutralize the foreign particles penetrating into the blood through the lungs. Experimental animals are used for the determination of air quality standards. These values express the highest permissible amounts of certain pollutants in the atmosphere. These concentrations are harmless either to man or to the majority of living organisms. In most highly industrialized countries the observance of these values is controlled by legislation.

In areas contaminated by fluorine, fluoride is introduced into animals by means of plants. Fluorine accumulates in animal flesh, bones and fat. This results in malformation of bones and denture, decrease of resistance, changing of the blood pattern and depressed growth, in short, appearance of the symptoms of fluorosis.

The impacts of polluted air on animals living in the wild are not well known. It is, however, known that several bird species migrate from towns where the air is polluted and these are mainly insectivorous species. It is, therefore, relevant that primarily insects are affected by air pollution and consequently it is their destruction that leads to bird migration. Owing to agricultural mechanization and the use of ever increasing amounts of insecticides based on organo-phosphate esters and chlorinated hydrocarbons, these chemicals can also become pollutants. Their excessive or irregular inexpert application has caused, also through air, serious incidents of similar size to the well-known fish kills caused by the pollution of certain lakes and rivers. Frequently, the arthropods of forests and meadows are killed instead of the harmful insects. This may upset the biological equilibrium. Mass killing of birds and mammals has also occurred. Chemicals used in agriculture may also decimate the number of man's domesticated arthropods, the bees.

Finally, in order to show that air pollution can cause genetic aberrations in the animal kingdom in a relatively short period, we mention the case of "industrial melanism". In English industrial districts the heath moth of the birch tree is common. At the beginning of the 19th century, its populations consisted mainly of light-coloured individuals. The frequency of black individuals was 0.2%. As a result of industrialization, soot settled on to the light-coloured tree-trunks, thus providing a favourable hiding colour for black moths. It has been established experimentally, too, that from among the moths set free in an area where tree-trunks were black, predominantly the light-coloured ones were eaten by birds. Owing to this selective advantage, at the beginning of the 1900s, the frequency of black moths had already reached 99% while, in areas with pure air, the original proportions had remained unchanged.

Air pollutants can cause great damage to agriculture. American scientists estimate that, for the area of California alone, the yearly damage done to agriculture amounts to 10 million dollars. It has been reported that odorous fumes emitted by the chemical industry had made wine undrinkable and that entire fruit-tree plantations had deteriorated because of the dust from cement factories and because of sulphur dioxide pollution. Apart from these drastic changes, the decrease in yield is also a continuous, though not such an obvious, process. In the literature on this topic yield decreases of some 50% have already been recorded.

Those changes which can hardly be expressed in economic terms should also be considered. The extent of the areas, preserving the natural landscapes and the animal and plant kingdoms of our countries and of our continent, have been continuously decreasing. It is possible to provide for the partial protection of these areas by rules and regulations but it is, however, impossible to protect them from the impacts of air pollution.

The effect of industrial air pollution on forests

In present-day environmental control the conservation of forests has gained in importance for two reasons: firstly, the forests need increased protection; secondly, in the future, they can be of greater help against environmental contamination. Industrial air pollution causes great damage to forests. These damages can be assessed by different methods. In the following, an attempt is described, aimed at developing an appropriate method for damage assessment.

An aluminium factory pollutes its environment with fluorine containing compounds, sulphur dioxide, dust and carcinogenic 3,4-benzpyrene bound to the dust. The endangered area is 280 ha. The factory that started operating in 1952, has caused the gradual destruction of the entire forest. Pine *(Pinus nigra)* proved to be one of the most sensitive species. Since 1955, afforestation work has been going on in the same area, but without any success. The redness of the needles of the pine trees, brown spots on the leaves of *Quercus petraea* (sessile oak), *Quercus cerris, Crataegus monogyna* (hawthorn) are the result of changes caused by fluorine. The above symptoms cannot be observed at places not subject to air pollution. In open plantations or in the case of single trees living at the edge of woods facing the aluminium works, the extent of the severe damage is visible to the naked eye. Leaves of *Robinia pseudoacacia* have suffered great distortions. The few scattered *Ailanthus* (tree of heaven) individuals with desiccated tops are also evidence of damage.

Symptoms of secondary pests, *Tischeria complanella* and on older individuals, those of *Dryomia circinans* can be observed. Egg clusters of *Lymantria dispar* occur near the base of the trunks of *Schizophyllum alneum* and *Gloeoporus adustus* can be observed, too.

Smoke damage can be assessed on the basis of annual wood laid down by the inner or wood cambium of trees. According to this, new cambium forms on top of last year's growth. The growth cycle of trees can be traced by means of the measurement of the width of annual rings or that of the radial growth or girth.

In the affected area annual ring chronological investigations were made. Auger samples were taken at chest height (1.3 m), at right angles to the wind direction. Figure 28 illustrates data obtained by the measurement of one of the sampled trees. It has been drawn so that values of annual ring width are marked above the number of the corresponding year. Connecting

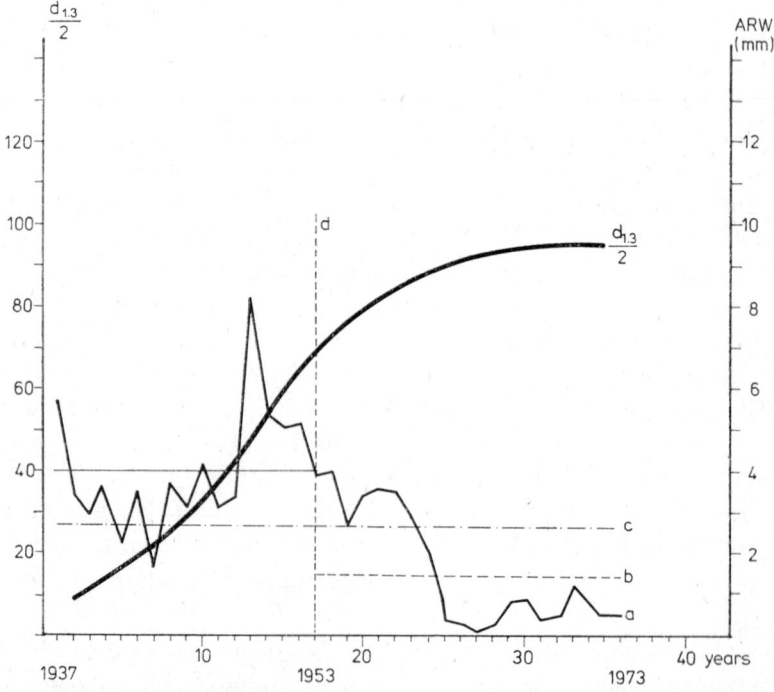

Fig. 28. Result of an annual ring chronological investigation. Average annual ring width prior to 1953, (*a*) after 1953, (*b*) average annual ring width, (*c*) average annual ring width in the year following the commissioning of the factory, (*d*) (ARW), annual ring width in mm $\left(\dfrac{d_{1.3}}{2}\right) : \dfrac{\text{annual growth in diameter (without trunk) at breast height}}{2}$

the neighbouring points by a dotted line, the diagram of annual rings is obtained ($\acute{E}_{sz}$"). The curve marked by $\frac{{}^d1 \cdot 3}{2}$ illustrates the changes in annual growth as measured by the half diameter without bark $\frac{{}^d1 \cdot 3}{2}$.

Study of the internal pattern of annual rings on a chronological basis has yielded data, showing a strong connection between the formation of annual rings and air pollution. As annual ring formation is also influenced by several other factors, future investigations should define their extent. Improvement of the method will make it possible to determine the losses in growth caused by the deterioration of the environment and also the consequent financial losses.

Table 4 illustrates the degree of air pollution tolerance for certain tree species.

Harmful effects on health

It is well known that pure air plays an important role in the preservation of health. A polluted environment does not provide the right conditions for adequate rest, relaxation and recreation. In order to eliminate the harmful effects of air pollution, the organism consumes energy, which means an unnecessary stress and the resistance of the organism decreases. Polluted air weakens the organism, thus causing illnesses, aggravating already existing ones and retarding recovery.

Sudden, but generally short-lasting pollutions of high concentration, cause acute illnesses. This kind of pollution acts selectively: it affects the more sensitive individuals and those already ill, even killing them. In the case of recurring smogs, for instance, it is the first one that increases mortality, as there remains no susceptible population for the second one to exert a harmful effect on. Chronic pollution, however, exerts its effects during the entire life of the individual, on each individual of the population and on several generations.

This lasting effect may change metabolic processes, causing chronic illnesses, even genetic aberrations. It is well known that historically major disturbances such as floods, earthquakes and other catastrophes have not affected the evolution of animal or plant types which, however, has resulted e.g. from relatively minor, but lasting changes in the atmospheric oxygen content, or in that of carbon dioxide or by temperature changes of only a few degrees in the climate of the Earth. The harmful effect of polluted

Table 4

Air pollution tolerance of certain tree species

Scientific name	Common name	Tolerance rating
Acer campestre	(Field maple)	2
Acer ginnala		2
Acer monspessulanum		2
Acer negundo	(Box-elder)	1
Acer negundo odessamum		1
Acer negundo variegatum		1
Acer platanoides	(Norway maple)	3
Acer platanoides globosum		2
Acer platanoides Reitenbachii		2
Acer platanoides Schwedleri		2
Acer pseudoplatanus	(Sycamore)	1
Acer sacharinum	(Silver maple)	4
Acer tataricum		4
Aesculus carnea		3
Aesculus hippocastanum	(Horse chestnut)	2
Ailanthus glandulosa	(Tree of heaven)	5
Alnus glutinosa	(Common alder)	2
Alnus incana	(European grey alder)	2
Betula pendula	(Warty birch)	4
Betula pubescens	(Hairy birch)	4
Carpinus betulus	(Hornbeam)	3
Carpinus betulus columnaris		3
Castanea sativa	(Sweet chestnut)	3
Castanea vesca		3
Catalpa bignonioides	(N. American catalpa)	3
Catalpa Bungei		3
Celtis austrialis		5
Celtis occidentalis	(Nettle tree)	5
Celtis siliquastrum	(Mediterranean judas tree)	4
Cornus mas	(Cornelian cherry)	4
Corylus colurna	(Turkish hazel)	3
Crataegus monogyna	(Hawthorn)	3
Eleagnus angustifolia		5
Evodia Daniellii	(Ewodia)	2
Fagus silvatica	(Beech)	3
Fagus silvatica pendula		3
Fraxinus americana	(White ash)	4
Fraxinus excelsior	(Ash)	4
Fraxinus diversifolia		3
Fraxinus ornus		4
Fraxinus pennsylvanica	(Green asn)	3
Gleditsia triachanthos	(Honey locust)	5
Gymnocladus dioica	(Kentucky coffee tree)	3
Juglans nigra	(Black walnut)	3
Juglans regia	(English walnut)	3
Koelreuteria paniculata	(Golden rain tree)	5
Liquidambar styraciflua	(N. American sweet gum)	2
Liriodendron tulipifera	(Yellow poplar)	2
Malus baccata	(Siberian crab)	2
Malus pumila	(Crab apple)	2
Malus pumila aldehamensis		2
Malus pumila Bileyi		2

Table 4 (*cont.*)

Scientific name	Common name	Tolerance rating
Malus Niedzwetskyana		2
Malus spectabilis		2
Morus alba		5
Morus alba Fegyvernekiana		5
Morus alba pendula		5
Morus alba nigra	(Mulberry)	3
Ostrya carpinifolia	(European hop hornbeam)	3
Paulownia tomentosa	(Foxglove tree)	2
Pyrus communis	(Wild pear)	4
Pyrus nivalis		4
Platanus acerifolia	(Plane)	4
Platanus occidentalis	(American sycamore)	4
Platanus orientalis	(Oriental plane)	4
Populus alba	(White poplar)	5
Populus alba Bolleana		5
Populus alba nivea		5
Populus alba pendula		4
Populus alba pyramidalis		3
Populus balsamifera	(Balsam poplar)	3
Populus canadensis		3
Populus canescens	(Grey poplar)	4
Populus nigra	(Black poplar)	4
Populus nigra italica		3
Populus nigra plantierensis		3
Populus robusta		3
Populus Simonii		4
Populus Simonii fastigiata		4
Populus sauveolens		4
Populus tremula	(Aspen)	4
Prunus canescens		3
Prunus cerasifolia		3
Prunus cerasifolia nigra		3
Prunus cerasifolia Hessei		3
Prunus cerasifolia Spaethiana		3
Prunus cerasus	(Wild cherry)	4
Prunus communis		3
Prunus mahaleb		3
Prunus padus	(Bird cherry)	3
Prunus pseudocerasus		3
Prunus serrulata		3
Quercus borealis	(Red oak)	4
Quercus cerris	(Turkey oak)	4
Quercus cerris Ambrozyana		4
Quercus conferta		4
Quercus lanuginosa		4
Quercus petraea	(Durmast oak)	4
Quercus robur	(Pendunculate oak)	4
Robinia hispida		3
Robinia pseudoacacia	(Black locust)	3
Robinia pseudoacacia Decaisneana		3
Robinia pseudoacacia pendula		3
Robinia pseudoacacia pyramidalis		3
Robinia pseudoacacia umbraculifera		3
Salix alba	(White willow)	5

Table 4 (*cont.*)

Scientific name	Common name	Tolerance rating
Salix alba vitellina		5
Salix alba pendula		5
Salix babylonica	(Weeping willow)	4
Sophora japonica	(Scholars tree)	5
Sophora japonica pendula		5
Sorbus aria	(Whitebeam)	4
Sorbus aucuparia	(Mountain ash)	4
Tilia americana	(American basswood)	4
Tilia cordata	(Small-leaved lime)	4
Tilia euchlora	(East European lime)	4
Tilia platyphyllos	(Large-leaved lime)	4
Tilia tomentosa		4
Ulmus americana	(American elm)	3
Ulmus campestris		3
Ulmus glabra	(Wych elm)	3
Ulmus hollandica		3
Ulmus var. petteursi		3

1: susceptible to pollution; 2: mostly susceptible; 3: averagely tolerant; 4: generally tolerant; 5: in all cases tolerant.

air on health has been established by statistical-epidemiological investigations. Diseases of the respiratory and circulatory systems are more frequent in populations living in such an environment.

According to a large-scale assessment by Dean (1968) city air pollution increases mortality caused by chronic bronchitis and lung cancer. If air pollution and smoking were eliminated—he says—mortality caused either by lung cancer or chronic bronchitis could be reduced to one tenth and to one half of the present value, respectively. The number of cancer cases affecting the respiratory system has been increasing all over the world. Generally, air pollution is suspected to be its cause. This is underlined by the fact that combustion products contain large amounts of different polycyclic aromatic hydrocarbons, which are carcinogenic. The same substances can be found also in cigarette smoke and it has been shown that they can cause cancer in test animals.

Pollutants may attack the lungs through five main sites of action or mechanisms: (*i*) In the respiratory system, which reacts by the initiation of a constrictive reaction of the bronchi reflex; (*ii*) in the blood vessels of the bronchus and its branches, which try to reduce the absorption of harmful substances through the bronchial mucosa; (*iii*) in the blood vessels of the lungs, where they react by decreasing absorption from the alveolar (pulmonary) capillaries; (*iv*) in the heart and large blood vessels taking part in the transport of toxic substances; (*v*) by penetration into organs, tissues or cells and by affecting metabolic processes.

The inhalation of larger amounts of pollutants slows down or even inhibits the motion of cilia. The base epithelium may become detached and hyperplasia or metaplasia may develop. Any disturbance in the functioning of the bronchial mucosa may favour the lodging of pathogenic and facultative-pathogenic microorganisms. The swelling of the bronchial mucosa and bronchioles, the cramp of the muscles of the alveoli bring about a restriction of the respiratory passages, affecting also the heart and the organs of the circulatory system (Fig. 29). Should the inhaled dust particles get into the alveolar ducts, the phagocytes present in the alveolar tissues will increase and engulfing the dust particles and other debris, migrate to the bronchioles whence by ciliary action and coughing they may be expelled. The inhaled pollutant may also directly destroy the tissues of lungs. Chronic bronchitis, frequently brought about by air pollution, predisposes to cancer and helps the penetration of the carcinogenic hydrocarbons into the respiratory system.

The following factors should be taken into consideration when morbidity is being examined: (*i*) malignant tumour of the tracheas, bronchial tubes and lungs, (*ii*) acute bronchitis and bronchiolitis, (*iii*) chronic bronchitis, (*iv*) inflammation of the conjunctiva and eyes. The overlapping effect of

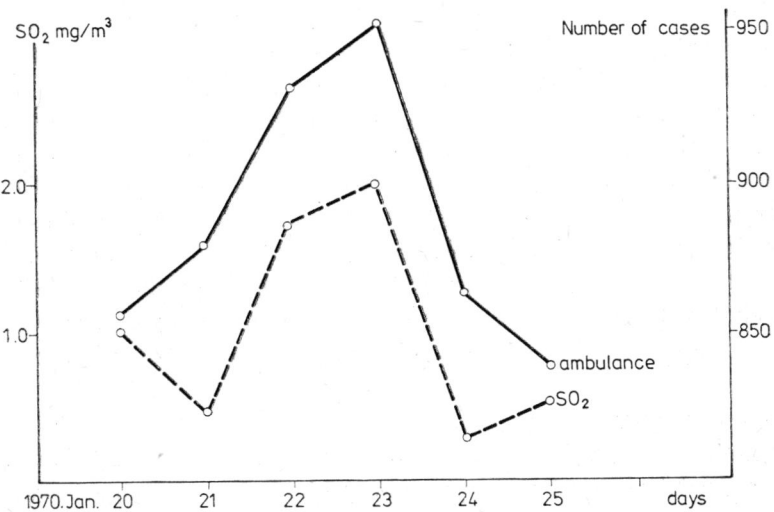

Fig. 29. Connection between the degree of air pollution and the number of sudden sicknesses expressed as the number of ambulant cases

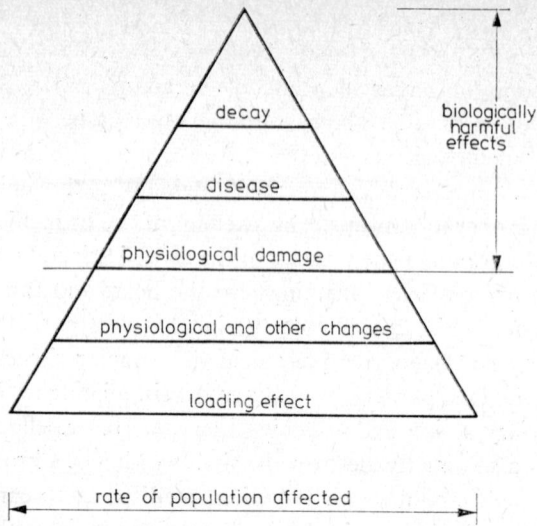

Fig. 30. The schematic diagram showing the biological effects of air pollution

numerous factors acting simultaneously, makes it very difficult to carry out a statistical–epidemiological investigation.

Physiological effects of air pollution depend on both external and internal factors, like the concentration of a certain pollutant, its toxicity, synergic or antagonistic effect of other pollutants, the duration and periodicity of exposure and also environmental factors, such as humidity and temperature. Internal factors are the general state and susceptibility of the exposed organism to a certain substance.

All these factors may cause death, acute and chronic illnesses, modification in the basic processes of metabolism (e.g. lung ventilation, oxygen transport), harmful effects (e.g. irritation of the eyes) and nuisances (e.g. offensive odours) (Fig. 30). It is assumed also that reproductive, genetic and human-genetic alterations may occur. Essentially, long-term and short-term effects should be distinguished. Numerous data are available on short-term effects. Long-term effects are, however largely undetermined and presumably much more complex than it would be possible to prove on the basis of our present knowledge.

In order to preserve the nature and health of the human population, the threshold concentrations of different pollutants are being experimentally determined. This is called the physiological limit. In most countries regulations or laws ordain that they should be respected. This forms the basis for the protection of the inhabitants from harmful effects. The definition

Table 5

Limit values of air quality (mg/m³)

Substance	USA		FRG		USSR	
	30'	24h	MIK$_K$	MIK$_D$	30'	24h
Acetaldehyde				4.00	0.01*	
Acetone				120	360	
Acrolein				0.1	0.3*	0.1
Ammonia	3.5			—		0.2
Aniline				0.8		0.03
Arsenic						0.003
Benzene				3.0		0.8
Beryllium		0.00001				
Acetic acid				5.00	15.00	
Ethanol				100		5.0
Ethylene		0.13**				3.0
Phenol				0.2		0.01
Fluorine	0.07	0.007			0.03*	0.01
Hydrogen fluoride						0.005
Formaldehyde						0.012
Mercury						0.0003
Sulphur dioxide		0.26	0.75	0.5	0.50*	0.15
		0.13				
		0.44				
		0.39				
Hydrogen sulphide	0.045	0.0075	0.3	0.15		0.008
Sulphuric acid	0.1				0.3*	0.1
Chlorine dioxide	0.3		0.6	0.3		0.03
Soot						0.05
Manganese						0.01
Methanol				15		0.5
Nitro-benzene				0.3		0.008
Nitrogen dioxide		0.18	2.0	1.0		0.085
Lead						0.0007
Oxidizing agents		0.1				
Dust	0.1	0.05			0.5*	0.15
		0.125				
		0.15				
		0.20				
Hydrochloric acid			1.4	0.7		0.006
Carbon disulphide						0.01
Carbon monoxide		16–33**			3.0*	1.0
Toluene				20		0.6
Trichlorethylene				30		1.0
Xylene				20		0.2
Dust deposit	0.15 g/m², month		indus-trial 0.85 g/m² month	other 0.42 g/m² month		

of physiological limit is, however, not very explicit. According to one attitude air pollution is only harmful, if it brings about measurable modifications in the organism, spoils health or mental capacity. The other approach regards those pollutant concentrations as harmful, which cause biochemical modifications or reactions in the central nervous system, even in those cases, where no clinical symptoms can be observed and the changes are spontaneously reversible. Therefore, e.g. in the USA, values are frequently higher than those accepted in certain European countries.

Table 5 illustrates the limit values for a few important substances.

References

Dean, G. (1968): Air pollution and health. *Royal Soc. of Health Journal* **68**: 31–33.

Garber, K. (1967): *Luftverunreinigungen und ihre Wirkungen*. Berlin.

Munn, R. E. and Bolin, B. (1971): Global air pollution, meteorological aspects. *Atm. Environ.* **5**: 363–402.

Peterson, E. K. (1969): Carbon dioxide affects global ecology. *Environmental Science and Technology* **3**: 1162–1169.

Robinson, E. and Robbins, R. C. (1970): Gaseous sulfur pollutants from urban and natural sources. *Journal of Air Pollution Control Association* **20**: 233–235.

Stern, A. C. (1962–68): *Air pollutions*. Vols I, II, III. New York.

Várkonyi, T. (1972): Areal distribution of atmospheric sulfur dioxide. (in Hungarian) *Energia és Atomtechnika* **25**: 164–196.

Chapter 6

Water pollution

WATER POLLUTION AND THE EUTROPHICATION OF LAKES

The water resources of the world

According to our present knowledge the total water resources of the world amount to 26.6 trillion t. Approx. 94.7% of this huge volume of water can be found in the lithosphere (rocky belt), its major part being bound to minerals which constitute the rock bed. This is called bound water (other names: water of crystallization, water of constitution). These waters form a part of the structure of minerals and are released only at high temperature. The remaining 5.3% can practically be found in the hydrosphere (water belt), the distribution of which is given in Table 6 (Entz 1964).

The oceans and seas form the greatest coherent volume of water to be found on the surface of the Earth. They cover 70.84% of the 510 million km^2 of surface area of our planet. Their depth exceeds, in more than one location, the height of the highest peaks of the continents. On the surface of the continents water appears in a more scattered form, covering 2.5 million km^2 of its territory. From this the area of fresh water amounts to 2 million km^2. The volume of fresh water is small in comparison with that of

Table 6

Water resources of the hydrosphere

Location and state of stored water	Amount 10^{12} t	Per cent
Seas	1,380,000	98.900
Polar and mountain ice and snow	16,700	1.077
Fresh water	25	0.002
Water vapour in the atmosphere	13	0.001
Underground water	250	0.020
Total	1,396,988	100.000

seas and oceans (Table 6). It amounts to barely 0.4% of the surface area of the Earth and to approx. 1% of the area of the continents.

In the Earth's interior, water occurs in various forms of underground water. Capillaries of granular soils are filled with coherent soil water. Soil binds water by means of capillary action (soil moisture), though the existence of subterranean streams should also be mentioned.

The quantity of biologically bound water, in comparison with the above forms, is insignificant. The biologically bound water means water that forms part of the structures of plants and of the bodies of animals. The so-called transpiration water, transpired by plants in the course of their metabolism should also be considered. In the form of invisible vapour and the condensed water of clouds, finely distributed water is also present in the atmosphere.

WATER BALANCE OF HUNGARY AND MEETING THE WATER DEMANDS

The average amount of precipitation falling on to the surface of the Earth yearly is approx. 930 mm. In view of the fact that the water resources of the atmosphere, oceans and seas are unchanged—this also applies to the water holding levels of the continent—the quantity of water evaporating from the surface of our planet can be regarded as practically constant. As to the water balance of certain continents or seas, evaporation and water precipitation is generally out of equilibrium. Precipitation falling on to the surface of continents is lost either by evaporation or in surface runoff.

The present state of the Hungarian water system is the result of a long geological development. Although at a different rate it is still being further developed and shaped. The entire territory of the country belongs to the catchment of the Danube. Therefore, the entire Hungarian water management is based on only a few greater rivers (Danube, Tisza, Dráva).

In a rainy year, the total volume of surface water resources can be estimated at 120 $km^3 \cdot year^{-1}$. In average dry years it amounts to approx. 100 $km^3 \cdot year^{-1}$. From the point of view of the water resources management of the country, this volume is not unfavourable. According to the water balance of the year 1965 (Csermák 1967), the annual consumption of the country amounted to 4 km^3, which was expected to rise in the future. For example, in the 1950s, the following values of water consumption were recorded: agriculture 0.85, industry 0.5, population 0.3 km^3. Ten years later, in the same sequence, these values had risen to 1.4, 1.5 and 0.6 km^3. Present water consumption may amount to as much as 14 km^3. According to our present knowledge the mean theoretical exploitation of surface waters in Hungary is 19%.

96–99% of the natural surface water resources of Hungary—depending on the season under study—is supplied by waters arriving from the neighbouring countries. This implies that both its quality and its quantity depend on interferences in foreign countries. As far as water management is concerned, the conventions concluded with the neighbouring countries for the utilization of water and the protection of their resources are of great importance. Therefore, in our country, special importance is attached to those measures of environment control aimed at the protection of the few water sources of Hungarian origin and the few lakes, which are also important for resort purposes.

CLASSIFICATION OF NATURAL WATERS

Natural waters which comprise all the waters of the continents are divided into two groups: seas and inland waters. Besides their vast extent and volume sea water can be characterized by a mean 3.5% dissolved solid content of which 2.73% is salt (sodium chloride). The volume of inland waters is less, their salt content being under 3%. The majority of them is so-called fresh water, with a dissolved solid content under 0.05%.

Waters can be classified according to several principles like organic matter content, temperature conditions, turbulence, vegetation, etc. Particularly in the case of lakes, numerous classifications are used. From among them Thienemann's (1926) classification can be regarded as the most comprehensive:

— ground waters
— springs
— running waters (from brooks to rivers)
— standing water: lakes, lagoons, pond or swamps, temporary waters
— waters of unusual temperature and chemical composition: thermal waters, snow and ice, sewage, brackish waters (with a salinity of 0.05–3%), highly-saline and natron (chemically rich) lakes and other waters with peculiar characteristics.

WATER AS AN ECOLOGICAL FACTOR AND ITS ROLE IN THE BIOSPHERE

In the history of the Earth, water appeared in the so-called azoical time before life appeared, when the drop in temperature had permitted the precipitation of water. This led to the formation of the hydrosphere, between the lithosphere and the atmosphere. Hydrosphere is a permanent body of water, gathered in the hollows of the Earth's crust, forming the oceans and seas. From that time on, water has taken over the role of the transformation of relief and that of the history of the Earth (Vadász 1957). During the following main stage of development, when the temperature had fallen to a value of approx. 80 °C, the emergence of life became possible which, of course, depended on water and presumably bacterial-like particles were its first representative. Even today bacteria are known to live in thermal sources at 82.5 °C and are capable of enduring even 89 °C (Sebestyén 1963).

Water, or more exactly sea water, is considered to be the cradle of life. This has been proved by two facts: (*i*) The concentration of sea water and that of the bodily fluid of marine animals is almost identical. (*ii*) The marine vegetation and fauna is far richer in species than that of fresh waters. The origin of aquatic life and its importance in building up organisms is illustrated in Table 7. It can be seen that organisms emerging from water preserve it within themselves as a certain relict.

Water means for organisms both life medium and environment. Soil, water and air, collectively the biosphere, is the scene of life on Earth. Water as a life medium differs from air in certain characteristics. Of these, the liquid state is the most important. This largely affects reproduction, movement, feeding, in one word, the vital processes of organisms. Planktons, the most characteristic members of aquatic organisms, spend their whole life in water (here they carry out all their life processes), independently of the substrate. The floating of planktons in water is not a physical phenomenon. As the specific weight of the protoplasm of living organisms is somewhat greater than one, the floating of planktons cannot be regarded as floatation in a physical sense. Consequently, planktons are slowly sinking. In order to counterbalance this, different appendages have evolved on the surface of the body (gelatinous materials, wing-like appendages, oildrops, vacuole filled with gas, etc.) making the floating of planktons possible (Fig. 31).

In water the community of floating organisms capable of displacement, irrespective of water movement, are called nekton (as opposed to benthon or plankton). In inland waters they consist almost entirely of fishes. Other

Table 7

Water content of certain living organisms expressed in percentage of the
total body weight
(Buddenbrock 1956)

Animal group	Species	Per cent
Cnidaria (Jelly fish)	Bell-shaped medusae	98.22
Platyhelminthes (Tapeworm)	*Diphyllobothrium latum*	84.70
Nematolminthes (Nematode)	*Ascaris lubricoides*	79.30
Annelida (Leeches)	*Hirudinoidea*	86.30
Mollusca	*Helix pomatia* (Roman snail)	84.42
	Planorbis corneus	88.28
Arthropoda	*Gammarus* sp.	73.91
	Caterpillar of *Pieris rapae*	83.00
	Leptinotarsa decemlineata	62–66
	Caterpillar of the varicoloured butterfly	78.00
Vertebrata	*Tinca vulgaris* (Flying lizard)	80.00
	Rana sp. (Frog)	77.00
	Lepus sp. (Rabbit)	69.00
	Sus sp. (Pig)	41–55
	Homo sapiens (Man)	59–66

aquatic organisms attached to the bed live on the surface of the mud (ben-thon). It is also known, that some other organisms form a characteristic coating (periphyton) on the surface of aquatic plants or stones. Certain, tiny little organisms adhere to the body of other animals (e.g. water flea species). Mainly on the surface film of still waters, communities of freely moving organisms with a larger body (pleustons) fixed to the coat and communities of microscopic organisms (neustons) may develop. Water as an environment is most complex. Water itself as a whole and its so-called influence factors affect aquatic organisms. Such influence factors are dissolved gases and salts, temperature, light, pollution and the circulation rate of water. The impact of these factors makes possible or, on the contrary, hinders the presence of certain species and thereby affecting the formation of the entire life community in one way or the other. A very characteristic example of this is the relationship between the salt content of western Westphalian sodium chloride waters and the number of their species (Thienemann 1926):

Salt content:	3%	3–10%	10–16%	16–20%	20%
Number of species:	64	38	12	1	0

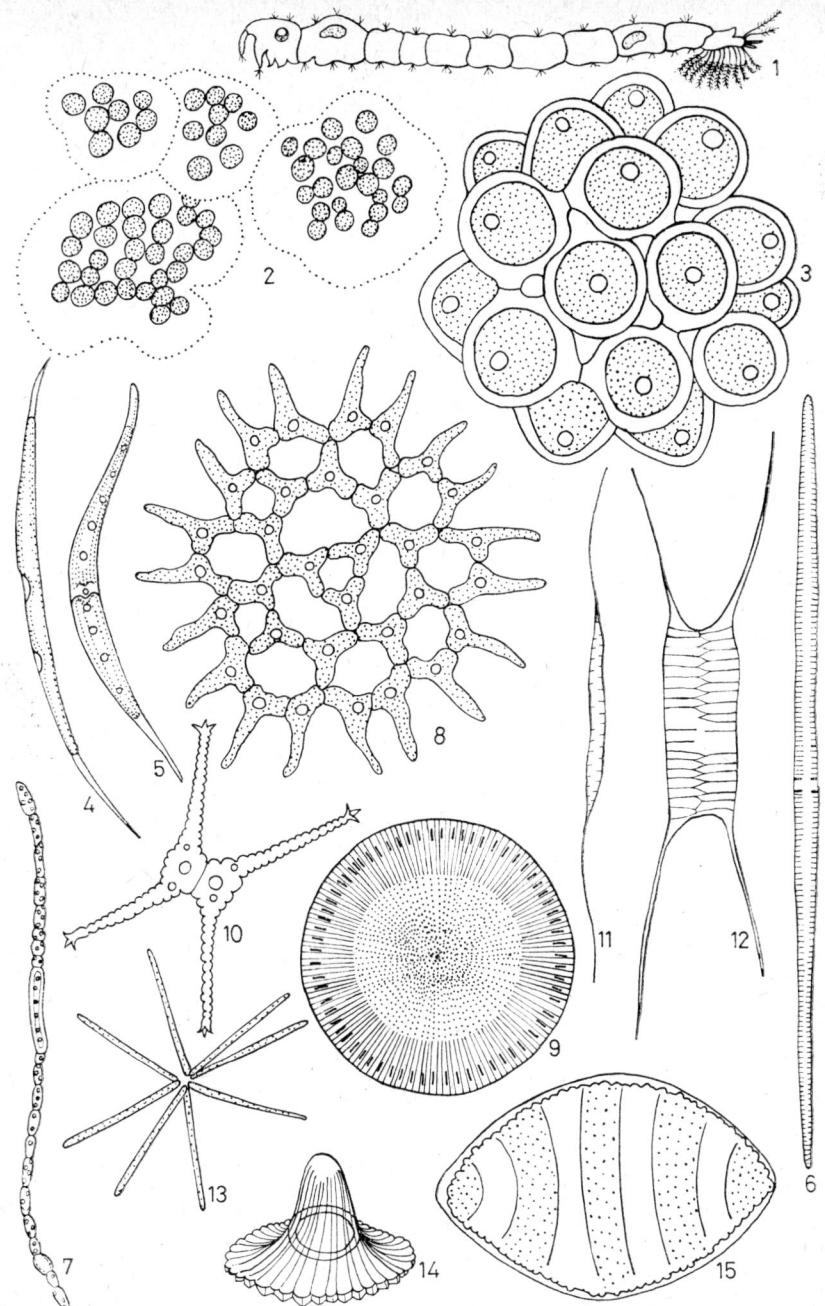

Fig. 31a. Plankton organisms with different structures, their floating is caused by the presence of gas (1,7), global form (3), elongated cell (4,6), thread-like form (7), sheet-like form (8–10), long appendages (11–13) and parachute-like form (14,15). 1: larva of *Chaoborus crystallinus* and back gas-bladder; 2, 7: blue-algae; 3, 4, 5, 8, 11: green algae; 6, 9, 10, 12, 13, 14: diatoms; 15: cyst of a suctorian. (after Sebestyén 1963)

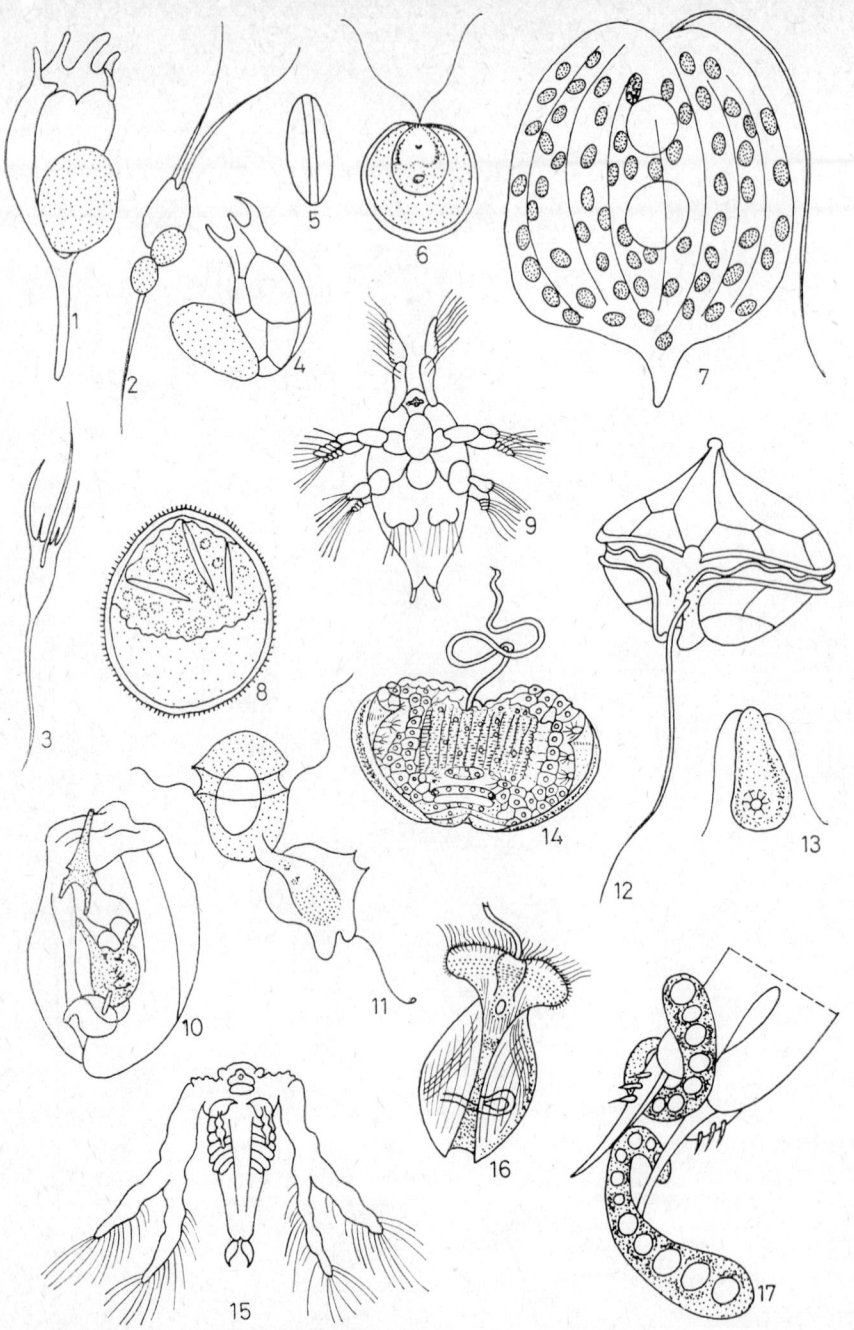

Fig. 31b. Aquatic organisms floating with active ciliary or flagellate motions, **1, 2, 3, 4, 10:** rotifera of different shapes; **6, 7, 11, 12, 13:** flagellates, **14, 16:** mollusc larvae; **15:** larva of a plankton fresh water shrimp; **17:** adhesive algae on top of the abdomen of a plankton shrimp. (after Sebestyén 1963)

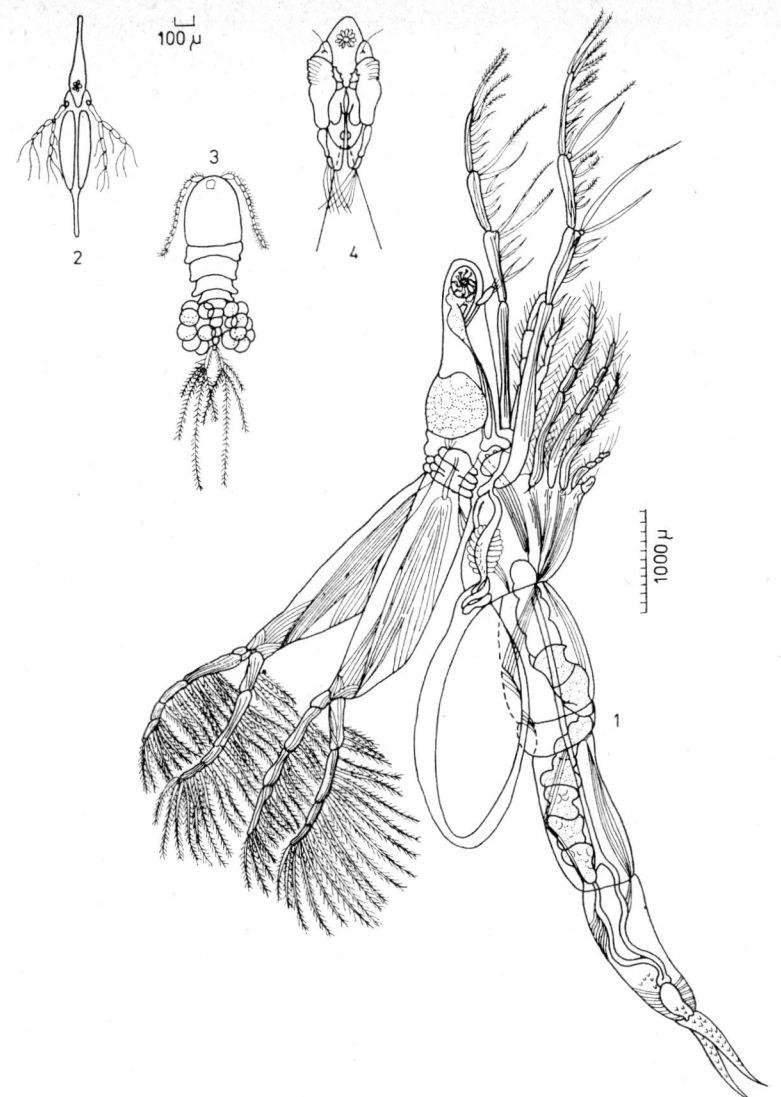

Fig. 31c. The actively moving carnivorous "glass" shrimp (1) prefers to eat other planktonic shrimps (2, 3, 4). (after Sebestyén 1963)

A similar example could be mentioned in connection with the carbonate waters of the area between the Danube and the Tisza. In these waters the total salt content (generally sodium bicarbonate) varies between 25.5–0.7 g. l^{-1} (Dvihally and Ponyi 1957), and, consequently, there is also a substantial variability in the number of their animal species.

The distribution of animals living in the well-developed reeds of Lake Balaton (Ponyi 1962) clearly illustrates the role and significance of dissolved oxygen in water and water movement. Animals with an increased oxygen requirement, which are resistant to the strong surge of wave action, are located in that part of the lake's reed belt, which is subjected to surge and is rich in oxygen. On the other side of the reed belt, facing the shore, there are organisms with small oxygen requirement and which prefer still, marshy places (Fig. 32).

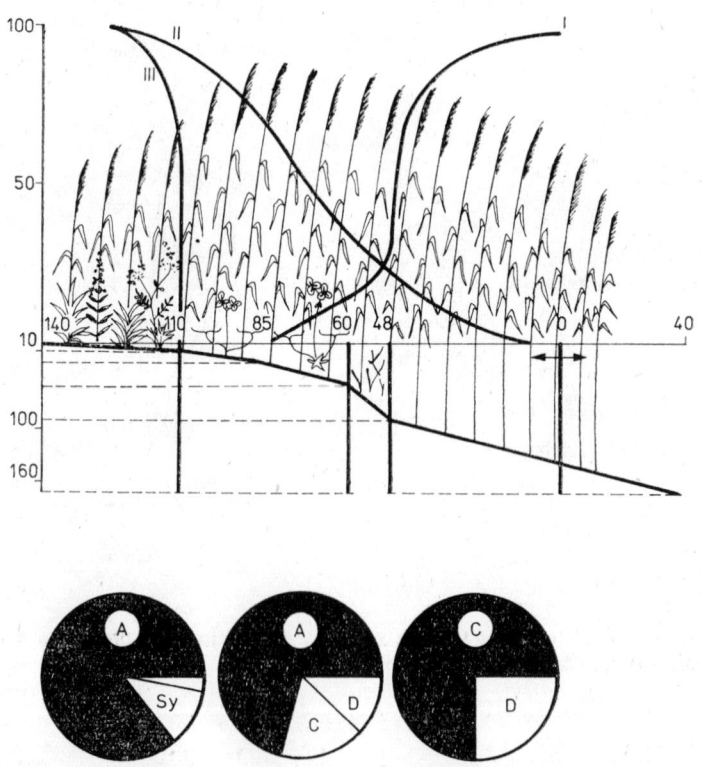

Fig. 32. Number of individuals and percentage composition of *Malacostraca*-species in the cross-section of reeds of Lake Balaton. (I) *Corophium;* (II) *Dicerogammarus;* (III) *Synurella* and *Niphargus;* (A) *Asellus;* (C) *Corophium;* (D) *Dicerogammarus;* (Sy): *Synurella.* (after Ponyi 1962)

Similarly to terrestrial life, light radiation also plays a basic role in the life of aquatic organisms. Without light aquatic life could not flourish in its medium. It is the presence of light and the transparency of water that render it possible among others for algae to produce organic matter—the main source of food for animals—from CO_2 and water dissolved salts. Thus, it is relevant that certain lakes are capable of self-preservation without any external interference. Waters entirely cut off from light, the so-called underground waters and lakes, are also known. Naturally, they are devoid of green plants. The little, generally white and blind animals which live in them, feed on detritus derived from the soil surface. These aquatic life communities are no longer capable of self-preservation.

Organisms living in an aquatic environment must adapt themselves greatly in order to survive. The most characteristic phenomenon is perhaps the development of the defence mechanism of the organisms cast on to a dry surface as a result of changing water level. We know several worms and snails which bury themselves into the mud during the "waterless" season. On the other hand, there are shells capable of living, with their shells tightly closed, for a long period without water. It is typical, especially for Daphnia species living in ponds that, prior to the drying-out they lay so-called resting eggs (ephippium), thus securing their survival. Other species bore themselves down into the mud and become encysted. When the dried out puddle becomes repeatedly filled with water they "revive". Many aquatic invertebrates react to the fluctuation of temperature in the same manner.

Feeding is one of the most important links between the living organisms of waters and this fact plays a vital role in the circulation of materials. Food interrelationships constitute a very complex food chain which, expressed for lake plankton is as follows: plankton algae→ filter-feeding Crustacea→ non-predatory plankton crab→ non-predaceous fish→ predaceous fish.

The study and knowledge of these food interrelationships are not only of theoretical importance but they also have practical implications. Such investigations have made it possible for modern fish hatcheries to breed such fish species (Fig. 33) which enable a proper distribution of consumers for each group of the available natural food (Antalfi and Tölg 1972).

The importance of water—as food sources—in the biosphere cannot be better illustrated than by the fact that from ancient times man has been interested in the living world of seas, lakes and rivers, utilizing the ample food supplied by them. To assess the present situation, it suffices to survey the important role fish plays in world nutrition. According to Ribiánszky and Woynarovich (1962) some 10–12 kg fish is consumed, compared with

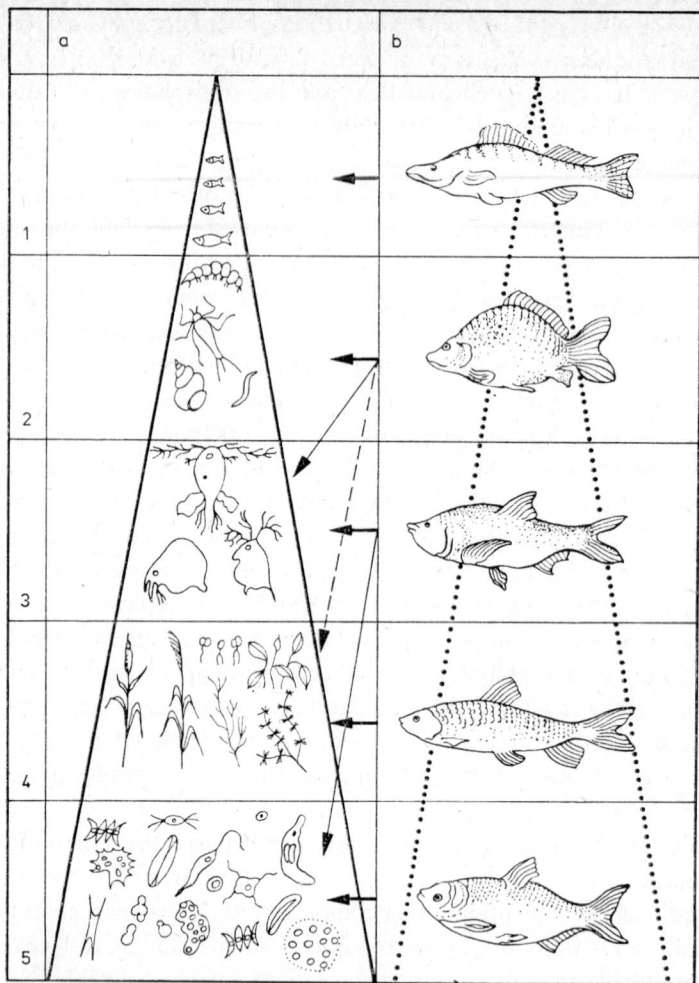

Fig. 33. Fish, living in modern fish hatcheries and their food. *(a)* groups of food, *(b)* feeding groups of fishes. Plankton algae *(5)* form the greatest mass among the food groups, they are followed by macrophytes and other aquatic plants *(4)*, plankton animals of small size *(3)*, organisms living in the silt and on the surface of plants *(2)*, and edible fish *(1)*. Thick arrow: main food; thin arrow: additional food; broken-lined arrow: periodical food. The two dotted lines converging upwards show a comparison of the natural production between the individual fish groups. (Antalfi and Tölg, 1972, partly modified)

approx. 17–18 kg/head of the flesh of warm-blooded animals, by the entire population of the world. Other data also refer to the rapid increase in fish consumption all over the world, which implies a 70% increase in the catch in comparison with those in the 1930s.

The connection between the biosphere and water cannot, actually, be restricted to the mere discussion of water belts and of the phenomena taking place in it. In brief, mention should be made of the characteristic zone at the boundaries of rock, water and air belts, namely, the soil which, owing to its special group of living organisms, is also called the "edosphere" and gives rise to edaphic factors. Soil constitutes a relatively thin crust of the Earth. Its properties and essential conditions are, however, entirely different from those of any other biotope. When comparing soil with a river, lake or even a forest, these differences readily spring to mind. Members of the plant kingdom (bacteria, algae, fungi) and those of the animal kingdom (protozoa, worms, arthropods, vertebrates) are equal components of the life community of the soil. The majority of these organisms spend their whole life in the soil and as a result of their beneficial action they add to the fertility of the soil. As in the case of aquatic life communities, there is a similar interrelationship between the members of the soil life community and the physical and chemical properties of the soil. Its characteristic active components determine the composition of the life community living in it. From among the many factors (structure, air content, chemical conditions of the soil, etc.) the water content of the soil must be stressed as one of the most important. Not only soil productivity and the existence of higher plants but also the water- and moisture-requiring organisms living in the soil depend on the water content of the soil (Fehér 1954).

We have already made mention of the role of vegetation covering the Earth in water transpiration. Nevertheless, it seems to be necessary to further elucidate some other aspects of the soil–vegetation–water interrelationship. The colour, exposure and vegetation can significantly modify the evaporating capacity of the soil. While both colour and exposure can increase the warming up process (and thereby also evaporation), vegetation is capable of reducing both of them. This may amount to 45–50%. The modifying role of vegetation in evaporation is twofold. Either the intensity of the exchange of humid air, caught in between the plants, is slowed down or a certain part of the precipitation is intercepted by vegetation. Therefore, the quantity of rainfall reaching the ground is reduced. The latter may reach even 60% of the annual amount of precipitation (Szarvas 1971). Apart from its quantity also several other factors influence the degree and speed by which rainfall penetrates into the soil such as the physical and chemical properties of the soil, and its cultivation.

Vegetation exerts a significant effect on the level of ground water. The larger the mass of vegetation on the territory in question, the deeper the level of soil water is (Sennykov 1953). Vegetation to be found alongside the

Table 8

Yearly transpiration of some soil water-consuming plants

Name	Transpiration mm/yr
Reed	1,500–2,000
Bulrush	2,250
Willows	750–1,300
Sedge and bent-grass	1,920
Tamarisk (*Tamarix*: *T. anglica* webb)	1,370–2,200
Poplars	1,500–1,800

different sources of water—depending on its composition—may consume 470–1,250 mm of water yearly. Table 8 contains data on the yearly transpiration of a few species which directly consume ground water (Szarvas 1971).

THE PROCESS AND SIGNIFICANCE
OF EUTROPHICATION

The expression eutrophication stands for the enrichment of the nutrient supply in stagnant waters. It is a rather complex concept. In order to be able to understand it, one has to be familiar with certain basic principles of the nutrient cycle in the life of lakes. Aquatic organisms are interrelated with each other by means of the food chain. When examining the manifold aspects of nutrition in a lake, one might recognise a certain order. The basis of this regular order is that by using solar energy aquatic plants (also the most important planktonic algae) synthesize organic matter from water, CO_2 and mineral salts. A simplified equation for this is the following:

$$6\ CO_2 + 12\ H_2O \xrightarrow[\text{pigment receptor}]{\text{light}} C_6H_{12}O_6 + 6\ H_2O + 6\ O_2$$

This is a primary product which is transformed and accumulated at a higher level by aquatic invertebrates. The latter are then consumed by fish.

Concerning their functions, aquatic organisms playing a part in this food chain can, principally, be divided into two groups: constructive organisms which build up organic matter and transferring organisms (Gere 1957). According to their functions within the group of transferring organisms, one can distinguish rebuilders, returners and decomposers (Sebestyén 1963). By rebuilders we mean such organisms which directly or indirectly feed on aquatic vegetation. Algae filtering zooplankton members, non-predatory fish feeding on them, or even carnivorous ones (pike, European eels, *Silurus glanis* L.) can equally be classed as rebuilders. Recuperant organisms are also animals feeding on plant and animal wastes. Their significance is interpreted variously in the literature in Hungary (Balogh 1953; Szabó and Marton 1956). Their real function is, among others, to consume bacterial colonies growing on detritus and by further splitting them up, helping bacterial decomposition. The expression returner, therefore, does not apply to the function of the animal group in question. The detritus eating Chironomid (midges) larvae, the main natural food of non-predatory fishes are also such animals. The term decomposer organisms, refers mainly to bacteria. If quantitative relationships are considered also in a feeding context, it can be observed, that the absolute quantities in the food chain show a pyramid-like decreasing tendency (Fig. 34).

Material recycling taking place in the life communities of lakes also implies energy flow. Consequently, the feeding of organisms practically determines the energy flow. The different trophic levels to be found in life communities, which are based on each other, can, therefore, be regarded as energy levels. These are denoted after the first letter of the English word "level" by λ (Lindeman 1942). The number of these levels is normally restricted to 4–5. These are fed by differing densities of various species. A certain percentage of solar energy (λ_0) is transformed, in the course of photosynthesis, in the bodies of algae, where it represents a potential quantum of energy (λ_1). Members of the animal plankton (e.g. Daphnia) consume a certain proportion of the plankton algae (λ_2); these are, in turn, consumed by zooplankton eaters (λ_3) e.g. glass crab (*Leptodora kindti*) and non-predatory fishes belonging to the third level. The latter may, then, be consumed by carnivorous fishes (λ_4).

In reality the matter and energy flow taking place along the food chain is far more complex. The connection between λ_1 and λ_2 in Lake Balaton is a case in point. Food interrelationships between plankton organisms have been fed into a computer, type CDC 3300 (Ponyi et al. 1975). It has been established that from among algae of the size 10–1,000 μ, only organisms of the size 10–40 μ were capable of reaching the second trophic level at a probability level of 0.1% (Fig. 35). As only two (*Keratella tecta* and *Polyarthra vulgaris*) of the 3 rotifera species, to be taken into consideration in the transport of algae, occur in large numbers this can happen only to a small extent. Filter-feeding *Crustacea* are only slightly bound to algae of the size 10–20 μ (P=5%), which clearly supports the fact that the exploitation of organisms smaller or equal to 10 μ is greater (Gliwicz 1969). Owing to this, experts are of the opinion that in Lake Balaton the organic

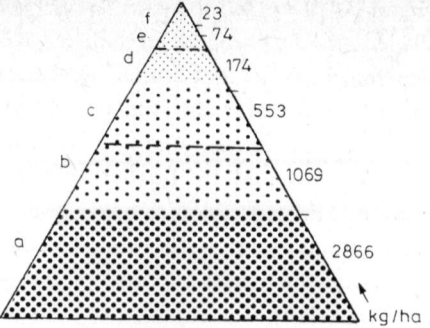

Fig. 34. Diagram expressing the weight ratio between organic matter and the biota of lakes. (a) dissolved organic matter, (b) phytoplankton, (c) bottom flora, (d) bottom fauna, (e) zooplankton, (f) fish. (after Sebestyén 1963, partly modified)

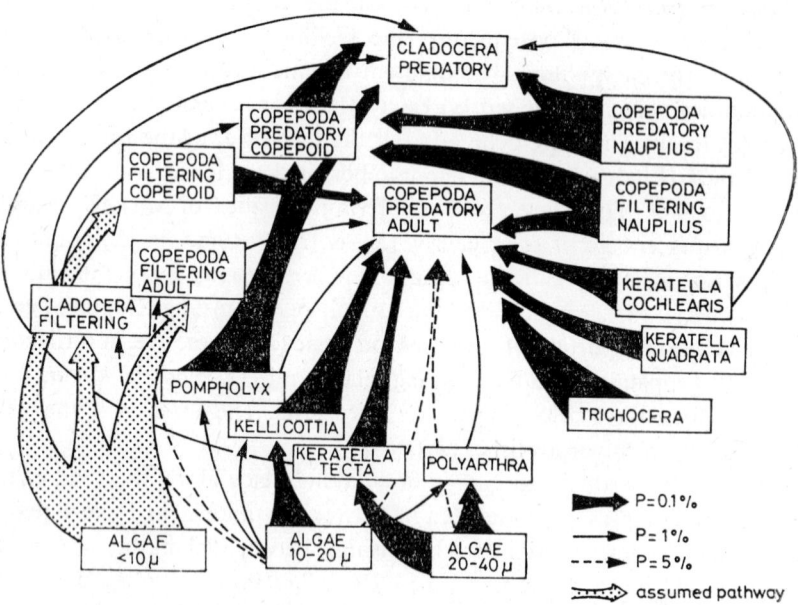

Fig. 35. Sketch of the food relations in the open water area of Lake Balaton. The arrows represent probability levels. (after Ponyi 1977)

matter produced by primary production, in the form of particles larger than 10 μ, will hardly be capable of passing through the filtering–sedimenting system of Lake Balaton to reach higher trophic levels. Other data, too, seem to indicate the important role of bacteria and micro-algae in the plankton system.

When making a detailed study of a particular trophic level, it can be observed that a certain quantum of energy is put into this level. The quantity of energy output is less than the input. The above-mentioned loss of energy is caused by several factors: energy needed for self-preservation, energy loss as a result of cannibalism and the loss of potential energy volume caused by death.

Once a substance has entered a living system a significant proportion of it will be involved in a perpetual circulation, whereas the energy bound to it will pass through the whole system only once (Fig. 36). At the different levels, the organic matter gradually gives off its energy and becomes in-organic matter. Photosynthesis will then build this inorganic matter into plants and the cycle starts again. The scheme outlined in Fig. 36 is a greatly simplified one. It must be taken into consideration that there are also processes opposing biological recycling; these lead matter and energy flow in the direction of abiotic transformations. Only that kind of organic matter will leave the circulation of substances of ecosystems, over which the co-ordinating effect (power) of the enzyme systems of living organisms has lost its power. This is generally the case when aerobic organisms are sub-jected to anaerobic conditions. Their cell walls dissolve, enzymes embedded in the plasma are freed and an uncoordinated process will start. In the course of post-lethal biocatalytic processes, the condensation of phenols

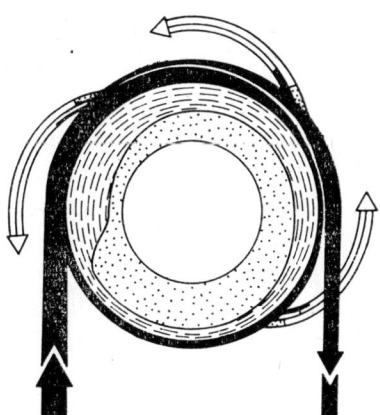

Fig. 36. Scheme of the matter and energy flow in a living community. Black arrow: in-coming and outgoing energy from the system; hatched arrow: amount of organic matter. Upon the net gain of solar energy, the amount of organic matter increases at the expense of inorganic matter. This relationship is reversed in the course of further processes. The three arrows pointing in the opposite direction to biogenic cycling represent the reverse process to "carbonification", when matter and energy are transferred by way of abiotic transformations. (Szabó and Marton 1956)

of different origin can be observed. These substances being already foreign to the structure of the organism do not take part in the material cycle. Such substances are the different components of humus. According to this interpretation, the energy-saving role of bacteria is relevant. Earlier it was believed that they, on the contrary, freed energy within the ecosystem (Szabó and Marton 1956).

Thus, it is easy to realise that the number of animal consumers is dependent on the feeding capacity of plants. The reproduction of aquatic plants is, however, determined by the amount of nutrients available in the water. Therefore, similarly to other biological systems, the aquatic life of lakes is dominated by the "quasi-stationary state", which is maintained, principally, by the matter and energy turnover (Fábián et al. 1975). Apart from the thermodynamical interpretation, it is also a characteristic of this special state that there are no "macroscopically" observable changes, though the building-up and decay processes constantly take place in the lake.

In spite of the fact that all the preconditions for the stability of aquatic life of lakes are given, one can distinguish the following phases in it: juvenile, maximal and senile. This can be accounted for by the fact that the functioning of aquatic plants, animals and bacteria, just because of changes in the margins of the lake, cannot be fully co-ordinated. Therefore the decomposition of organic matter is also inadequate, i.e. a certain proportion of organic matter collects in the sediment. Thus, owing to its own nutrient production, the aquatic living space becomes rich in nutrients. This process is called eutrophication. Man-made effects can accelerate this process, which is called artificial eutrophication. While the former process has been going on for thousands of years, the latter is taking place now, within a lifetime. Eutrophication can hardly be influenced. Since artificial eutrophication is the result of the activities of man, it can be naturally controlled, slowed down or accelerated.

According to the impact of human activity on the eutrophication of lakes, five major groups can be distinguished: (i) The impact of river-regulation and water impounding works, (ii) agricultural activity and its impacts, (iii) forest and sylvicultural works, (iv) industrialization, (v) impacts of urbanization.

The indirect impact of water regulation and water engineering control works on the eutrophication of a lake will be illustrated by the example of Lake Balaton. The most important work of water regulation, in the case of Lake Balaton, has been the drainage of marshes surrounding the lake (beginning of 18th and the middle of 19th century). When casting a glance at an earlier map of the lake (Fig. 37) it will be relevant to note

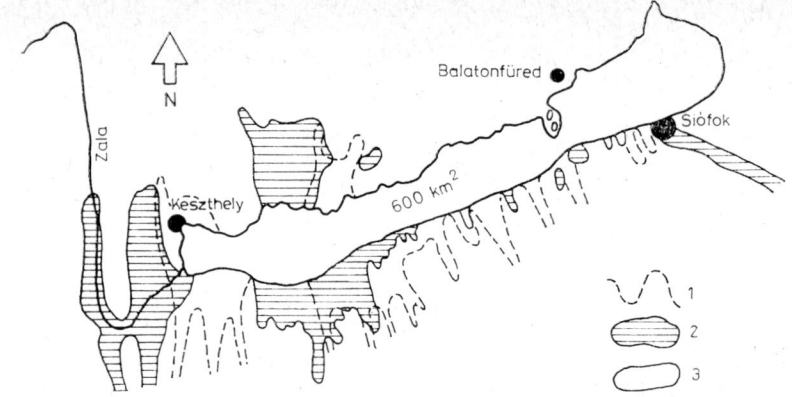

Fig. 37. Changes in the area and water level of Lake Balaton. Extension of the lake before the 15th century (1), in the 16–17th centuries (2), and the present area (600 km²) of the lake (3) (NWA Centre for Water-reserve Management, 1968)

that earlier, every watercourse of significance had to pass through an area of marshland to reach Lake Balaton. As these marshes were directly connected with the lake, they effectively filtered the natural watercourses and precipitated the larger proportion of the alluvium. At that time these areas were covered by aquatic plants of great stature (reed, rush, bulrush). These plants together with the bacteria and algae covering their submerged stems, took up a certain proportion of the water-dissolved nutrients. In the so-called spreading water, most of the suspended matter was able to sink down. As a result of marshland drainage and river control engineering works, the concentration of dissolved substances rose in Lake Balaton. At the same time, the rate of siltation had also further accelerated.

The impact of agriculture on the eutrophication of lakes is brought about by the rivers entering the lake and carrying a different quantity and quality of nutrients of agricultural origin. Mainly infiltration, agricultural effluents, less frequently wind or carelessness are the main means by which these substances get into water reservoirs. Nitrogen and phosphorus fertilizers play a significant role in the eutrophication of lakes. Nutrient enrichment manifests itself in the growing mass of algae and aquatic vegetation. In Hungary, the application of fertilizers is increasing at a considerable rate (Table 9), which calls special attention to the growing danger. It is practically impossible (in the case of nitrogen) or else very expensive, (for phosphorus) to remove these substances from watercourses.

In the catchment of Lake Balaton, for instance a huge amount of of active ingredients was spread on agricultural land in 1971. According to

Table 9

Fertilizer consumption in Hungary (Déri 1971)

Years						
1915	1925	1935	1945	1955	1965	1970
9.8	16.5	7.7	0.1	54.3	357.2	818.0

Data relate to 1000 t active ingredient.

Szabó (1973) some 10–15% of chemical fertilizers spread over the soil get washed into subsoil or surface waters. This would imply that in 1971, only by this means, 50–7,000 t of active principle might have reached Lake Balaton (Fig. 38). If the entire quantity had reached Lake Balaton, a concentration of approx. 2.8–3.8 mg of active ingredient per litre of the average volume of water would have been reached. These data are based on mere estimates. Nevertheless, they clearly demonstrate the size of the impacts reaching the lake, in other words, the extent of the danger.

The spread of intensive, factory-like livestock husbandry is another source of pollution. Slurry might flow directly into watercourses. Although, in Hungary, we have no available data on these processes as yet, according to foreign assessments they give rise to a significant problem.

Inadequate protection of the soil and obsolete agricultural practices result in significant amounts of top-soil getting into surface waters. According to Szabó (1973) the quantity of plant nutrients reaching Lake Balaton by way of arable soil can be estimated at 2,650–2,700 t. This increases the total amount of nutrients available for plants by 1.49 mg/l. This source, which accelerates eutrophication, can be controlled only by soil-conserving cultivation that can be regarded, in this respect, as a system of water conservation and environmental protection.

The role of forests is not exhausted only in the transpiration of water and in the control of the level of subsoil water, but they also play an important part in the binding of the soil. As a result of great efforts in reforesting, it has been achieved during the last decades that the area of forests exceeds 15% (Déri 1971). Forests, situated alongside waters to be controlled (e.g. Lake Balaton where along the northern coastline the danger of erosion is imminent), play an especially significant role. On the hillside facing the lake the number of crop-lands requiring intensive cultivation (e.g. vine) is continuously increasing although it would be most preferable to increase the afforested territory. In order to illustrate this in Table 10 we demonstrate the essence of Sylvester's (1961) already classical experiments, after Felföldy and Tóth (1970).

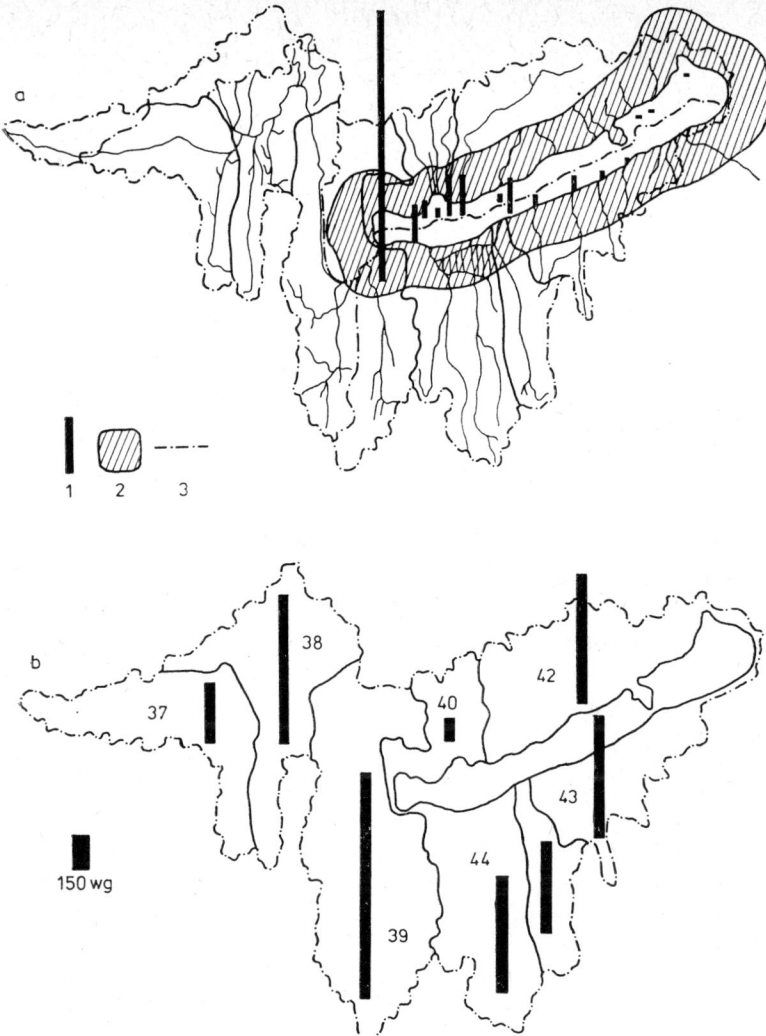

Fig. 38. Distribution of the water conservation area of Lake Balaton and the amount of chemical fertilizers applied in 1971. (*a*) (1) average discharge of the more important watercourses (m³/s), (2) area controlled by the regional development project of Lake Balaton, (3) border of the suggested conservation area, (*b*) black columns represent the amount of chemical fertilizers spread. The figures indicate the numbered catchment districts (after Szabó 1973, partly modified)

Table 10

Average nutrient content of drainage waters from afforested and
agriculturally cultivated areas (mg/1)

	Total-P	Dissolved-P	NO_3-N	Kjeldahl total-N
Unpopulated woodland without agriculture	0.069	0.007	0.130	0.074
Irrigated agricultural territory with drainage	0.216	0.184	2.690	0.172
Irrigated agricultural territory, surface water	0.215	0.162	1.250	0.205

The impact of urbanization and industrialization on the process of eutrophication of lakes cannot be distinguished. That is to say, in both cases, the production of mineral substances getting into the lake promotes the proliferation of algae and aquatic weeds. Here, too, nitrogen and phosphorus-containing substances are the most important.

We may take Lake Constanz as an example where as a result of urbanization PO_4-P has increased (Szarvas 1971). Prior to World War I it could not be detected at all. In 1950 there was a PO_4-P concentration of 2–3 mg/m^3 which by 1958 already increased to 9 mg/m^3 and brought about an intensive algal production. The total PO_4-P concentration of Lake Balaton, compared with other lakes, has been found to be high (Felföldy and Tóth 1970). The mean value of 35.4 mg/m^3 in the north-eastern and that of 84.0 mg/m^3 in the southern basin indicates the eutrophication of the lake. It must, however, be considered that in lake water, especially when in a disturbed state, considerable quantities of water-insoluble phosphorus forms can be present (these are not available for algae). On the basis of its production of algae Herodek and Tamás (1974) class the major part of the catchment of Lake Balaton in the category of natural eutrophic lakes.

WATER POLLUTION

A great number of scientific papers deal with water pollution and changes deriving from it. They speak for the fact that the "sewage-question" has become a central problem of humanity. Hungary is not an exception either. The growing demand for water and simultaneously, the increasing volume of industrial effluents are well-traceable processes. According to data by Illés and co-workers (1969), in 1969 the total water demand of Hungarian

industry amounted to 4 billion m³/year which, owing to significant development meant an already increased demand and consumption, in comparison
with previous conditions (Table 11).

The expression "water pollution" seems to be clear to all. Nevertheless,
it is worth determining its real meaning as this has changed in the course
of time. Felföldy's (1972) precise definition is the following: "Water pollution is every impact which changes the quality of our surface and subsoil
waters to such a degree that its suitability either for human consumption
or for the support of man's natural life processes will decrease or cease".

On the basis of the use of water domestic, industrial and agricultural
sewage can be distinguished. These are very different in their composition
and even within a certain group great differences can be observed concerning
their content. As to the biological impact of substances to be found in
sewages, they can be divided into two main groups: nutrients and biologically active substances, i.e. poisons.

Organic matter utilizable by heterotrophic organisms (bacteria, worms,
arthropods, etc.) constitute the first group of nutrients, while the inorganic
nutrients utilized by autotrophic organisms (algae) belong to the other one.
In this context it should be mentioned that there are two important water
quality indicators: (i) The accumulation of decaying organic matter available for heterotrophic organisms results in nothing else but saprobity. (ii)
The amount of inorganic (mineral) substances available for algae represents
the degree of trophicity.

Biologically active substances (poisons) form two main groups. Group 1
contains inorganic matter (microelements: fluorine, zinc manganese, etc.;
active residues: NO_3; different gases, etc.), whereas organic matter (detergents, plastics, pesticides, phenols and different kinds of tar) belong to
Group 2. The toxic effect of waters, which can hinder or even prevent
aquatic life, is expressed by toxicity as an index of water quality.

Sewage modifies the water quality of surface waters. It has been established
that downstream of the source of pollution, after a while, polluting matters

Table 11

Forecast water demand and wastewater discharges
(million m³/year) (Illés et al. 1969)

	1965	1970	1975	1980
Total water demand	3,700	4,800	6,400	8,700
Fresh water demand	1,600	2,100	2,800	3,900
Sewage discharges	390	500	665	900
Fully purified sewage	70	120	330	630

gradually disappear and water regains its original state. This process is called self-purification. It is the result of physical, chemical and biological processes in which living organisms play the most important role. From among the physical factors, water movement, viscosity, temperature and light condition can be underlined. Hydrolysis and oxidation of polluting matters are the most important chemical processes, interrelated with the metabolism of life communities, which take place in two phases. In the anaerobic phase (decomposition and actual decay) bacteria decompose organic matter in the absence of oxygen. In the aerobic process, in the presence of oxygen besides bacteria also plant and animal organisms take part in decomposition. It is, however, impossible to determine the exact boundaries between the two processes.

Aquatic living organisms have been studied by numerous scientists. It has been established that the occurrence of certain organisms is an indication of a particular degree of pollution. This can be explained by the fact that aquatic organisms have adapted themselves to the varying degree of pollution and to the differing chemical conditions derived from it. Among the organisms of the plant and animal kingdom, the single celled animals (Protozoa) are of special importance, though there are also other organisms which render it possible to assess the degree of water saprobity. In his classical work Liebmann (1962) distinguishes 4 degrees by which he characterizes the state of pollution by domestic sewage (Table 12).

The polysaprobic type of water is highly polluted with a great amount of protein, high molecular weight N-containing compounds, polypeptides, grease and their decomposition products. It has an offensive odour. As oxygen is generally absent, the process of self-purification starts under anaerobic conditions. At the beginning of decomposition there is a great number of bacteria present.

The α-mesosaprobic type water is characterized both by the increase of dissolved oxygen and by the presence of amino acids derived from the decomposition of proteins. Besides the still great number of bacteria, the presence of algae is also significant. The oxygen demand is still great, though

Table 12

Characterization of the degree of water pollution

Degree of pollution	Saprobity	Colour of water
Very severely polluted	Polysaprobic	red
Strongly polluted	α-mesosaprobic	yellow
Moderately polluted	β-mesosaprobic	green
Slightly polluted	Oligosaprobic	blue

the water does not smell so badly as polysaprobic sewages do. Waters of the β-mesosaprobic type are characterized by a significant oxygen content for which there is only little oxygen demand. While the number of bacteria decreases, it is rich in other species and individuals of microscopic organisms. This life community is very sensitive to the impacts of sewage.

The oligosaprobic water contains a great amount of dissolved oxygen, whereas the number of bacteria is still insignificant. It is rich in species but poor in individuals. This life community reacts to changes in the composition of water very sensitively. Its members are not capable of enduring poisonous substances even in very small concentrations. It is not only the quality and quantity of living organisms that renders it possible to get information on the degree of water saprobity but also the chemical characteristics of the water (quantity of organic matter, biochemical oxygen demand, processes in connection with the oxygen cycle, etc.).

As a result of the agricultural use of chemicals, pesticides, which belong to the class of biologically active substances, have become one of the most wide-spread poisons. According to the type of organism to be killed, nearly 200 poison types are known (acaricide- mite-, larvicide (mosquito)-, nematicide (roundworm) killer, etc.). Concerning their active ingredient they are most varied (zinc and arsenic compounds, chlorinated derivatives, phenoxy derivatives, DDT and its derivatives, etc.). The number of the most frequently applied poisons exceeds 60 (Felföldy and Tóth 1967). Numerous authors described tragic cases in foreign countries where lakes and rivers suffered from pesticide kills. These substances may penetrate into the living-space in three ways: (a) by direct treatment of the water surface; (b) by wind, from the treated arable land; (c) from treated land, by way of water infiltration.

Data in the international literature seem to indicate a tendency towards the application of pesticides with a short time of decomposition. In this way the amount of damage can be reduced. Certain pesticides persist in the soil for a very long time without losing their action. Thus, e.g. DDT, methoxy-chlorine and pentachlorphenol persist for 15 years, aldrin, dieldrin, BHC (benzene hexachloride), heptachlor for 9–12 years, toxaphene (camphecor) for 5 years. In spite of certain objections it seems to be proved that the remnants of persistent herbicides are carried into waters from land either in the form of wind-blown dust and washed-off deposits or without it, in diluted or suspended form. The large-scale fish kill in Lake Balaton, in 1965, was also caused by DDT and γ-BHC (Lindane) (Baron et al. 1967). While these components were hardly detectable in water the organisms serving as food for fishes contained, on the contrary, large amounts of them (Ponyi et al. 1968). Therefore it was concluded that the accumulation of poisons had taken place along the food chain (algae→ invertebrates→non-predatory fish→predatory fish).

Because of the widespread use of pesticides it is a very complex and difficult task to protect against them. Sufficient protection can be achieved by the sensible choice and application of pesticides though the quantity of chemicals applied should also be reduced. According to Szabó (1973) in 1971, in the catchment of Lake Balaton alone, in large-scale agricultural production 994.3 t of pesticides had been used up. On the basis of preliminary investigations (Czeglédi-Jankó et al. 1973) it can be concluded that the Lindane pollution of watercourses is widespread in this region. A residue of 2,4-D can also be detected (Pfeifer et al. 1978).

Synthetic detergents contain large molecular organic compounds. They exert their action either directly or indirectly. Frequently used detergents of Hungarian origin (Rapid, Ultra) are poisonous for a very large number of aquatic organisms. The production and use of synthetic detergents is rapidly increasing in Hungary, therefore, their danger must be taken into serious consideration. From among other pollutants, mineral oil should be mentioned. In Hungary, the pollution of rivers occurs most frequently, though lately, the number of accidental pollutions of Lake Balaton has been steadily increasing. When entering Hungary the oil carried by the river Danube amounts to 190 t. day^{-1}. At Budapest unpurified sewage discharges are the source of a substantial part of the oil pollution of the Danube (27.0 t. day^{-1}).

CONTROL OF NATURAL WATERS

Owing to the impact of domestic sewage the quality of our natural living waters significantly changes. In the case of lakes this is more dangerous. Should, for instance, purified or unpurified sewage flow into a river its original state will be recovered within a limited period (a few months, perhaps a year). In lakes, however, polluting substances have a prolonged action. Concerning lakes, inorganic plant nutrients and the increase in the trophic degree are the real problem areas of water pollution, since modern water purification methods render it possible to get rid of organic matters relatively easily but leave inorganic nutrients in the water of watercourses. Similarly there is great concern on how to remove pesticides from sewages. According to the literature on the subject in spite of the technical facilities available, no sewage can be discharged into lakes without causing serious danger. In the catchment of these lakes, the water quality of which is to be protected, agriculture cannot develop irrespective of the requirements of water conservation. In the case of Lake Balaton, too, the agricultural structure, the control of erosion, afforestation, etc. must be revised within the catchment of the lake or else in 15–20 years the water quality of the entire Lake Balaton, similarly to the bay of Keszthely, will degrade to that of a fish-pond.

ALGAE AND MACROPHYTIC VEGETATION OF LAKE BALATON AND THEIR RELATIONSHIP WITH EUTROPHICATION

Eutrophication of Lake Balaton

During the last decade the study of the effects leading to the eutrophication of Lake Balaton and of measures to be taken in order to prevent this process have been major issues. There are some very useful studies aimed at surveying the sources of the sewage load of Lake Balaton. The latest results of these studies were reported at the session of the Executive Committee of Lake Balaton in 1974 by Pásztó. On this occasion he analysed both the direct and indirect effects of sewage and stated that the concentration along the shore line of Lake Balaton varied. As seen in Fig. 39 substantial deviations could be observed in the different basins. The greatest concentration could be measured in the eastern basin and at the end of the bay of Keszthely. When expressing these values per unit of water volume, the values summarized in Table 13 can be obtained. Pásztó writes furthermore: "Even if we knew those effects which favourably contribute towards hindering the process of eutrophication of Lake Balaton (prevailing wind and wave directions, morphology, favourable gradient on the southern side, etc.) it is inevitable that the signs of polluting impacts should be observed here, in the bay of Keszthely".

Investigations into the artificial eutrophication of Lake Balaton, carried out by the Research Institute for Water Management, are also remarkable. From among them the ideas published in the research reports for 1969–1970 are especially useful (Tóth 1972b). As the formation of phosphate compounds is considered to be of vital importance, we think useful to quote the following statement: "In connection with the artificial eutrophication of surface waters, the study of phosphorus circulation has gained impetus in the course of the last few years. The visible and, from the point of view of man,

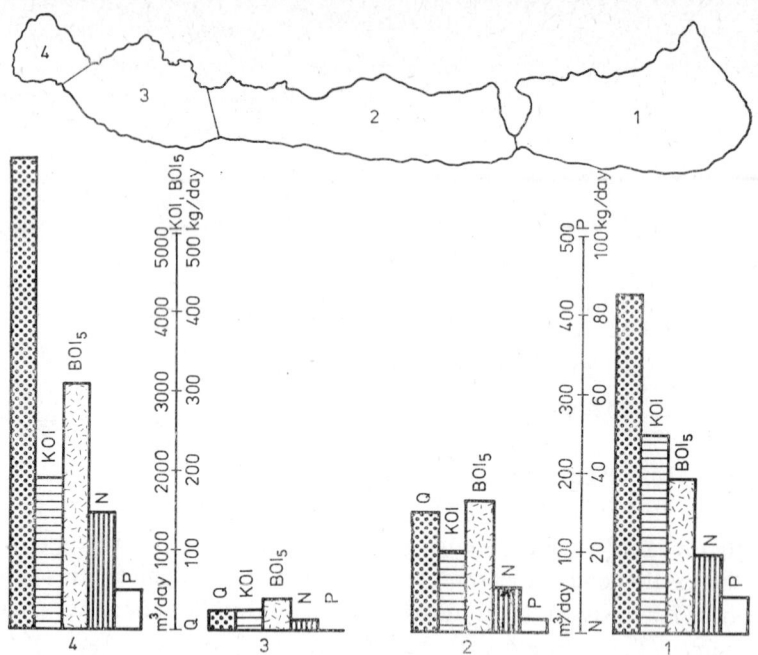

Fig. 39. Distribution of the sewage-load in different areas of Lake Balaton (August 1972) (Pásztó 1974, ined.)

the most unpleasant consequence of the mass spread of algae is eutrophication. In the life of aquatic algae phosphorus seems to be the main limiting factor. It is relevant to note that the lack of nitrogen can be compensated —also in a natural way—by elementary nitrogen-fixing organisms. In contrast to this, phosphorus—apart from its poor natural occurrence—is enriched only by man's polluting activities. The study of phosphorus circulation is more promising than that of the similarly important nitrogen. First of all, the amount of PO_4-P can be measured by a very sensitive and accurate method (Vogler 1965). Because of the absence of oxidation pro-

Table 13

Degree of eutrophication of Lake Balaton

	BOD_5 kg/day $10^8 \, m^3$	P kg/day $10^8 \, m^3$
Eastern basin	25.4	1.34
Middle basin	23.8	0.49
Western basin	9.6	0.12
Bay of Keszthely	238.1	7.14

Table 14

Phosphorus content of Lake Balaton in 1969 (Tóth 1972)

Sampling point	15 April			20 May			21 July			8 September		
	mg/l Suspended matter	mg.m^{-3} Total P	PO$_4$-P	mg/l Suspended matter	mg.m^{-3} Total P	PO$_4$-P	mg/l Suspended matter	mg.m^{-3} Total P	PO$_4$-P	mg/l Suspended matter	mg.m^{-3} Total P	PO$_4$-P
Füzfő, north-eastern corner	23.0	—	0.0	57.0	26.0	0.0	3.4	39.0	0.0	2.4	35.0	0.0
Between Füred$^+$ and Siófok*	95.0	—	0.0	21.0	22.0	0.0	13.2	41.0	0.0	1.4	25.0	0.0
Tihany, spring	45.0	—	0.0	26.0	21.0	0.0	13.2	41.0	0.0	1.1	30.0	0.0
Between the bays of Földvár* and Bozsa	31.0	100.0	0.0	37.0	46.0	0.0	12.4	41.0	0.0	3.4	40.0	0.0
Szemes, the middle of the Lake*	35.0	80.0	0.0	38.0	62.0	0.0	2.6	40.0	0.0	2.4	50.0	0.0
Révfülöp–Boglár$^+$ –	23.0	—	0.0	—	—	—	3.7	30.0	0.0	12.7	80.0	0.0
Badacsony$^+$ – Fonyód*	18.7	56.0	0.0	30.0	76.0	0.0	4.3	38.0	0.0	8.2	90.0	0.0
Szigliget	30.7	74.0	0.0	62.0	119.0	0.22	12.3	39.0	0.0	10.5	60.0	0.0
Bay of Keszthely (Western end)	26.3	86.0	0.0	87.0	137.0	0.20	13.2	50.0	0.0	4.1	50.0	0.0

* Southern shore
+ Northern shore

Table 15

Phosphorus content of Lake Balaton in 1969–1970 (Tóth 1972)

Sampling point	13 October 1969			2 December 1969			27 January 1970			23 February 1970		
	mg/l Suspended matter	mg.m^{-3} Total P	PO$_4$-P	mg/l Suspended matter	mg.m^{-3} Total P	PO$_4$-P	mg/l Suspended matter	mg.m^{-3} Total P	PO$_4$-P	mg/l Suspended matter	mg.m^{-3} Total P	PO$_4$-P
Fűzfő, north-eastern corner	5.8	50.0	0.0	—	—	—	—	—	—	—	—	—
Between Füred+ and Siófok	4.8	60.0	0.0	—	—	—	—	—	—	2.5	58.0	4.0
Tihany, spring	1.0	50.0	0.0	—	—	—	—	—	—	—	—	—
Between the bays of Földvár* and Bozsa	1.6	50.0	0.0	—	—	—	—	—	—	—	—	—
Szemes, middle of the Lake*	5.0	55.0	0.0	111.1	150.0	10.0	—	—	—	—	—	—
Révfülöp–Boglár	11.2	60.0	0.0	—	—	—	2.6	60.0	0.0	7.3	52.0	4.0
Badacsony+ –Fonyód*	14.1	85.0	0.0	83.0	150.0	10.0	—	—	—	—	—	—
Szigliget	18.1	75.0	0.0	84.4	140.0	25.0	2.6	60.0	14.0	6.0	52.0	14.0
Bay of Keszthely (western end)	17.5	115.0	35.0	80.7	160.0	25.0	2.1	70.0	45.0	6.4	124.0	34.0

* Southern shore
+ Northern shore

cesses, so characteristic of nitrogen, special groups of bacteria play no part in the formation of P-forms (Tóth 1972).

In 1969–1970 experts of the Scientific Research Institute for Water Management studied the range of phosphorus compounds in the different parts of Lake Balaton. From among the phosphorus compounds the amount of total P and the dissolved PO_4-P content were studied (Table 14). For practical reasons, in order to avoid the inconvenience of using several zeros, the results are expressed in terms of elemental P. m^3 or its equivalent in litres; 1 mg.m^{-3} = 0.001 mg/l.

As Table 15 shows, no dissolved PO_4-P had been detected in the open water by the end of October. Its presence could be established only by analyses over the winter months (December–January–February). The amount of total P varied between 20–160 mg. m^{-3} and showed a decreasing tendency from the bay of Keszthely towards Balatonfűzfő. To be precise, the concentrations of phosphorus in the northern and southern basins are totally different (Tóth 1972). According to Tóth (1972), who has compared the range of phosphorus concentrations in Lake Balaton with the data of literature, Lake Balaton shows the characteristic features of a lake with unpolluted water. On the basis of investigations it can also be established that the concentration of phosphorus in the different areas of Lake Balaton shows deviation (Table 16). During the major part of the year, however, phosphorus could not be detected. According to Tóth this allows for two conclusions: either at the time of its release or when introduced into the lake it is absorbed by living organisms or, on entering the lake, because of a chemical reaction it becomes precipitated in a water-insoluble form. Apart from emphasizing the significant role of phosphorus eutrophication, experts regularly study the formation of other macro- and micro-nutrients in the water of Lake Balaton.

Table 16

Concentrations of phosphorus in Lake Balaton (Tóth 1972)

	mg. m^{-3}	Total
	average	extreme values
Northern basin	35.4	21–60
Southern basin	84.0	41–160

The flora of Lake Balaton

In the course of investigations of the process of eutrophication wider attention is given to the study of algal and aquatic weed flora and to the wetland plants forming in the shallow waters and shore line habitats and also to their role (Kárpáti 1974*a,b;* Kárpáti 1977; Kárpáti et al. 1977). In the following sections, the qualitative and quantitative formation of algal and aquatic weed growths will be discussed.

The composition of the phytoplankton

The presence of 660 species of free-swimming algae has been detected in the upper layers of Lake Balaton, their distribution being as follows: Cyanophyta 80, Euglenophyta 126, Cryptophyta 38, Chrysophyta 106, Chlorophyta 310.

In winter and spring it is the diatoms that can be found in the greatest quantity. Nitzschia and Synedra species have been frequent cause of water colourations in the last few decades. The worst of these was observed, between November 1974 and March 1975, in the basin of Keszthely and Szigliget. In earlier times, in summer the phytoplankton of Lake Balaton consisted predominantly of *Ceratium hirundinella* (Chryptophytae).

In the summers of the last decades the blue-green algae (Myxophyceae) have regularly caused algal blooms. Similarly, substantial changes have been observed in the north-eastern basins as *Ceratium* receded and algal species of smaller size became dominant, forming blooms. Species which are indicators of the process of eutrophication in the Lake Balaton are recorded in Table 17.

Phytoplankton biomass

Regular investigations into phytoplankton biomass have been going on since 1965 (Tamás 1967, 1969, 1972, 1975; Herodek and Tamás 1976, 1978; Vörös 1978).

In the case of each algal species, the number of individuals has been determined by Utermöhl's (1958) plankton microscope. The volume of an average individual of the species has been determined by additional measurements. Assuming a specific weight of one, the mass of certain species and that of the entire phytoplankton has also been calculated (Tamás 1974).

Table 17

Alga species indicating the eutrophication of Lake Balaton

Tribes	Species
Cyanophyta (Blue-green algae) (Myxophyta)	*Anabaena constricta* (Szafer) Geitler *A. solitaria* Klabahn *A. spiroides* Klabahn *Aphanizomenon flos-aquae* (L.) Ralfs *A. issatschenkoi* (Ussaczew) Proschkina-Lavrenko *Aphanocapsa delicatissima* W. et G. S. West (Anacystis) *A. grevillei* (Hass.) Rabenhorst *Microcystis flos-aquae* (Wittrock) Kirchner *Romeria elegans* (Woloszynska) Koczwara *R. gracilis* Koczwara
Euglenophyta (Euglenoid flagellates)	*Euglena klebsii* (Lemm.) Mainx *Phacus longicauda* (E.) Dujardin *P. pseudonordstedti* i Pochm.
Pyrrophyta (Dinoflagellates) (Cryptophyta)	*Cryptomonas erosa* Ehr. *C. ovata* Ehr. *Ceratium hirundinella* (O. F. Müll.) Schrank *Peridinium insonspicuum* Lemm.
Chrysophyta (Golden-yellow algae)	*Planktonema lauterborni* Schmidle *Centritractus belonphorus* Lemm. *Tetrakentron tribulus* Geitler *Chrysococcus rufescens* Klebs. *Dinobryon divergens* Imh. *Salpingoeca frequentissima* (Zach.) Lemm. *Melosira granulata* *M. granulata* var. *angustissima* *Nitzschia acicularis* W. Smith *N. palea* (Kütz.) W. Smith *Stephanodiscus dubis* (Fricke) Hust.
Chlorophyta (Grass-green algae)	*Ankistrodesmus falcatus* (Corda) Ralfs. *A. falcatus* var. *mirabile* W. et. G. S. West *A. falcatus* var. *spirilliformis* G. S. West *Carteria stellifera* Nyg. *Chlamydomonas* sP. *Closterium aciculare* West *C. paruulum* Naeg. *Crucigenia tetrapedia* (Kirch.) W. et G. S. West *Dictyosphaerium pulchellum* Wood. *Lagerheimia genevensis* Chod. (Chodatella) *Scenedesmus acuminatus, arcuatus,* dispar. *ecornis, spinosus, quadricauda* and var. *longissima* *Schroederia setigera* Lemm. *Tatraedron caudatum,* var. *incismu, minimum, muticum, hastiferum* *Planktomyces békefii* Gimesi (aquatic fungus)

At Tihany, the phytoplankton biomass has risen fivefold since 1975, and exceeds 5 mg wet weight per litre in summer. Whereas in 1967 the biomass had reached 7 mg wet weight per litre at Keszthely, in the summer of 1977 already 53 mg wet weight per litre was recorded (Vörös, personal communication). Such an algal density already seriously endangers the suitability of the water for bathing. Similarities can be observed between the phytoplankton biomass densities recorded at Balatonalmádi–Tihany and Szigliget–Keszthely (Herodek and Tamás 1974, 1975a,b).

Primary production of phytoplankton

According to Rodhe (1969) primary production is most suitable for expressing the degree of eutrophication of lakes. The most sensitive method for the measurement of phytoplankton production using ^{14}C, was elaborated by Steeman-Nielsen (1952). The essence of this method is that radioactive carbon ($Na_2^{14}CO_3$) of known activity is introduced into water samples taken from natural water. The bottles are then returned to the original sampling point and in situ, exposed for a given period of time. Following this, using membrane filters, the algae are filtered and their radioactivity measured. In addition to this a duplicate is also prepared in order to measure the so-called dark fixation, the amount of CO_2 which is not fixed photosynthetically. These duplicates are placed in the dark. Knowing the specific activity of the carbonic acid in the samples, the total concentration of fixed carbon can be calculated on the basis of the radioactivity of the algae. Using this method the first preliminary investigations into the water of Lake Balaton were carried out as early as 1961 (Böszörményi et al. 1963). From May to September a total of twelve measurements were carried out at Tihany, on each occasion at a depth of 1 m. At eight other locations two subsequent measurements were made, the first, at the end of August, the second in mid-September and each time at a depth of 1 m. Samples were being exposed for 6 h, radioactivity was measured by a Geiger counter. At Tihany the average primary production amounted to 7 μg C/l/h while the values of the two measurements at Keszthely were 8 μg C/l/h and 4 μg C/l/h; consequently, there was no striking difference between the values obtained at Keszthely and Tihany. Measurements made at other locations of the lake yielded similar values.

Detailed investigations into the primary production of phytoplankton were started in 1972, production being measured at Tihany (1972–1973), Keszthely (1973–1974), in the basin of Szigliget (1974–1975) and of Balatonszemes (1976–1977) and in 1977, repeatedly at Tihany (Herodek and Tamás 1978; Herodek et al. 1978a,b). These regular investigations, with fortnightly sampling, at four different depths (0.25, 1, 2 and 3 m)' were carried out throughout the year. The 200 ml samples were divided into two parts. The algal content of the first was counted by microscope, according to Utermöhl (1958). The second 100 ml was poured into hermetically sealed glasses which, following the addition of 20 μCi $Na_2^{14}CO_3$, were submerged again at the original depth from which they had been taken. They were then exposed for 4 h. Radioactivity was measured by liquid scintillation methods. Using this technique the drying of samples can be omitted which, in the case of Geiger counter measurements, might lead to loss of carbon. Assuming that the samples taken from the upper zone represent a half-meter high column and the others a one meter high column of water, respectively, the production was calculated for the unit area. The area under the curve connecting the daily production values, calculated for the unit area, expresses the yearly production.

In the case of a lake with a large water surface, strong wave motion can arise and large waves will then disturb the shallow water. It is not the algae, but the amount of silt floating in the water that basically affects water transparency. Whilst in a strong storm only 2% of the light reaching the surface penetrates to a depth of 1 m, in a windless period more than 10% reaches the bottom. It is due to disturbance of the sediment that, from time to time, the vertical distribution of primary production at Tihany and Szemes (Fig. 40) differs from that of other lakes. In a strong storm, the uppermost water layers show the highest productivity while in calm weather it is the samples taken from the lowest level that display the maximum productivity. In most cases, however, because of the too strong radiation, on the surface, the intensity of light becomes a limiting factor. Therefore, maximum productivity is shifted to a depth of 2 m. At a depth of 3 m, the lack of light considerably restricts production.

In the basin of Szigliget and especially in that of Keszthely, algae play the main role in determining transparency. In these areas, with the exception of only a few instances, it has been impossible to detect even 1% of solar radiation reaching the water layers at a depth of 2 m. Under this value plant respiration, generally, exceeds photosynthesis. By 1973 the former weed beds so typical of the bays of Keszthely and Szigliget had disappeared, which may have been brought about by the lack of light caused by algae. The vertical distribution of the primary production of phytoplankton in the south-western basins also displays features typical of strongly polluted hypertrophic lakes. In this case the highest productivity can always be

156

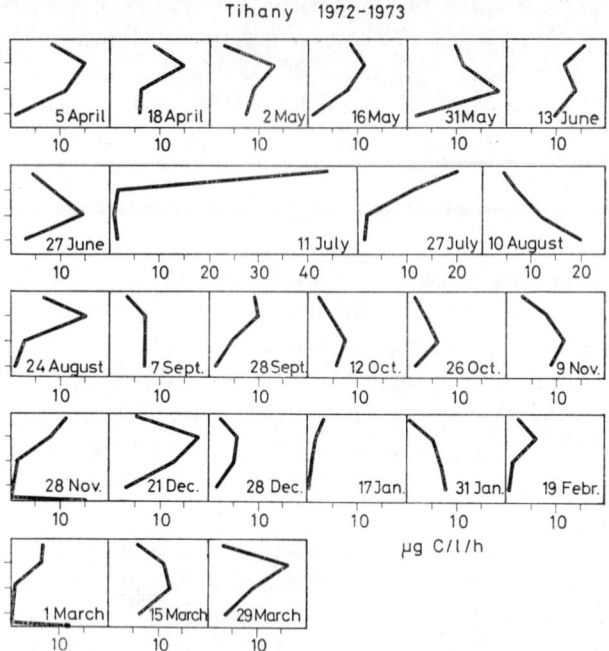

Tihany 1972-1973

μg C/l/h

Fig. 40. Distribution of phytoplankton production and variation with water depth in Lake Balaton at Tihany in 1972-1973. (Herodek and Tamás 1976)

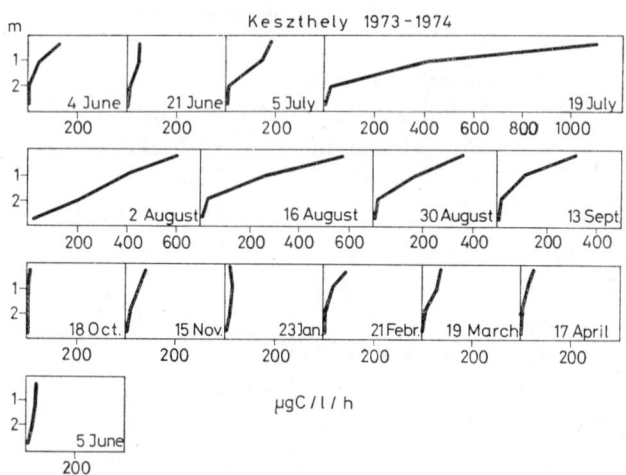

Keszthely 1973-1974

μgC/l/h

Fig. 41. Distribution of phytoplankton as a function of water depth in the bay of Keszthely in 1973-1974. (Herodek and Tamás 1976)

detected in the uppermost samples, while, at the depth of 1 m, productivity is already considerably reduced. At a depth of 2 m, and even lower than that, owing to the self-overshading of algae there is no definite photosynthesis (Fig. 41). This may lead to a very dangerous situation as algae forming in the upper water levels fall like a "rain of plankton" to the bottom. Their decomposition consumes the oxygen of the level where, because of the lack of light, there is no oxygen production. In windless weather this may lead to the lack of oxygen in the vicinity of the bottom layer.

Primary production, calculated for a unit area, was one order of magnitude higher in the Keszthely basin than the values measured at Tihany the previous year and the production of samples taken in the Keszthely basin 12 years earlier (Fig. 42). From 1972 to 1977, primary production at Tihany has doubled (Fig. 43) which indicates that the whole lake has reached the stage of rapid eutrophication and that only immediate measures can preserve it in a state suitable for bathing. In a water column of 1 m² basic area, the values of photosynthetically fixed carbon, over a period of one year, are as follows: in 1972–1973 at Tihany 96 g, in 1977 171 g, in 1976–1977 at Balatonszemes 274 g, in 1974–1975 at Szigliget 301 g, in 1973–1974 at Keszthely 830 g. Concerning the scale of trophication the values measured at Tihany still fall into the eutrophic range, while those found at Keszthely can be considered to indicate the high hypertrophication (Fig. 44). If converting the above data into wet weight—in order to help better understanding—it can be seen that the yield of algae at Keszthely, over a period of one year, was 83 t/ha. In the bay of Keszthely algal blooms are regular

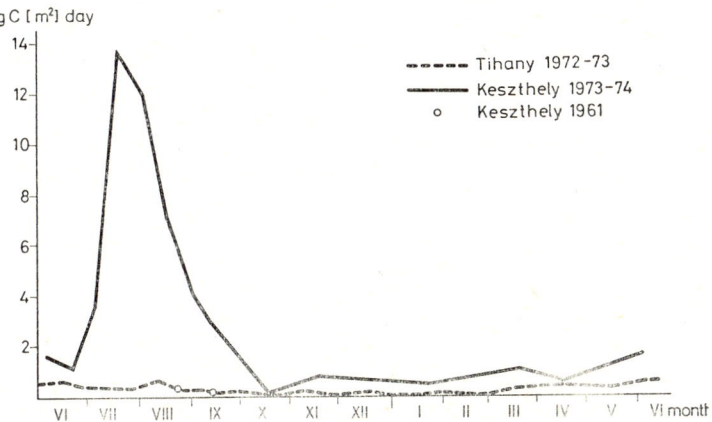

Fig. 42. Phytoplankton production expressed for the basic area, at Keszthely, as compared with values measured in 1961 at Keszthely and 1972–73 at Tihany

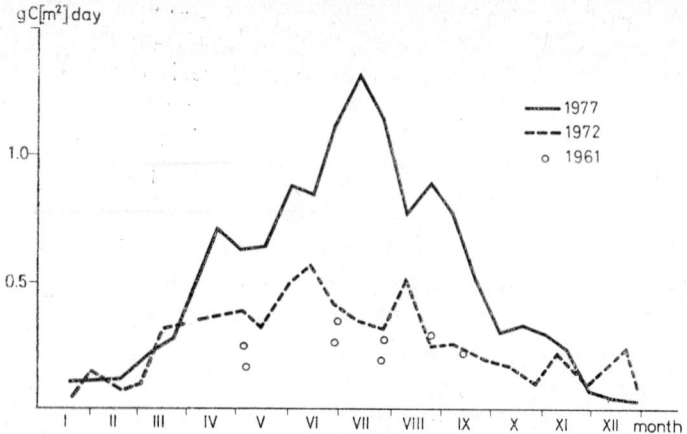

Fig. 43. Phytoplankton production expressed for the basic area at Tihany, in 1961, 1972 and 1977. (Herodek et al. 1978b)

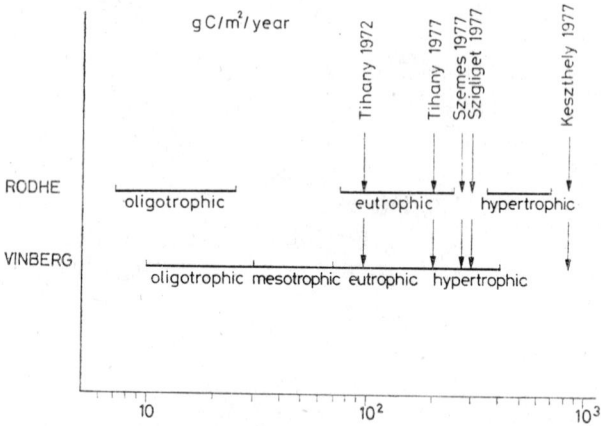

Fig. 44. Position of different basins of Lake Balaton in the trophicity scale of lakes compiled on the basis of the primary production

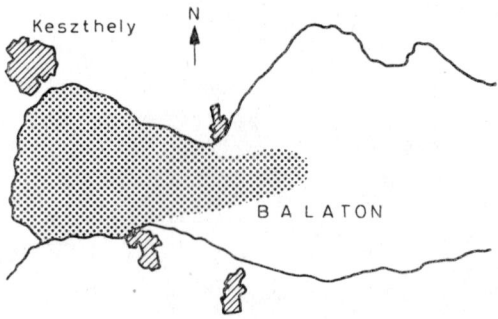

Fig. 45. The extent of algal blooming in bay of Keszthely in 1964. (Hortobágyi and Kárpáti 1967)

Fig. 46. Aphanizomenon flos-aquae causing algal blooms, (Hortobágyi and Kárpáti 1967)

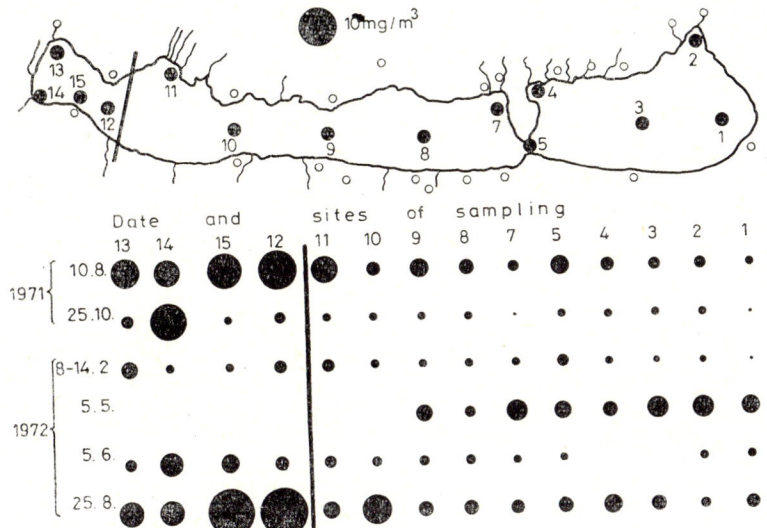

Fig. 47. The chlorophyll content of water samples from Lake Balaton. (Pásztó 1974, ined.)

phenomena (Fig. 45 and Fig. 46). The primary production is clearly illustrated by the localised variations of chlorophyll concentrations in samples taken from this area (Fig. 47).

The composition of aquatic weed flora

Mainly as the result of a survey all the characteristic weed species of the lake were known as early as 1928. By 1932 Soó had identified already 24 weed species. According to recent studies there are 30 weed species in the lake. (Species capable of indicating eutrophication are summarized in Figs 48 and 49) (Kárpáti and Kárpáti 1967, 1968, 1974; Kárpáti et al. 1979; Kárpáti and Lantos 1979, 1981).

Fig. 48. Plant species indicating eutrophication. (*1*) *Batrachium circinatum,* (*2*) *Nuphar lutea,* (*3*) *Nymphaea alba,* (*4*) *Utricularia vulgaris,* (*5*) *Trapa natans.* (drawing by K. Bíró)

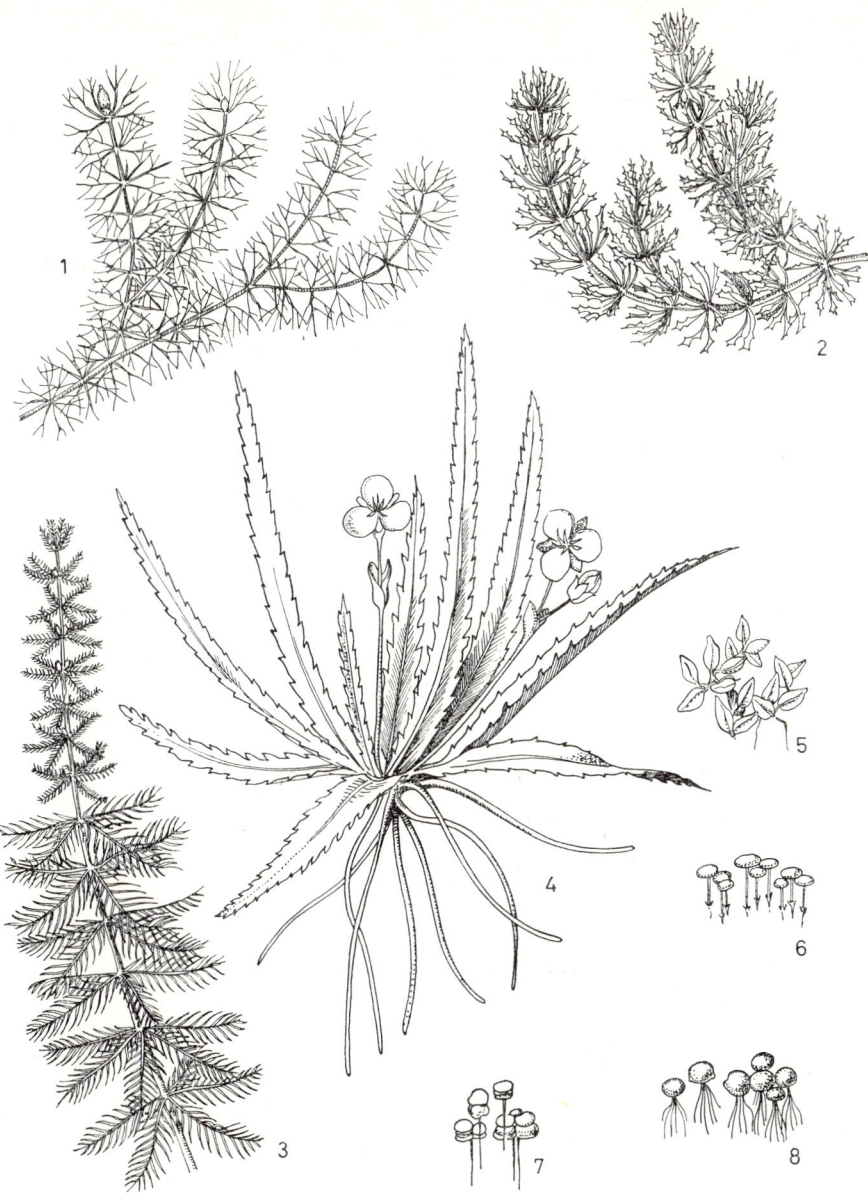

Fig. 49. Plant species in Lake Balaton indicating eutrophication. *(1) Ceratophyllum submersum, (2) Ceratophyllum demersum, (3) Myriophyllum verticallatum, (4) Stratiotes aloides, (5) Lemna trisulca, (6) Lemna minor, (7) Lemna gibba, (8) Spirodella polyrhiza.* (drawing by K. Bíró)

EMERGENT SPECIES

Floating: *Spirodela polyrrhiza* (Great duck weed)
Lemna gibba (Fat duck weed)
Lemna minor (Common duck weed)
Wolffia arrhiza (Duck weed)
Hydrocharis morsus-ranae (Frogbit)
Stratiotes aloides (Water soldier)

Rooted: *Nymphaea alba* (White water-lily)
Nuphar lutea (Yellow water-lily)
Trapa natans (Water chestnut)
Polygonum amphibium (Amphibious bistort)
Potamogeton natans (Broad-leaved pondweed)
Potamogeton gramineus (Various-leaved pondweed)

SUBMERGENT SPECIES

Floating: *Lemna trisulca* (Ivy-leaved duckweed)
Ceratophyllum demersum (Rigid horn wort)
Ceratophyllum submersum
Utricularia vulgaris (Greater bladderwort)
Stratiotes aloides f. *submers* (Water soldier)

Rooted: *Potamogeton perfoliatus* (Perfoliate pondweed)
Potamogeton pectinatus (Fennel pondweed)
Potamogeton lucens (Shining pondweed)
Potamogeton crispus (Curled pondweed)
Potamogeton pusillus (Lesser pondweed)
Myriophyllum spicatum (Spiked water-milfoil)
Myriophyllum verticillatum (Whorled water-milfoil)
Najas marina (Holly-leaved naiad)
Najas minor
Anacharis canadensis (Canadian pondweed)
Batrachium circinatum (*Ranunculus* subgen.)
Zanichellia palustris (Horned pondweed)

The mass ratio of the aquatic weed coenoses

Pondweed (*Potamogeton perfoliatus*) can be considered to be the most characteristic aquatic species. Its submerged populations can be found even at depths of 3–4 m. Its rooted, overwintering, short shoots develop an intensive growth in spring and at an undisturbed place, their coverage will remain almost unchanged over many years. They build either nearly ring-shaped polychormones or fairy rings (atoles), the middle of which ripen to ring-shaped spots. According to our investigations *Myriophyllum spicatum* can also be found in large quantities. Until 1976 it had been the mass spread of *Ceratophyllum demersum* which indicated the degree of eutrophication. This species occur mainly at the point where strongly polluted streams discharge into the lake. In contrast to this, recent observations have established increased growths of *Myriophyllum spicatum*.

Aquatic weed biomass is being studied at certain selected sampling stations by the scientific staff of the Department for Botany of the Agricultural University of Keszthely. In the course of these investigations sub-surface quadrate of 1 m² area were examined and the weight of weed measured at various water depths (Kárpáti and Kárpáti 1975a). Changes in both form and extent of the cover at the above-mentioned sampling spots (300×600 m) were determined by air photography (Fig. 50). It was aimed to establish the relationship between the area of the weed cover and

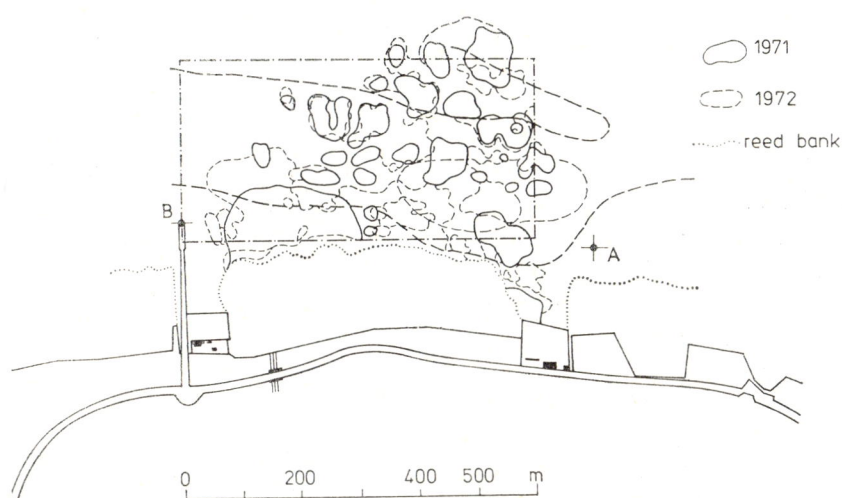

Fig. 50. Map of Szigliget-bay macrophytes prepared on the basis of measurements in 1971 and 1972

164

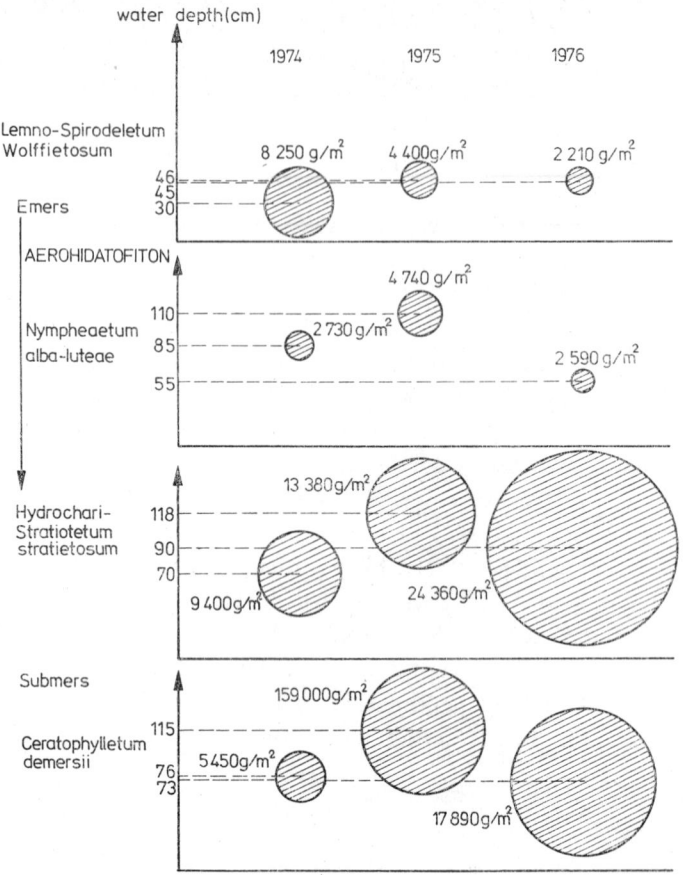

Fig. 51. Macrophytic production (wet weight) in Little-Balaton. (Kárpáti 1977)

their density or biomass (Kárpáti and Varga 1970; Kárpáti et al. 1971; Kárpáti et al. 1972*a*, *b*). On the basis of several hundred measurements per year with a total of more than one thousand, it has been possible to establish a correlation between the percentage cover and biomass production. This determination has been carried out for each species separately at intervals of 0.5 m water depth. The shape of the resulting graphs differs from year to year, being accounted for by varying ecological conditions (climatic factors, water flow, etc.) (Kárpáti and Varga 1970).

It is interesting to survey the quantitative changes in production of algae and macrophytes over the period of the last 10 years. The great increase in the production of microphytes, which increases following artificial eutrophication, significantly decreases the production of submergent macrophytes. On the basis of experiments it can be concluded that the cut back of weed growth is due to the shading effect of algal plankton. Very little light penetrates into the water under those conditions and consequently photosynthesis and also the intensive growth of weed is hindered. Naturally, these processes are also influenced by the weather (Herodek and Tamás 1973).

Since 1974 investigations have been going on into the Little Balaton, which adjoins Lake Balaton on its western side and which can be considered as the most eutrophied bay. The weed production as a function of annual water movement, very well reflects the macrophytic production on the open surface of Little Balaton (Fig. 51). The comparison of the open water plant communities, as a function of annual water movement, allows the following conclusions: in *Lemno-Spirodeletum* communities a yearly decrease in the fresh "primary production" $(g \cdot m^{-2})$ could be established, which is all the more interesting as the water level had changed by only a few centimeters during the course of study. Naturally, production is also influenced by the nutrient supply. The above-mentioned samples were taken from one of the most isolated channels of Little Balaton, which is subjected to the least polluting effects. Several papers have established the spread of Stratiotes in the two open water bays of Little Balaton. During the three years of vegetation studies the changes in water depth affected the growth of Stratiotes to a lesser extent than the amount of autotrophic organisms did. In waters very rich in autotrophic nutrients they produced an ever increasing mass (Fig. 51). In comparison with the first year, the Hydrocharis–Stratiotes community produced a threefold quantity in 1976. At the very same spot of sampling, during the same period, it could be established that the amount of *Ceratophyllum demersum* had been steadily and significantly increasing. It is known that *Ceratophyllum* favours eutrophic waters and so the increase in the values of primary production also refers to the degree of eutrophication. On the basis of characters investigated it can be concluded that both *Stratiotes aloides* and *Ceratophyllum demersum* appropriately indicate the degree of eutrophication. Therefore, they are the most suitable as biological indicators (Kárpáti 1977).

Concerning the strong spread of *Stratiotes* in the open water of Lake Balaton, experts of the Scientific Research Institute for Water Management take the view that it could have been brought about both by nutrient increase and by the initial water level in the spring. Experts of this institute and those of the Department for Botany of the Agricultural University of Keszthely have also called attention to the intensive spread of *Anacharis canadensis* (Fig. 52) as well as *Potamogeton pectinatus*. They also consider

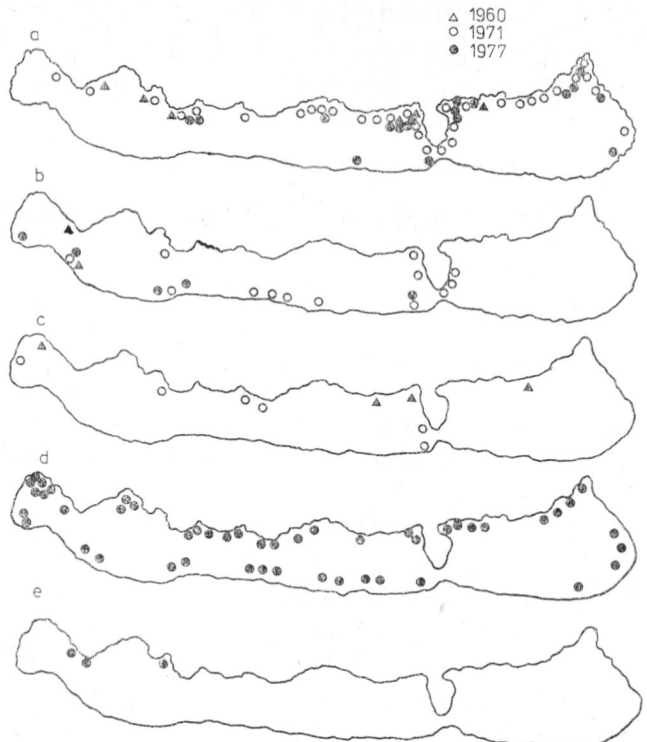

Fig. 52. Occurrence of blanket-weed species in Lake Balaton in 1960 and 1971. (*a*) *Stratiotes aloides*, (*b*) *Anacharis canadensis*, (*c*) *Spirodela polyrrhiza*, (*d*) *Ceratophyllum demersum, C. submersum, (e) Trapa natans* (Tóth 1972, completed with data from Tóth 1972 and Kárpáti 1971 and 1977)

it worth mentioning that after the cutting of the reed covered area downstream of the water purification works of Badacsony, *Spirodela polyrrhiza* could spread massively and form a coherent green cover. At Vonyarcvashegy, in the vicinity of the camping site, the increasing spread of *Trapa natans* is due to the enrichment of water in nutrients.

Co-workers of the Department for Botany of the Agricultural University of Keszthely have carried out interesting plant ecological studies in the south-western bays of Lake Balaton. The increased capability of aquatic macrophytes for nutrient accumulation is already known (Kárpáti et al. 1979, 1980). It has been furthermore established that the emergent or surface dwelling unrooted and rooted macrophytes can accumulate nearly the same amount of biogenic elements. The nutrient concentration capacity of submergent unrooted and rooted macrophytes, mainly in respect of microelements, very often exceeds that of the floating community. This investigation has verified in the first place the significant water-purifying capacity of submergent aquatic species and since macrophytes, not removed from the water, return their nutrients to the water, investigations of the decomposition of biogenic elements became necessary. The rate and quantity of decomposition allow for conclusions as to the capacity of the returned biomass to lead to eutrophication. Since 1974 the decomposition of the biogenic elements of the aquatic flora has been regularly studied under laboratory conditions using a percolation method (Kárpáti et al. 1979). The amount of elements released in the course of decomposition (N, P, Ca, Na, K, Mg, Zn, Fe) expressed as a percentage of the total amount of determined elements, is illustrated in Fig. 53. Should the elements, released in the course of decomposition, repeatedly increase the degree of trophication of the lake, the biomass of the macrophytes not removed from the water, does not play apparently a water-purifying role. These are intriguing thoughts for the specialists keeping an eye on the nutritive enrichment of Lake Balaton. The high tendency to spread of the previously

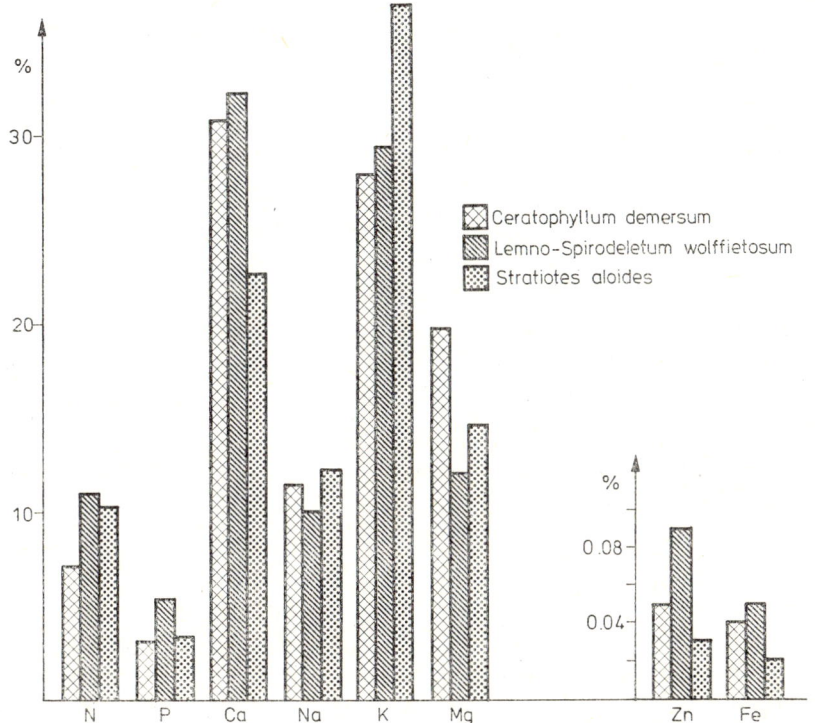

Fig. 53. The amount of elements released during decomposition (measured in 1975–1976)

mentioned species, urges their continuous monitoring which could supply useful information completing the chemical analysis of silt, water and plants.

For practical purposes, mainly connected with engineering works on water drainage the use of biological, mechanical or perhaps chemical means for the total destruction of weeds is often proposed. As it has been unmistakably proved that the aquatic vegetation of the higher plants plays a very important role in the self-purification processes of the water, these measures would basically be wrong. Reduction of the amount of sewage and chemicals to a minimum will also result in the restriction of aquatic beds to the required level.

HYDROBIOLOGICAL STUDY OF THE DANUBE

Origin of the research

The Congress of the International Society of Limnology (SIL) held in 1956 in Helsinki, had already made the scientific world aware of the rapid pollution of rivers and the almost incalculable damage resulting from it. It was stated that investigations of large rivers had been lagging far behind the successful limnological study of lakes. In its resolution SIL stated that the intensive study of rivers was necessary and it had been agreed to carry out a limnological study of a larger European river.

The Danube, the largest river of Central Europe, which had relatively clear water, was the unanimously chosen subject for a co-operative study. An international organization had been founded for the study of the Danube which, running through eight countries, is fed by water drained from twelve countries (Liepolt 1965–1967; Jaág and Vogel 1975).

The Danube as a living environment

As far as its size is concerned the Danube is the largest river in Central Europe. In Europe it is surpassed only by the river Volga. Its length amounts to almost 2,900 km and it is a real international river, as the Danube passes through 8 countries to reach its delta. Three capitals—Vienna, Budapest and Belgrade—and the administrative centre of a region, Bratislava, are also situated along the Danube. Apart from this, 10 larger and 30 smaller towns, 350 villages and communities with approx. 10–12 million inhabitants

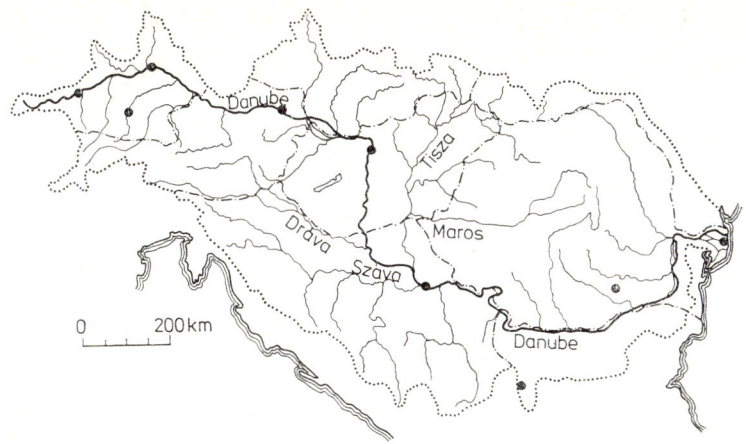

Fig. 54. River Danube and its catchment area (Puskás 1967)

can also be found alongside the river. Within its huge drainage area, comprising 817,000 km², there live about 70 million people.

The 2,900 km long main catchment of the Danube, its completely or partly isolated tributaries and its flood area constitute an "environment" which is divided into many parts from the biological point of view. Its ecologically different territories and reaches offer various environmental conditions for the living world (Lászlóffy 1965) (Fig. 54).

In the course of the hydrobiological study of the Danube, one of the most important tasks is to estimate those influences which result from human activity. While in the 18th century the original, natural factors—geomorphological, hydrographical and meteorological ones—entirely determined the flow, drift speed, rate of silt deposition, light and temperature conditions and the bankside formation of rivers, now the anthropogenic effects and human interference play an important part in the life of even such a large river as the Danube. The construction of dikes, drainage channels, dams, power stations, riverside walls, etc. are extreme forms of this interference (Liebmann and Reichenbach-Klinke 1967; Liepolt 1974).

Under the influence of natural or artificial factors each living space—aquatic or terrestrial—will be transformed. This transformation may be positive or negative. Because of this, it is an essential requirement to know the relationships between the life of a river and practical water management as the lack of such knowledge might have serious consequences (Breinich 1972). The thorough scientific study of rivers is an urgent necessity. A river serves not only practical purposes—such as shipping, freightage, construction of power stations, reception of waste waters, drinking water supply, etc.—but it is the home and living space for large numbers of organisms which play an active part in biological self-purification. Without their functioning our rivers would really become sewers to the disadvantage of public health.

Inhabitants living alongside the Danube and particularly those within its catchment, load the river with discharges on average of 200–500 l/person/day of sewage, which can be estimated as containing 12 g nitrogen and 3 g phosphorus nutrient per person. Apart from domestic sewage, the so-called urban waste water, the effluents from rapidly developing industry alongside the river, also mean a heavy load for the Danube.

Natural and anthropogenic (man-made) effects along the Danube

Only a mosaic-like outline of the limnological study of the river can be given, divided into the river-head, Upper-, Central- and Lower Danube, the river beyond the Kazan-pass and the delta area. To serve this aim some typical ecological problems are described.

River-head. The microorganisms of the rivers Breg and Brigach are ecologically well known. Biologically and for their saprobic classification these springs were ideal for comparison. While the Breg runs through an area free from human settlements, the river Brigach is contaminated at several locations. Backhaus's (1968) field and laboratory investigations of microphytic benthos (bottom-dwelling organisms) might serve as an example for similar ecological studies.

Upper Danube. The flow in the upper reaches of the Bavarian Danube section is well regulated. The narrow river bed is separated from the tributaries by power stations and dams. On its banks there are all sorts of industrial plants and densely populated urban areas. Even the tributaries enter the Danube with a heavy load of pollution.

Living organisms, from microorganisms to fishes, which populate the waters, are very sensitive and react to the harmful, polluting effects. The quality and quantity of their species, the changes in their composition, life functions, the appearance of new species, the lack of others—in several cases—are even better indicators of the damaging changes affecting water quality than physical instruments. The following examples illustrate well the major sources of pollution: The cellulose factories above Ulm exert their damaging effect on the Bavarian stretch of the Danube. The biochemical oxygen demand (b.o.d.) reaches the values of 70 mg/l. The municipal sewage discharges of Ulm and Neu-Ulm, from 150,000 inhabitants receive only mechanical (primary) clarification before entering the Danube. The river that only has a small natural flow at this point, takes in the cooling and process effluents from power stations at Grundremingen although its dilution is inadequate and therefore the heat pollution has an adverse effect on water quality. The river Lech carries the municipal sewage from Augsburg and effluents from the local machine and textile industries. While the industrial effluents flowing into the Danube, at Ingolstadt, are properly purified, the municipal domestic sewage, however, lacks treatment. At the town of Kehlheim, the synthetic fibre and sulphite cellulose manufacturing mills exert detrimental effects. In these reaches the natural self-purification processes would need a longer distance to become effective. The river, however, soon has to suffer from the great loads of municipal and industrial effluents from Regensburg. The river Naab carries the effluents from steel and aluminium smelters. The water of the Inn discharging into the Danube at Passau is, in comparison with the Danube, ample and clear, therefore it has a beneficial effect on water quality.

Knöpp (1967) has published several studies on the problems of oxygen-balance of the Bavarian Danube stretch. Liebmann's saprobiological activity (1954, 1958–1960) is truly reflected in his surveys, biocoenosis assays and comprehensive papers in this field. In order to show the degree of pollution of the Danube, Liebmann—based on the method used by Reichenbach-Klinke (Liebmann et al. 1967) in Munich—has compiled the water quality map of the Danube from its source to the delta. Investigations of the benthic fauna and the present element recycling—with a special emphasis on limnology—are being carried out by Kothé (Russev and Kothé 1972).

At the German–Austrian border the concentration of ammonia, nitrate, phosphate, iron, oxidizable matter and of detergents significantly exceeds the accepted limits. Also the results of plankton and benthos examinations reflect the impact of pollution.

Austrian stretch of the Danube. Limnological investigations of the Danube, under direction of Liepolt, started in 1956–57, within the framework of the international organization.

Thus, it is relevant that the limnological survey of the Austrian Danube reach is a multidisciplinary task. Knie (1966) published a complete survey of both the physical and chemical properties of, not only the Austrian Danube reach, but also that of the entire Danube. Weber (1967, 1973) has also published several papers on the limnological impacts of power stations, regulating lakes and dams. Eckl (1967) gives a survey of industrial sites situated alongside the Danube. Frantz (1966) has reported studies on the radioactive pollution of the entire Danube.

At present, the river Aschach is one of the main sewage carriers, bringing the effluents from the local chemical industry. The river Linz loads the Danube with effluents from fertilizer-, herbicide-, insecticide-manufacturing processes and also from other large industrial factories; its sewage content is also remarkable. To illustrate this, it should be mentioned that the ammonia concentration of the river, below Linz, reaches a figure as high as 5 mg/l. The rivers Traun, Enns and Ybbs carry mainly industrial effluents (from paper, cellulose, plastic works, car factories, etc.) into the Danube. The sewage purification plant of Vienna has already been started with substantial financial expenditure. The water of the Danube channel at Vienna having been analysed it was established that the storage of carps, in holding tanks, to be sold in the markets of Vienna is not permissible. Consequently, other costly facilities had to be constructed for the storage of living fish. From among the industrial pollutants, those from the refineries load mainly the Danube. The polluting impact of the Vienna catchment area can still be detected even in Hungary. According to Liepolt (1965–1967) the algal blooms caused by *Asterionella formosa* are not exceptional, which, otherwise is unusual in such a swiftly flowing river of alpine character.

To sum up the increase in polluting factors in the Austrian region of the Danube can be considered as insignificant. Nevertheless, water quality investigations at the Austro–Hungarian border have established that water quality lies between the α- and β-mesosaprobic classifications.

Therefore, the water quality of the Danube leaving Czechoslovakia should be better than it was at its entrance at Bratislava (Märki 1972).

Hungarian section of the Danube. The National Water Authority with its different institutions and research institutes is the main guard and protector of water purity in the Hungarian Danube section. Dolánszky and Thurnay (1973) have compiled a study on behalf of NWA and WRC (Water Resources Centre) on the state of the water purity of the Danube over a period of 5 years. They analyse in detail the sources of pollution of the Upper Danube and of the industrial and domestic sewages polluting the Danube.

The common Czechoslovakian–Hungarian Danube section. The bacteriological conditions of this area have already been the subject of several thorough limnological investigations.

Mucha et al. (1966) and Mucha and Daubner (1971, 1972, 1973) conducted the hydrobiological investigations, in the course of the international study of the Danube. Examination of the microflora of saprophytes and pathogens, hydromicrobiological studies, determination of the degree of self-purification, and detection of unlawful water pollution showed—in comparison with other limnological disciplines—a lack of progress in the countries lying along the Danube. However, since the organization of the hydrobiological study of the Danube a great improvement has been experienced in this field. This was stated at the Danube Conference in Bratislava in the autumn of 1973 (Daubner et al. 1974). Producer and consumer microorganisms are already known, mainly from the studies of Hanzlikova (1972*a,b*), Juris (1972, 1974), Rothschein (1973) and Vranovsky (1972). The results of their qualitative and quantitative plankton investigations roughly agree with those of the Hungarian observations made in this area.

The heavy pollution of the Czechoslovakian rivers detrimentally affects the Hungarian Danube section. In the neighbourhood of Morava, the oil refineries and sugar works are the main sources of pollution. Czechoslovakia's 30 sugar works, mainly in the peak season of production, strongly pollute all the rivers which enter the Danube. The domestic sewage of Bratislava enters the Danube without being purified. At Moson, the Danube carries the industrial waste waters of the river Lajta from Austrian territory. The polluting impact of the town of Komarno, situated on the left bank of the Danube, can be detected even at Budapest. In Hungary, the industrial plants of Szőny, Almásfüzitő, Lábatlan and Nyergesújfalu are the main sources of pollution. Upstream from Esztergom, the integrated paper mill of Štúrovo has already exerted detrimental effects on the water quality of the Danube on several occasions. It can be stated that in the Czechoslovakian–Hungarian Danube section ammonia concentration (1.9 mg/l) increases which is a most disquieting phenomenon. Also the quantity of oxidizable materials shows an enhancement. Literáthy and Szebellédy (1969) have established that also phenols and heavy metals are present in the river. Both in the Czechoslovakian and Hungarian investigations, the study of the ecological impacts of water power-stations and dams to be expected has become of increasing importance. In 1973, Rothschein mentioned the probable changes in the fauna of water.

**Hydrobiological investigations of the
Hungarian Danube section**

Adopting the proposals of Endre Dudich, the Hungarian Academy of Sciences and the Eötvös Loránd University of Budapest have provided facilities for the limnological study of the country's section of the Danube.

The remarkable activity of outstanding Hungarian water and civil engineers for decades, provided the necessary hydrographical–hydrological background for these investigations.

The dialectical study of water ecosystems comprises hydrobiological investigations, i.e. the analysis of physical, chemical and biological environmental factors and that of the components of life communities which help to get to know the interrelationships and the whole material energy flow.

The Hungarian Research Station for the Danube explores physico-chemical interrelationships of the river, its vegetation and fauna, as well as their life processes in a multidisciplinary manner. According to local demands and facilities and applying hydrobiological criteria, it is concerned with the fact that 70% of Hungarian water resources is supplied by the Danube and its water quality affects 40% of the population. The Danube also is the source of the water supply of Budapest and therefore, practical reasons also justify the need for certain basic research projects.

The optical study of the water of the Danube. The proper quality and quantity of available light is one of the basic requirements for the existence of micro- and macroscopic vegetation. There are, however, a lot of factors which influence the transmission of the different types of radiation. Investigations of the Danube have verified that, in very muddy water, the amount of light radiation impinging on the surface becomes entirely lost before reaching 1-m depth. In the water of the Danube, the yellowish-green light has the greatest transmission and beyond a certain depth only this part of the spectrum means the "light". For photosynthesis, however, unfortunately this is the least effective. In clear, or in only mildly turbid low water, light penetrates deeper and since it is rich in red and blue rays, its spectral composition is also more favourable (Dvihally 1959).

Chemical analyses of the water. When comparing the results of investigations of the years 1969–1974 with those of earlier years, there is evidence from several parameters, which illustrate changes in the water quality of the Danube. A great number of such chemical analyses have been made over the entire stretch of the Hungarian Danube section. On the basis of the evaluation of the large number of statistical data, characteristic mean values were calculated (Dvihally 1962, 1971, 1973). According to the lengthy investigations of the Hungarian Danube section, startling changes have taken place in the concentration of nitrite (NO_2), nitrates (NO_3), ammonia (NH_3) dissolved oxygen (mg/l) and the oxygen absorption and further increases are to be expected. Concerning the future of the Danube, which was considered to be pure or even the least polluted river in Europe, this is a phenomenon giving ground for anxiety.

Table 18

Changes in the chemical properties of the water of the Danube (1964-1974) (Dvihally 1976-1977)

Yearly averages

	1964	1965	1966	1967	1968	1969	1970	1971	1972	1973	1974
Dissolved O_2 mg/l	—	—	10.9	10.6	9.9	9.2	8.3	9.2	8.6	7.8	8.0
O_2-saturation %	—	—	95	98	96	82	73	84	77	70	72
NO_3^- mg/l	6.9	6.4	6.1	5.8	4.8	5.7	3.7	4.9	4.9	5.1	5.9
SiO_2 mg/l	5.2	4.4	3.8	3.3	3.0	3.0	2.0	0.9	1.15	2.5	0.5
Oxygen absorption	—	—	7.7	7.1	8.1	9.5	8.8	9.0	8.8	9.1	7.4
NO_2^- mg/l	0.078	0.087	0.098	0.091	0.079	0.095	0.129	0.077	0.080	0.080	0.084
NH_4^+ mg/l	0.47	0.37	0.45	0.54	0.61	0.62	0.54	0.98	1.15	0.82	0.89
Fe^{+++} mg/l	—	—	0.013	0.012	0.011	0.032	0.021	0.051	0.079	0.04	0.06
Dissolved CO_2 mg/l	—	—	3.0	4.1	1.7	4.5	4.0	1.5	1.2	1.0	2.4
Total dissolved solids mg/l	303	321	366	324	304	337	321	334	347	344	311
Number of samples analysed	140	173	32	54	51	50	51	41	49	50	52

Continuous study of the oxygen balance of the Danube has clearly indicated that—in comparison with earlier data—circumstances have recently deteriorated, though the great volume of water of the Danube, secures temporarily the proper dilution of pollutants, which is favourable for biological production (Dvihally 1976–1977) (Table 18).

Contamination of watercourses and of drinking water abstracted from the Danube

Contaminated water exerts a detrimental impact on the natural environment, endangering its living organisms. The pollution of rivers increases water purification expenses and in general, it decreases the suitability of the water for manifold uses.

In the context of pollution and the protection of the Danube it should be emphasized that the water demand of Budapest, which occasionally exceeds 1 million m^3/day, is basically met from the Danube. Riverbank filtration wells supply 900,000 m^3 water per day. The Water Works of the capital process 230,000–250,000 m^3 so-called "surface raw water" taken directly from the Danube, into potable water (Szemes et al. 1963).

The North-Transdanubian District Water Authority carried out weekly measurements at the Rajka reach of the Danube over a period of 5 years in order to determine the organic matter pollution. The figures for oxygen absorption, calculated from the permanganate value ($KMnO_4$-P.V.I), showed a worsening quality from year to year (Benedek et al. 1973).

Year		
1967	5,100	Mass-flow (g/s): multiple of $KMnO_4$ oxygen
1968	5,740	absorption and rate of flow
1969	5,800	
1970	6,500	
1971	7,200	

The final conclusion of the above investigations is that, assuming an average deterioration of 5% per year, the present organic matter content of the Danube will double in 20 years' time. This is a most dangerous and alarming process (Fig. 55).

To characterize the entire Danube section, monthly measurements were made from Rajka to Mohács, in several reaches. The values of oxygen absorption from $KMnO_4$ were illustrated in graphs. It was established that

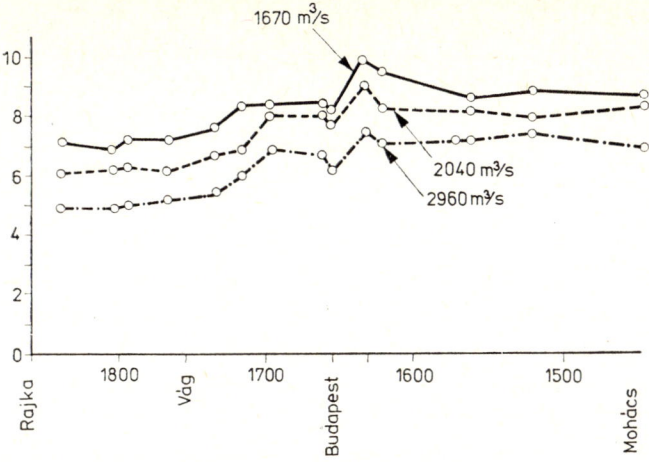

Fig. 55. The organic matter load of the river Danube

the organic matter pollution of the Danube entering Hungary shows a yearly increase of 5%, which means that the river is no longer capable of eliminating its pollution load before it reaches the southern border.

Kozma (1975, 1976–1977) determined the quantity of both the oxidizable organic matter and of the water-suspended bioseston, separately. Parallel with the plankton surveys he also observed their changes with time. According to him, the seasonal changes are rather characteristic. While in summer the quantity of suspended (already formed) organic matter increases considerably, in winter a decrease takes place. The amount of dissolved organic matter is approximately ten times that of the matter in suspension.

The Water Resources Centre of the NWA and the North-Transdanubian District Water Authority have made a joint, detailed study of the water balance of the major industrial plants in the area of Ács–Esztergom–Dorog. At the same time the Central Danube Valley District Water Authority has thoroughly analysed the load of polluted water of the Danube, at Budapest. According to their assessment, the quantity of prepurified effluent entering the Danube along the right bank, amounts to 700,000 m³. Through the open sewers of the sewerage system of the capital a further 100,000 m³ flows into the river on the right bank. Through the discharge pipes of the industrial plants nearly 300,000 m³ of industrial effluent discharges to the Danube, 260,000 m³ of which—i.e. the larger part—flows into the Danube from the left bank.

Benedek and co-workers (1973) carried out investigations and calculations in an attempt to determine what distance the sewage of Budapest had to cover before it became purified. At present this distance amounts to 50–70 km! The construction of the new sewage purification plant of Budapest, with a capacity of 1.5 million m³/day, is of great significance concerning the protection of the water of the Danube. In their paper Benedek and his co-workers (1976) point to the fact that the cross-sectional distribution of concentrations is in strong correlation with water-flow, turbulence conditions and the hydraulic interrelationship between the polluting sources and the river. Changes in both the river bed profile and the speed of its individual discharges affect the distribution of floating matter, therefore, the whole ecosystem. The large amount of data, of the chemical analyses made between 1968–1973 as well as the values and loads at each sampling station are given.

All the results are illustrated quarterly and yearly, with the mean, standard deviation, maximum and minimum of the values.

Bacteriological and microbiological study of the Danube

Numerous institutions, among them the National Institute of Hygiene, the Centre for Sanitation and Epidemiology, the Laboratory for Health of the Hungarian State Railways, the Water Canalization Works of the capital have been carrying out bacteriological investigation of the Danube. The Centre for Sanitation and Epidemiology and the Waters Works of Budapest are especially concerned with the intensive study of the bacteriological conditions of the Danube with respect to potable water production from direct abstraction and from the filtration wells alongside the river. The water which leaves Budapest is strongly polluted and 15 years of investigations indicate that the pollution reaches its peaks in autumn.

Some of the pathogenic bacteria (Salmonella) are rather resistant to self-purification. Unfortunately, from the bacteriological point of view, by the 1970s the water quality of the Danube had deteriorated to such a degree, that the Centre for Sanitary and Epidemiology of Budapest—on health grounds—forbade free bathing in the area of the capital in the summer 1973. In years of low water levels, the bacteriological water quality—irrespective of the places of sampling—deteriorated by one order of magnitude on average.

At the Danube Congress in Vienna, Mucha and Daubner (1973) disclosed the results of bacteriological investigations along the entire Danube while at the international congress, at Visegrád, they made known a report on the then existing situation. Concerning the bacteriological investigations of the Hungarian Danube section they referred to the papers of Bozzay (1972), Némedy (1972) and Némedy and Pietrasko (1972). In his book on water microbiology Daubner (1972) also gives a detailed survey of the bacteriological pollution of the Danube.

The microscopic flora of the Danube

Since the foundation of the Hungarian Danube Research Station, phyto- and zoo-plankton investigations have been carried out continuously. These were concentrated mainly on one sector at Alsógöd, though several measurements have been made from Ásványráró to Mohács. Up to 1965, the presence of 1,568 plant microorganisms had been detected from the source to the delta of the Danube (Szemes 1967*a, b, c*). According to more recent studies the number of taxa amounts to 2,272 (Table 19).

Between 1956–1958 the maximum number of phytoplankton individuals was around 8–9 individuals/ml. This number has been increasing with the years. More recently especially in floodless months—under the still favourable temperature and light conditions—the maximum number of phytoplanktons reached 30,000–40,000 individuals/ml. This process indicates the eutrophication of the Danube. Changes in the composition of the various coenoses have also shifted in the direction of pollution. Also the results

Table 19

Number of plant and animal taxa in the water of the Danube
(Szemes 1967, 1970; Dudich 1967)

Plant kingdom	Number of taxa in	
	1967	1970
Bacteria	30	30
Mycophyta (Fungi)	18	25
Cyanophyta (Blue-green algae)	274	345
Euglenophyta (Euglenoid flagellates)	124	195
Xanthophyceae-Chrysophyceae (Yellow algae flagellates)	91	130
Bacillariophyceae (Diatoms)	402	709
Pyrrophyta (Dinoflagellates)	41	58
Chlorophyta (Grass-green algae)	579	771
Rhodophyta (Red algae)	9	9
Bryophyta (Liverworms and mosses)	28	28
Pteridophyta (Ferns-horsetails)	2	2
Angiospermae (Vascular flowering plants)	121	121
Total	1,719	2,423

Table 19 (*cont.*)

Animal kingdom	Number of taxa in	
	1967	1970
Flagellata (Non-ciliated protozoa)	107	
Ciliophora (Ciliates)	113	
Porifera (Sponges)	4	
Cnidaria (Jellyfish-sea-anemones)	8	
Platyhelminthes (Flat worms)	57	
Nemertoea (ribbon worms)	1	
Aschelminthes (includes rotifers, nematodes)	225	
Bryozoa hydrozoa (Hydra)	2	
Annelida (true worms and leeches)	99	
Mollusca (snails, limpets-mussels)	128	
Tentaculata (sea gooseberries)	8	
Rhizopoda (Sarcodina)	5	
Arthropoda	724	
Vertebrata	111	
	1,734	
Zoobenthos (additional list by Russev 1967)	154	
Total	1,888	

of the above-mentioned investigations illustrate this tendency. Occasionally the diatom *Stephanodiscus hantzschii* appeared in such a great mass that it resembled an invasion. Since 1970 *Sceletonema subsalsa* has also appeared in large numbers.

The impact of flood on plankton and phytobenthic communities

At the time of high water levels and floods, the velocity of the river increases. It carries much suspended matter and becomes significantly less transparent. These unfavourable impacts destroy the flora of the algae of the river. Broken up colonies of algae, alga strands and algae deprived of their floating setae, are good examples of this (Szemes 1968).

The great flood of the Danube, in 1965, arrived in six waves. Each time the phytoplankton suffered great losses. The increased velocity, in particular, strongly flushed out plankton members. When the speed of the flow exceed the value of 1 m/s, the majority of these did not find favourable living conditions in the river (Behning 1928). With increasing speed the time of the rivers outflow becomes shorter. Therefore, the residence time for plankton formation also decreases. As far as the total length of the Danube is concerned, flood waters reach the sea 30–40 days later (Tőry 1952). The disturbed processes of metabolism may decisively decrease the quantity of plankton.

Under the changed, new conditions algae have a definitely smaller assimilational capacity. One of the other reasons for the deterioration of the processes of assimilation is the growing turbidity and decreasing light transmission that can be observed simultaneously with the rise in water level. Thus, as it can be deduced from Dvihally's (1972) investigations, the light conditions in the water of the Danube are the most favourable at permanent low waters in autumn and winter. On such occasions there is relatively little suspended silt in the water, consequently, approx. 6–10% of the light reaching the surface can penetrate to a depth of 1 m. At the time of flood, when the quantity of suspended sediment increases, the loss of light is significant even at a depth of a few centimetres. At a depth of approx. 20 cm, only 10% of the light getting on to the surface can be measured. At this time, riverside algae (phytobenthos) covered with sediment, sand and silt—which are cut off from light—deteriorate even more rapidly than does the plankton. Changing water conditions eliminate the building up of larger lodgements of algae alongside the river. Following the partial stabilization of the water level, generally, 8–10 days are needed for the more intensive formation of microvegetation on the river banks. The height of water level (low, medium and high water levels) and the so-called little, average and large river beds exert both a qualitative and quantitative influence on the composition of the species and benthos (Berczik 1966).

Distribution of phytoplankton in successive reaches of the Hungarian Danube section

The qualitative and quantitative composition of phytoplankton was studied at 12 locations, along a more than 400 km long stretch of the Danube. Samples were taken monthly on the same day (Fig. 56). Roughly speaking, the whole phytoplankton flora consisted of the same species. The sampling points were the following: Ásványráró (1818 rkm*), Gönyü (1788 rkm), Komárom (1768 rkm), Esztergom (1719 rkm), Vác (1684 rkm), Budapest (1647 rkm), Ercsi (1614 rkm), Dunaújváros (1581 rkm), Dunaföldvár (1561 rkm), Paks (1531 rkm), Baja (1476 rkm), Mohács (1448 rkm). Occasional differences in the quantity of plankton were the result of flood waves. A relatively small amount of phytoplankton was detected in samples taken at such times when the entire river was affected by flooding. Comparing the sampling locations, the highest amount of plankton was observed at

* rkm = Distance from river mouth.

182

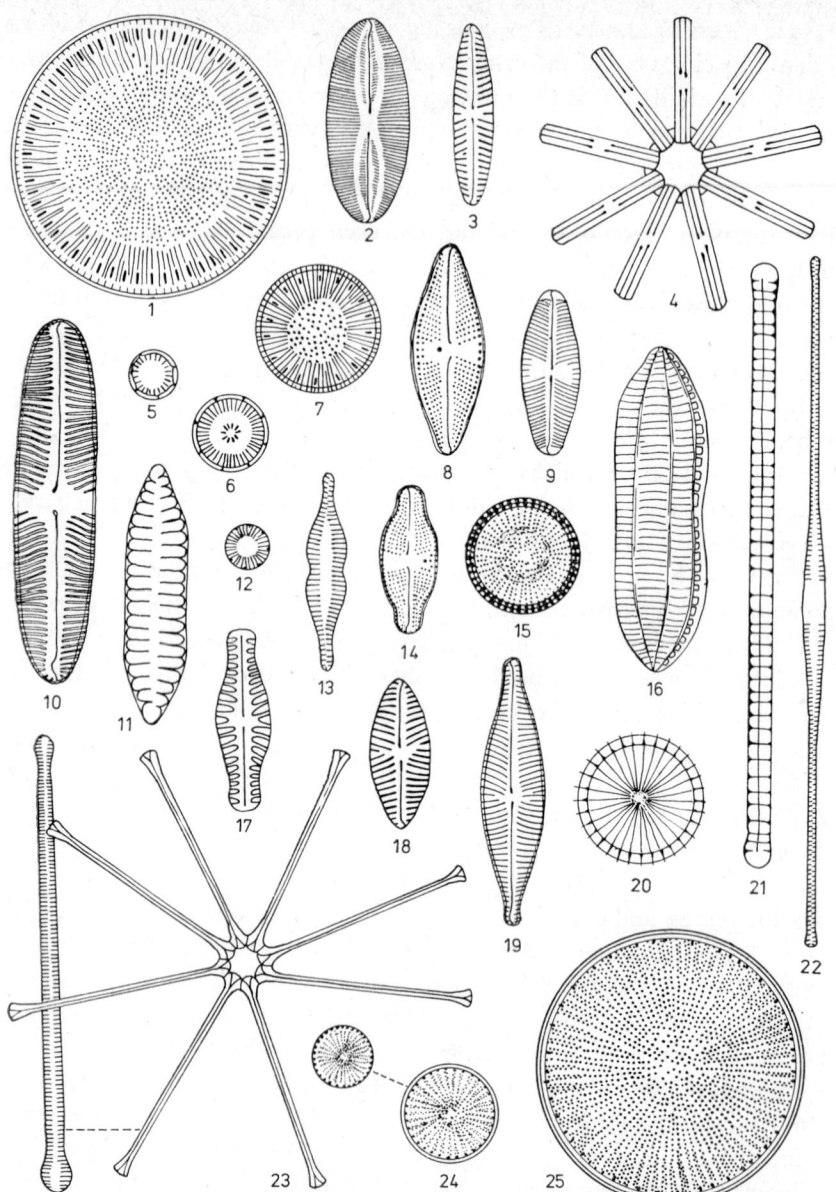

Fig. 56a. From among the diatoms (bacillariophyceae) very rich in species and individuals living in the Danube, the drawings illustrate a few so-called plankton-tags (members) found in suspension in rivers. Many of them can be indicators of different degrees of water pollution 1: Cyclotella, 2–3: Navicula, 4: Tabellaria, 5–7: Cyclotella, 8–9: Navicula, 10: Pinnularia, 11: Surirella, 12: Cyclotella, 13: Synedra, 14: Navicula, 15: Stephanodiscus, 16: Nitzschia, 17–19: Navicula, 20: Stephanodiscus, 21: Diatomsa, 22: Fragilaria, 23: Asterionella, 24: Stephanodiscus sp.

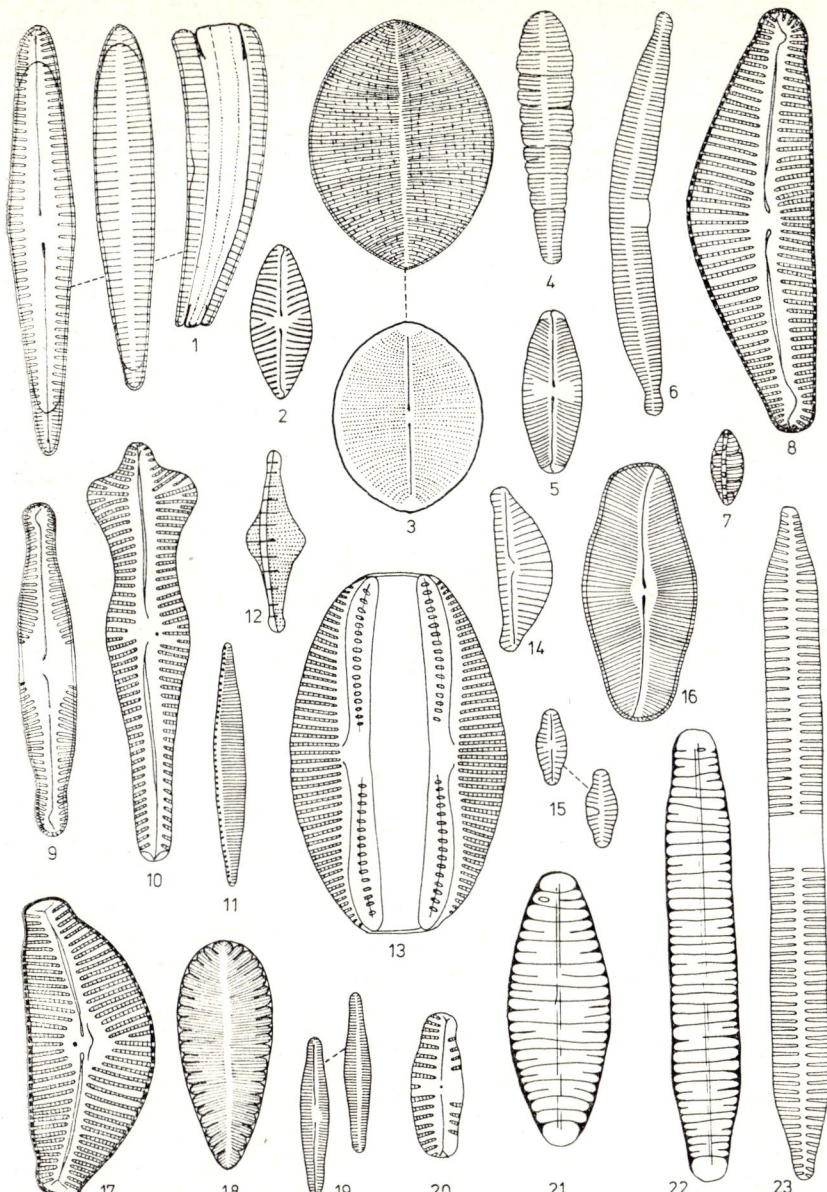

Fig. 56b. Diatoms, living on the stones of the banks of the Danube, on its stone walls and structures and pontoon covers and on aquatic plants are members of the benthos, though they are often washed off by the scouring, wavebreaking force of water and become part of the plankton community. (*1*) Rhoicosphenia, (*2*) Navicula, (*3*) Cocconeis, (*4*) Meridion, (*5*) Navicula, (*6*) Ceratoneis, (*7*) Denticula, (*8*) Cymbella, (*9*) Pinnularia, (*10*) Gomphonema, (*11–12*) Nitzschia, (*13*) Amphora, (*14*) Cymbella, (*15*) Achnanthes, (*16*) Eucocconeis, (*17*) Cymbella, (*18*) Surirella, (*19*) Achnanthes, (*20*) Cymbella, (*21–22*) Diatoma, (*23*) Synedra sp

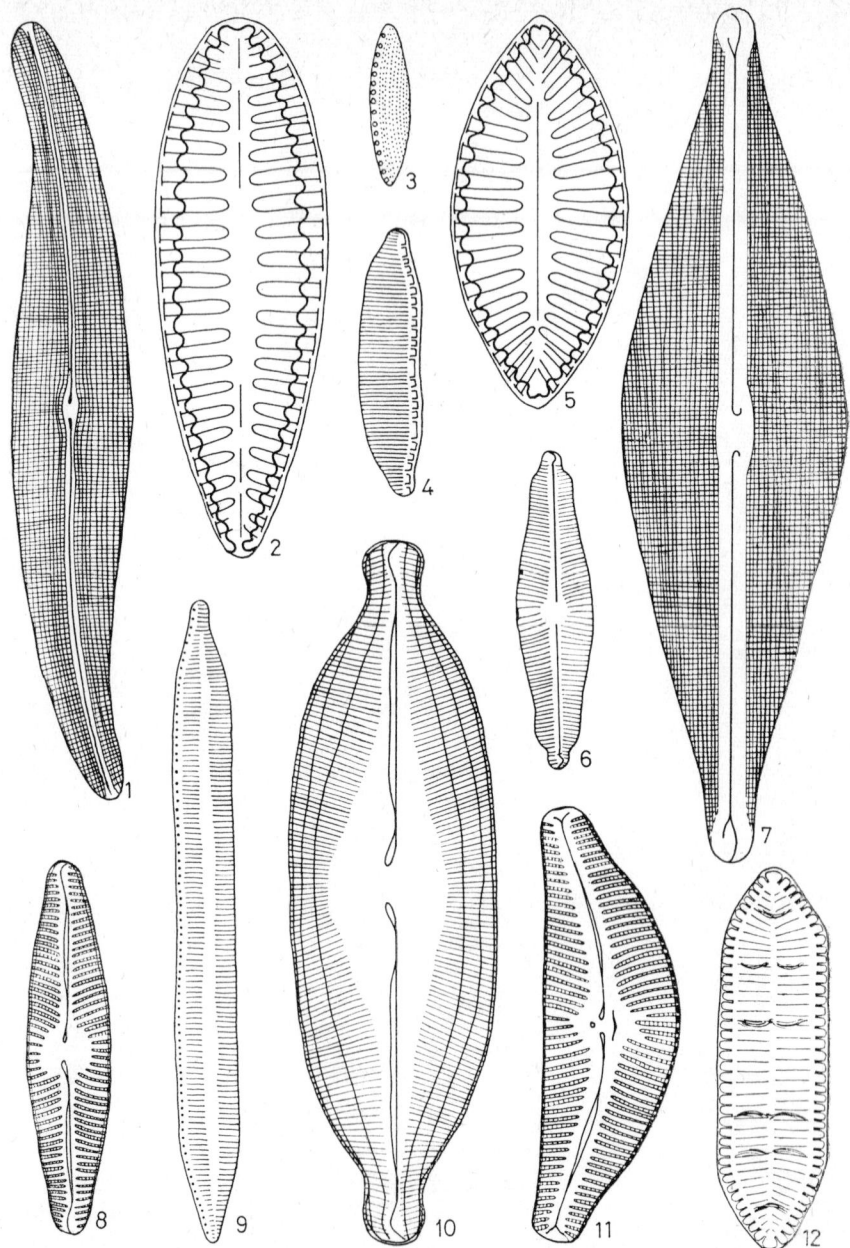

Fig. 56c. Diatoms frequently present in silt and on the sandy littoral regions. (*1*) Gyrosigma, (*2*) Surirella, (*3*) Nitzschia, (*4*) Hantzschia, (*5*) Surirella, (*6–8*) Navicula, (*9*) Nitzschia, (*10*) Caloneis, (*11*) Cymbella, (*12*) Cymatopleura sp.

Paks–Baja–Mohács (Szemes 1964, 1969a,b, 1971). Studies by Uherkovich (1966), Vörös (1974) and Uherkovich et al. (1978) also illustrate the richness of this area in species. In his study Hortobágyi (1973) gave a good account of the microflora of the settling and infiltration basins of Budapest.

Seasonal periodicity

During the months of spring, besides diatoms, blue and green algae also appear in greater quantities. In the summer months the number of taxa and that of the individuals of green algae also increases. In certain years their number had been close to, occasionally even higher than that of the diatoms. In winter it is also the diatoms that play an important part in the plankton population, though the number of their species and individuals is far less than in the more favourable growth seasons. The formation of phytoplankton in the Danube is, however, basically determined by factors which are dominant during the season of low and high flows.

Fish and fisheries

From time to time, on the basis of investigations into the fauna of the Hungarian Danube section, new species are taken under revision (Tóth 1960). The analyses of population dynamics have shown that parallel with the growing pollution of the river, the particularly rheophile sterlet (*Acipenser ruthenus*) and barbel (*Barbus barbus*) (favouring places with strong currents) deteriorate strongly. Neither feeding nor reproductive conditions are adequate for them, therefore their number recedes permanently. It is in the case of the stocks of pike, that the greatest changes have been observed, in the Hungarian section of Danube, during the last decades. The pollution of the river, the ecological conditions of tributaries and flood waters exert a similar impact on the stocks of pike-perch. Changes in the different biotopes of the river are well supported by the changes of ecological relationships of fishes (Tóth 1960, 1969, 1974, 1975).

Several studies have been published on the fish fauna and fisheries of the river. Busnita (1967) featured the fish and fisheries of the entire Danube. Balon (1968) analysed the impact of fishing on the fish stock of the Danube. In their paper Jancovic et al. (1974) revealed the biological and economical aspects of the fisheries. In a study Velev et al. (1974) tried to answer the question as to what extent water abstraction affects the water quality and drinking water supply as well as fishing and shipping on the river. Bacal-basa and Dobrovici (1974) also discussed the impacts of water extraction on fishing.

Impact of human activity on the Lower Danube

At the Danube Research Conference, in Visegrád, Rudescu (1972) pointed to the fact that, in spite of the large territorial gains of agriculture, the losses due to the construction of expensive dikes, the losses of fishery, flood washlands and forestry were great. Beautiful landscapes have also disappeared. On the same occasion Naidenov (1972) emphasized that protective embankments built along a long reach of Lower Danube had deprived the river of its connection with the more or less isolated channels, backwaters and marshlands. This has contributed to the enrichment of its plankton stock.

Hydrobiological investigations of the Romanian Danube section are well described in a large monograph compiled by a team led by Banu (1967). Busnita (1970) co-ordinated a study by several workers, which dealt with the hydrobiological investigation of the stretch of the Danube below the Iron Gate and of its tributaries. Data furnished by these studies serve as the basis for the comparative investigation of new ecological conditions brought about by the hydroelectric power station and dam at the Iron Gate and also that of the recently established biocoenoses.

The power station at the Iron Gate. As a result of hydrotechnical works at the Iron Gate, the water level was raised by 20–30 m. Simultaneously approx. 17,000 ha on the Romanian side of the Danube became covered with water. Trial borings have shown, that with only one year having elapsed, the river bed has changed. Sand and later on large quantities of silt have formed a deposit on top of the originally rocky base. The quantity of suspended particles has decreased and is 5–6 times less in the storage lake at the Iron Gate than it used to be in the original water. The increase in transparency of 1–2 m is significant.

The former river characteristics have been replaced by those pertaining to a lake. In the bay of Orsova, algal blooms were observed as early as the first year. *Pandorina morum* was detected at a density of 20,000 individuals/ml. Under the new ecological conditions, green algae like *Gonium pectorale* and *Erratela bornhemiensis* have also been observed. In the 628–612 river km points of the Lower Danube, *Cyclotella chaetoceras* has appeared only recently. Its occurrence in the storage lake of Orsova is frequent. In the long-separated backwater of the Hungarian Danube section—in Lake Szelid—it can be also detected in the presence of other species character-istic of brackish water. Investigations have been launched on both the Romanian and Yugoslavian sides. These cover both plant and animal plankton and benthos (Brezeanu 1974; Cure et al. 1974; Jancovic et al. 1974; Weber et al. 1974; Petcu 1974; Obuskovic 1975, etc.).

The impact of human activity on the Danube delta. The territory of the Dan-ube delta is 500.000 ha. It is a vast marsh and area of lakes, the water of which is of varying salt concentration. Its lake system is more or less connected with the sea and has an extremely rich flora and fauna. At its entrance to the sea, the Danube is divided into 3 main branches.

In his informative survey Rudescu (1972) compares the deterioration of ecological conditions and further that of the biocoenoses in the Szulina Channel—caused by 90 years of damaging human interference, shipping, river control activity—with the St. George's Channel where natural con-ditions have been maintained.

At present the river is 8–10 m deep in the Szulina Channel which, to-gether with the straightening of its banks and covering them with rocks and heaps of stones, is a main shipping channel. As a result of riverbed dredging the former 7% water volume carried by the river, has increased to 14%. Accordingly, the speed of flow has also increased and has reached the value of 1 m/s. The quantity of mud carried by the river has also doubled. Transparency amounts to 30 cm. These data illustrate that the hydro-technical interferences have brought about fundamental, negative changes in the natural lymnological conditions of the Szulina Channel. In the branches of the Danube delta, e.g. in 1971 a total of 1,800 t of fish was caught whilst only 700 t was caught in the Szulina Channel. It is an even more conspicuous fact that, according to estimates, the production of the river, at the mouth of Szulina Channel, is 130 kg/ha, while at the mouth of the St. George's Channel it is almost three times this amount: 370 kg/ha. It is striking that the quantity of sturgeon caught in the St. George's Channel was 3,547 kg while, in the Szulina Channel, at the same time, it amounted to only 151 kg. The great difference in production is explained by the more favourable ecological conditions of the St. George's Channel. There are also similar examples of this: the water depth was 4–6 m, the quantity of water carried has dropped from 25% to 16%. The speed of flow has fallen to 0.5 m/s. The quantity of silt has greatly decreased and transparency rose to 45 cm. In the St. George's Channel, which is situated in the original, natural environment, the conditions are definitely more favourable than in the canalized Szulina Channel. The damaging impact of human interference may serve as a warning for the future (Rudescu and Banu 1974).

Regulation of the Hungarian Danube reaches and of its tributaries

Though river regulation is a basic requirement for the security of shipping, passenger transport and shipment, at the time of its implementation the principles of nature conservation must strictly be respected. In the past, regulation of the Danube was limited, almost entirely, to the elimination of danger caused by water, ice and the shallows which had meant an obstacle for shipping. The present state of the Danube and its biological character are the result of the technical, mainly, regulatory interferences over a period of almost 100 years. Since the years following the Second World War, water regulation and control have become a manifold task. The requirements concerning the regulation of our rivers have risen. From the *Statistical Handbook of Hungarian Shipping 1945–1968* one can get a full picture of the many aspects of shipping. Here is a short quotation from it: "Apart from the increasing realisation of earlier objectives—prevention of flood and ice damage, the improvement of waterways—it is also an important task to increase the supply of industrial and potable water, agricultural water utilization, the establishing of water conservation works in the service of water management, the reliable functioning of barrages meant for the storage of irrigation water and to utilize hydroelectric energy. This has to be carried out by means of the regulation of the longest possible stretches within the scope of the above-mentioned institutions" (Fekete 1971).

A minimum water depth and width of river bed are preconditions for the safety of shipping. While cross dams built into the river control water depth, by means of river-bank protection works it is possible to secure the required width of the river. Ports, loading docks and different edifices along the bank of the river, these all influence its hydrological and hydrographical conditions and consequently, the development of living organisms and their changes. Unfortunately the lack of research data makes it impossible to establish exactly the changes which have taken place before and immediately after the river control works on the Danube. Naturally, Hungarian regulations have had far-reaching impacts on the life of the river. Along the 417 km long Hungarian Danube section

58 km (20.4%)   are regulated
287 km (68.7%)   are partly regulated
21 km (5.1%)   still require regulation
24 km (5.8%)   do not need regulation.

As a result of the 30 by-pass channels, the originally 472 km long Hungarian Danube section has been shortened by 11.6%, to a length of 417 km. Water, now flowing with an increased speed through the narrower cross-section brought about by the regulations, exerts its impact on the biology of the Danube and gradually, the river is losing its natural character.

In addition to the main branch, the subsidiary channels of the Danube —with an overall length of 212 km—also play a significant role. It is desirable that, in order to help the self-purification of the river, these should be preserved in their natural state. Human interference has been successful also in this field. From the total 212 km length of the Danube channels

72 km (33.9%)   are partly regulated
39 km (18.4%)   still need regulation
101 km (47.7%)   do not yet need regulation.

The impact of shipping on the Danube, as a living space, is also partly reflected by the figures for shipments. Thus, e.g. between Rajka and Gönyü in 1960, 2.5 million t of cargo was transported while, in 1968 it amounted to 4.5 million of t. In 1985 this is expected to amount to 15 millions of t on the Upper Reaches of the Danube. It is an important task to secure the safety of this water traffic. On the Upper Reach of the Danube, as already mentioned, the improvement of shipping conditions has been going on at an increasing rate since 1974. This involves the deepening of the river bed, the removal of river crossings. etc. A survey on Danube shipping has been given by Fekete (1967). Technical and also limnological aspects of the great international waterway are discussed by Michaelis and Kothé (1974).

Planned waterways in Europe and their possible effects on water quality and on the living organisms of the Danube

The construction of a common European water network and the modernization of waterways will also increase the transport of goods and passengers. A Rhine–Main–Danube canal is being built in the Federal Republic of Germany. This 141 km long waterway connects the North and Black Seas opening the way to the North Sea.

This 3,500 km long waterway, passing through 8 countries, will give a lot of work to hydrobiologists studying the water system. It is, however, questionable to what degree the ecological conditions and consequently the flora and fauna of the river and the capacity for self-purification will be modified. Will the environment control directives prove effective in the course of different works? Another great waterway planned, the Danube–Oder canal and the connected Oder–Elbe canal, will join the North Sea and Baltic Sea with the Black Sea. This will also make a significant contribution towards increasing water traffic on the Danube.

Although strict provisions have been provided for the avoidance of water pollution caused by shipping, long-term protection of water quality and for the steadily increasing shipping, material, cargo and passenger transport, the larger and newer ports alone may mean sources of increasing pollution. That section of the Danube which is situated in the Carpathian basin will be almost the central area for transit traffic. Between Rajka and Gönyü the waterway is at present full of shallows and river crossings, which, especially at the time of low river flows are a hazard to river traffic.

Power stations and dams of the Danube reaches in the Carpathian Basin

Presumably in the near future the construction of the barrage-system between Gabčikovo (below Bratislava) and Nagymaros (above Budapest) will be started with Czechoslovakian–Hungarian co-operation. The proposed water reservoirs at Hrusov and Dunakiliti and the barrages at Gabčikovo and above Nagymaros will result in new hydraulic, hydrographic and different ecological conditions at the same time. Dams exert a long-lasting impact on the life of the river. Water depth and speed, the width or the river bed, light conditions, the chemistry of the water, etc. all will be changed. It is to be expected that the landscape of the above-mentioned areas will almost completely change.

An important requirement which supports the building of dams for hydro-electric power stations, is the demand of Budapest and other urban areas lying along the river for an adequate supply of potable and industrial water. When artificially interfering with the river regime, in the course of construction of barrages and other engineering works, the greatest care should be taken to maintain the ecological features of the river and to safeguard the processes of self-purification. It is of prime importance to survey the present ecosystems, their hydrobiological properties in the territories that are to be subject to change. The study of the physical–chemical interrelationship of water, the quantitative and qualitative study of its living organisms, the analysis of plant and animal associations and the results of these works will help to quantify the changes brought about by the dams.

As the National Water Authority, sponsored by the World Health Organization, has designated the Hungarian Upper Danube as a "water quality regulation model territory", the most modern scientific approach is provided for this investigation. By utilizing a large amount of data the automatic measuring stations largely promote the general recognition of the Danube and of the capacity to control its water quality, with respect to the requirements of nature conservation, for the benefit of the people.

**International team involved in the investigation
of the Danube**

The first step for the Danube Limnological Team was to collect, arrange and evaluate all the literature available on the hydrobiology of the Danube. This was followed by the development of a common work programme, which considers the differing environmental properties of the individual Danube sections and the relevant tasks. Bacteriologists, botanists, zoologists, water-chemists, hydrologists, geomorphologists, paleolymnologists, climatologists, hydraulic-engineers, etc. are working in this team. In the individual countries concerned, a national society organizes, leads and co-ordinates these investigations. The number of participants in this collective investigation is nearly 300.

Gradually some main themes have evolved. The leaders of the specialist groups make suggestions for them and they also compile the directives. At the annual conferences reports of the results are exchanged. As a result of this common activity, the monograph entitled *Limnologie der Donau* (1967) has been compiled. Several volumes have been published on the limnological research projects of the individual countries.

The number of papers on limnological subjects amounts to 2,000. They all bear witness to both the theoretical and practical approaches of the problem and to the commendable international collaboration in this work.

References

Antalfi, A. and Tölg, I. (1972): *Herbivorous fishes* (in Hungarian). Budapest.

Bacalbasa, N. and Dobrovici X. (1974): Wasserentnahme und ihre Auswirkungen auf die Fischerei. *Societas Internationalis Limnologie Arbeitsgemeinschaft Donauforschung* **16**: 136–146.

Backhaus, D. (1968): Ökologische Untersuchungen an den Aufwuchsalgen der obersten Donau und ihrer Quellflüsse. *Arch. f. Hydrobiol. Suppl.* **34**: 24–73, 251–320.

Balogh, J. (1953): *The Principles of Zoocoenology* (in Hungarian). Budapest.

Balon, E. K. (1968): Einfluss des Fischfangs auf die Fischgemeinschaften. *Arch. f. Hydrobiol. Suppl.* **34**: 228–249.

Banu, A. C. (1967): *Limnologia sectorului Romanesc Al Dunarii-Studiu monografic*. Editura Academiei Republicii Socialiste Romaina.

Baron, F., Csonti, F. and Ponyi, J. E. (1967): Investigations of pesticide residues in fish and other aquatic organisms of Lake Balaton and some other aquatic habitats (in Hungarian). *Annal. Biol.* **34**: 117–128.

Behning, A. (1928): Das Leben der Wolga. Zugleich eine Einführung in die Flussbiologie. *Die Binnengewässer* **5**: 1–162.

Benedek, P. and Literáthy, P. (1979) *Water Quality Control in Environmental Protection* (in Hungarian). Budapest.

Benedek, P., Hock, B., Kádár, L., Puskás, M. and Rymorz, P. (1973): Determination of water quality in order to evaluate the efficiency of sewage purification plants planned in Budapest (in Hungarian). *Vízügyi Közlem.* **2**: 167–191.

Benedek, P., Literáthy, P., Jolánkay, G. and László, F. (1976): Water quality problems in the Hungarian section of the Danube (in Hungarian). *Hidrológiai Közlöny.* **56**: 49–58.

Berczik, Á. (1966): Über den Einfluß einiger hydrobiologischen Faktoren auf die Besiedlungsmöglichkeiten der Fauna der Mittleren-Donau. (Danubialia Hungarica, XXX.). *Ann. Univ. Sci. Budapestiensis Sect. Biol.* **8**: 25–32.

Bozzay, E. (1972): Clostridium-Untersuchungen des Budapester Wasseraufarbeitungswerks—SIL Arbeitsgemeinschaft Donauforschung, 15. Arbeitstagung in Ungarn, Kurzreferatum, Budapest.

Böszörményi, Z., Cseh, E., Felföldy, L. and Szabó, E. (1963): Some methodical questions on photosynthetic measurements with radioactive tracer C^{14}-techniques in Lake Balaton (in Hungarian). *Annal. Biol.* **29**: 39–63.

Breinich, M. (1972): Ungarn wasserwirtschaftlich gesehen. SIL Arbeitsgemeinschaft Donauforschung 15. Arbeitstagung in Ungarn.

Brezeanu, Gh. (1974): Die physikalisch–chemischen und hydrobiologischen Charakteristiken des Stausees „Eisernes Tor" (rumänischer Abschnitt) in den Bedingungen des Jahres 1973. 17. Arbeitstagung der Internationalen Arbeitsgemeinschaft Donauforschung 23–29. September 1974. Galatz—Rumänien.

Buddenbrock, W. (1956): Ernährung, Wasserhaushalt und Mineralhaushalt der Tiere. *Vergleich. Physiol.* **3**.

Busnita, Th. (1967): Die Fischerei und Fischwirtschaft. *Limnologie der Donau* **4**: 26–41.

Csermák, B. (1967): Water resource management. In: Puskán (ed.): *The surface waters of Hungary* (in Hungarian). Budapest.

Cure, V., Schneider, A., Naziru, M. and Mencinicopschi, Gh. (1974): Die Dynamik des Zoobenthos im Stausee am Eisernen Tor in den Jahren 1972-73. Kurzreferate 17. Arbeitstagung der Internationalen Arbeitsgemeinschaft Donauforschung 23–29. September 1974. Galatz–Rumänien.

Czeglédi-Jankó, G., Ponyi, J. and Csonti, F. (1973): Contributions to the pesticide-pollution dynamics of Lake Balaton (in Hungarian). *Halászat* **19**: (66), 74–75.

Daubner, I. (1972): *Mikrobiologie des Wassers.* Berlin.

Daubner, I., Karolcek, J. and Kohl, W. (1974): Saprophytische und pathogene Microflora und ihre Bedeutung für den Stoffkreislauf und die Gewässergüte. SIL Arbeitsgemeinschaft Donauforschung, Bratislava **16**: 213–226.

Déri, J. (1971): The effect of human activity on natural water resources (in Hungarian). *Vízügyi Műszaki Gazdasági Tájékoztató 16*, VIZDOK, Budapest.

Dolánszky, F. and Thurnay, B. (1973): Water quality of the Danube section above Budapest during the past 5 years. Personal communications.

Dudich, E. (1967): Systematische Verzeichnis der Tierwelt der Donau mit einer zusammenfassenden Erläuterung. *Limnologie der Donau* **3**: 4–69.

194

Dvihally, Zs. (1959): Visual inspection and investigations of the Alsógöd section of the Vác-branch of the Danube (Danubialia Hungarica II.). *Hidrol. Közlem.* **39**: 357–364.

Dvihally, Zs. (1962): Der gelöste Sauerstoffgehalt, die Schwebestoffmenge und die Trübung des Oberflächenwassers der Donau im Laufe des Jahres 1959. *Arch. f. Hydrobiol. Suppl.* **1**: 72–84.

Dvihally, Zs. (1971): Untersuchung der Primärproduktion im ungarischen Donauabschnitt (Danubialia Hungarica LVIII.). *Ann. Univ. Scient. Budapestiensis Sect. Biol.* **13**: 33–43.

Dvihally, Zs. (1973): Die Gestaltung der wasserchemischen Verhältnisse im ungarischen Donauabschnitt (Danubialia Hungarica LVIII) *Ann. Univ. Scient. Budapestinensis, Sect. Biol.* **15**: 23–30.

Dvihally, Zs. (1976–77): Die Änderung der chemischen Verhältnisse des Donauwassers zwischen 1964—1974. (Danubialia Hungarica LXXXIV.). *Ann. Univ. Sci. Budapestiensis Sect. Biol.* **18.19**: 29–33.

Dvihally, Zs. (1981): Zum Sauerstoffgehalt und zur Primärproduktion in der Donau. *Arch. f. Hydrobiol. Suppl.* **52**: 350–370.

Dvihally, Zs. and Ponyi, J. (1957): Charakterisierung der Natrongewässer in der Umgebung von Kistelek auf Grund ihrer chemischen Zusammensetzung und ihrer Crustacea-Fauna. *Acta Biol. Acad. Sci. Hung.* **7**: 349–363.

Eckl, E. (1967): Industrie. *Limnologie der Donau,* Stuttgart **4**: 60–70.

Entz, B. (1964): Hydrobiology (in Hungarian). Personal communications.

Fábián, Gy., Jeanplong, J., Nagy, M., Rády, M. and Széky, P. (1975): Ecology (in Hungarian). Personal communications.

Fehér, D. (1954): *Soil biology* (in Hungarian). Budapest.

Fekete, Gy. (1967): Schiffahrt. *Limnologie der Donau, Stuttgart* **4**: 49–59.

Fekete, Gy. (1971): The statistical manual of Hungarian shipping 1945–1968 (in Hungarian). Budapest.

Fekete, Gy. (1973): La navigation sur le Danube. Wasser- und Energiewirtschaft. Cours d'eau et energie. Sonderheft Donau/Danube. Schweizerische Monatsschrift. *Revue Mensuelle Suisse* 3/4: 128–138.

Felföldy, L. (1972): Biological control of water quality (in Hungarian). Personal communications.

Felföldy, L. and Tóth, L. (1967): The effect of agricultural use of chemicals on water management. I. Pesticides (in Hungarian). *Vízügyi Szakmai Világszintbeszámolók 18.* VIZDOK, Budapest.

Felföldy, L. and Tóth, L. (1970): The effect of agricultural use of chemicals on water management. II. (in Hungarian). *Vízügyi Műszaki Gazdasági Tájékoztató 25,* VIZDOK, Budapest.

Frantz, A. (1966): Die Radioaktivität in der Donau. *Limnologie der Donau* **2:** 84–96.

Gere, G. (1957): Production-biological classification of living things and their role in life communities (in Hungarian). *Állattan. Közlem.* **46:** 71–78.

Gliwicz, Z. M. (1969): Studies on the feeding of pelagic zooplankton in lakes with varying trophic states. *Ekol. Polsk. A.* **17:** (No. 36), 663–708.

Hanzlikova, G. (1972a): Der Einfluss der Donaualgen auf einige chemischen und physikalischen Eigenschaften des Wassers. SIL 16. Arbeitstagung der Internationalen Arbeitsgemeinschaft Donauforschung in der ČSSR. Kurzreferate (in Slovakian).

Hanzlikova, G. (1972b): Dynamik der Veränderungen des Phytoplanktons im tschechoslovakischen Donauabschnitt. *Ac. Rer. Natur. Mus. Nat. Slov. Bratislava* **19:** 57–76.

Herodek, S. (1977): Recent results of phytoplankton research in Lake Balaton (in Hungarian). *Annal. Biol.* **44:** 181–198.

Herodek, S. and Tamás, G. (1973): The primary production of phytoplankton in Lake Balaton. *Annal. Biol.* **40:** 207–218.

Herodek, S. and Tamás, G. (1974): The primary production of phytoplankton in Lake Balaton. *Annal. Biol.* **41:** 205–216.

Herodek, S. and Tamás, G. (1975a): Phytoplankton production in Lake Balaton. *Symp. Biol. Hung.* **15:** 29–34.

Herodek, S. and Tamás, G. (1975b): The primary production of phytoplankton in the Keszthely basin of Lake Balaton, in 1973–4. *Annal. Biol.* **42:** 175–190.

Herodek, S. and Tamás, G. (1976): The phytoplankton biomass, its production and the eutrophication of Lake Balaton (in Hungarian). *Hidrológiai Közlöny* **56:** 219–228.

Herodek, S. and Tamás, G. (1978): The phytoplankton biomass, its production and the eutrophication of Lake Balaton II. The Szigliget-basin 1974–75 (in Hungarian). *Hidrológiai Közlöny.* **58:** 384–391.

Herodek, S., Vörös, L. and Tóth, F. (1978a): The mass of phytoplankton, its production and the eutrophication of Lake Balaton III. The Szemes-basin 1976–7 (in Hungarian). Personal communications.

Herodek, S., Vörös, L. and Tóth, F. (1978b): The mass of phytoplankton, its production and the eutrophication of Lake Balaton IV. Siófok-basin 1977 (in Hungarian). Personal communications.

Hortobágyi, T. (1973): *The microflora in the settling and underground water infiltration basins of the Budapest waterworks.* Budapest.

Hortobágyi, T., Kárpáti, I. (1967): Algal "blooms" in the south-western district of Lake Balaton (in Hungarian). *Botan. Közlem.* **34:** 137–142.

Illés, I., Kelemen, L. and Szépkuti, L. (1969): The development of industrial water management and its aims (in Hungarian). *Hidrol. Közlem.* **49**: 61–69.

Jaág, O. and Vogel, H. E. (1975): Aus den Anfängen des Europäischen Gewässerschutzes. *Öster. Abwasser Rundschau.* Jubiläumausgabe, 3–9.

Jancovic, D., Bogatu, D. and Bacalbasa, N. (1974): Biologische und wirtschaftliche Probleme der Donaufischerei. 17. Arbeitstagung der Internationalen Arbeitsgemeinschaft Donauforschung. Galatz–Rumänien. Personal communications.

Juris, S. (1972): Prispevek k poznaniu fytoplanktonu československého useku Dunaja a ustia hlavnych pritokov z nasho u uzemis. *Acta Rev. Nat. Mus. Slov.* **18**: 19–27.

Juris, S. (1974): Niektore poznatky o zmenach kvantity fytoplanktonou Dunaja. *Acta Rev. Nat. Mus. Slov.* **19**: 103–111.

Kárpáti, I. (1974a): Botanical investigations for the protection of the water of Lake Balaton. Results of the investigations into environment control in 1973. MÉM. Budapest, 1974. April.

Kárpáti, I. (1974b): Higher plants in the vegetation of Lake Balaton and its littoral area (in Hungarian). In: *Balaton monográfia,* Budapest.

Kárpáti, I. and Kárpáti, V. (1967): Die Sukzessionsdynamik der Laichkrautvegetation des Balatons (in Hungarian). *Hidrológus Napok Programja* **17**: 5–6.

Kárpáti, I. and Kárpáti, V. (1968): The succession relations of the aquatic vegetation in Lake Balaton (in Hungarian). *Bot. Közlem.* **55**: 51–58.

Kárpáti, I. and Kárpáti, V. (1974): Die Anwendung der TWR-Indikatorkonzeption auf Wasser- und Auen-Ökosysteme. *Acta Bot. Acad. Sci. Hung.* **20**: (1–2), 83–92.

Kárpáti, I. and Kárpáti, V. (1975a): Jährliche Primärproduktion der Makrophytenökosysteme im Balaton, *Symp. Biol. Hung.* **15**: 109–112.

Kárpáti, I. and Kárpáti, V. (1975b): *Einfluss des intensiven Pflanzenbaus auf die Ökosysteme von Gewässern.* XVII. Georgikon Napok Keszthely, 10–13. June 1975.

Kárpáti, I. and Lantos, T. (1979): Study of the distribution of water macrophytons as bioindicators in Lake Balaton. *Agrártudományi Egyetem Keszthely Közleményei* **21**: (9), 1–41.

Kárpáti, I. and Lantos, T. (1981): Die Nitellopsis Obtusa Phase des Primärproduktionsrhythmuses im Balaton. *BFB-Bericht* **42**: 109–118.

Kárpáti, I. and Varga, Gy. (1970): Results of investigations of reedgrass vegetation of Keszthely-bay (in Hungarian). *Keszthelyi Agrártud. Főisk. Közlem.* **12**: 3–67.

Kárpáti, I., Varga, Gy. and Novotny, I. (1971): The phytomass production of the reedgrass vegetation of Szigliget-bay, in 1970 (in Hungarian). *Agrártud. Egyetem Kiadványai,* **13**: 3–39.

Kárpáti, I., Novotny, I. and Varga, Gy. (1972*a*): Aerial photographs for the assessment of the primary production of the macrophytic vegetation of Lake Balaton, and its variation. Communication at the XIIth Congress of the International Society for Photogrammetry Ottawa, 1972.

Kárpáti, I., Kárpáti, V. and Varga, Gy. (1972*b*): Die methodischen Fragen der Auswertung der Phytomassen-produktion und der Vegetationskartierung von Potametea-Gesellschaften. Bericht über das Symposion der Internationalen Vereinigung für Vegetationskunde 1970 in Rintel. Den Haag.

Kárpáti, I., Kárpáti, V. and Herodek, S. (1977): *Production of macro- and microphytes in Lake Balaton.* Symposium on the effects of man on life in Fresh Waters.

Kárpáti, I., Varga, Gy. and Lantos, T. (1979): Water macrophytons as bioindicators in Balaton (in Hungarian). Vándorgyűlés Keszthely. *Magyar Hidrológiai Társaság.* 1–7.

Kárpáti, I., Kárpáti, V. and Pomogyi, P. (1980): Nährstoffakkumulation bei Wassermakrophyten. *Acta Bot. Acad. Sci. Hung.* **26**: 83–90.

Kárpáti, V. (1977): Aquatic vegetation of Little-Balaton and the ability of typical species to accumulate nutrient (in Hungarian). *VEAB Értesítő* **3**: 131–140.

Kárpáti, V. and Pomogyi, P. (1979): Accumulation and release of nutrients by aquatic macrophytes. *Symp. Biol. Hung.* **19**: 33–42.

Knie, K. (1966): Physikalisch–chemische Eigenschaften des Donauwassers. *Limnologie der Donau* **2**: 51–83.

Knöpp, H. (1967): Zum Stoffhaushalt der Donau. *Limnologie der Donau* **2**: 97–119.

Kozma, E. V. (1975): Untersuchungen über die Veränderungen des organischen Stoffgehaltes des Donauwassers. *Ann. Univ. Sci. Budapestiensis Sect. Biol.* **17**: 31–39.

Kozma, E. V. (1976–77): Über die organischen Stoffgehaltveränderungen des Donauwassers beim Stromkm 1669. (Danubialia Hungarica LXXIX.) *Ann. Univ. Sci. Budapestiensis Sect. Biol.* **18–19**: 39–46.

Lászlóffy, W. (1965): Die Hidrographie der Donau. (Der Fluss als Lebensraum.) *Limnologie der Donau* **1**: 16–57.

Liebmann, H. (1954): Biologie der Donau und des Mains. *Münch. Beitr. Anw. Fisch. u. Flussbiol.* **2**: 111–208.

Liebmann, H. (1958–1960): *Handbuch der Frischwasser und Abwasser Biologie.* I–II. Jena.

Liebmann, H. (1962): *Handbuch der Frischwasser- und Abwasser-Biologie.* Band I., Jena.

Liebmann, H. and Reichenbach-Klinke, H. (1967): Eingriffe des Menschen und deren biologische Auswirkung. *Limnologie der Donau* 4: 1–25.

Linderman, R. L. (1942): The trophic-dynamic aspect of ecology. *Ecology* 23: 399–418.

Liepolt, R. (1965–1967): *Limnologie der Donau* 1: 1–57, 2: 1–119, 3: 1–326, 4: 1–146.

Liepolt, R. (1974): Limnologie und Wasserbau. SIL Arbeitsgemeinschaft der Donauforschung.

Literáthy, P. and Szebellédy, L.-né (1969): The determination of oil pollution in water and sewage, the present state of the oil pollution of the Danube (in Hungarian). *Vegyip. szennyv. és levegőszennyezés* 5: 43–60.

Märki, E. (1972): Die Bewertung des chemisch–physikalischen Zustandes der Gewässer im Donaueinzugsgebiet im Hinblick auf eine künftige Reinhalteordnung. Symp. Biol. Hung. SIL Arbeitsgemeinschaft Donauforschung 15. Arbeitstagung in Ungarn.

Michaelis, H. and Kothé, P. (1974): Der Ausbau der Donau als Grossschiffahrtsstrasse in technischer und limnologischer Hinsicht. Societas Internationalis Limnologieae. Arbeitsgemeinschaft Donauforschung. 87–109.

Mucha, V. (1974): Die Beziehung der Limnologie und Wasserhygienie. SIL Arbeitsgemeinschaft Donauforschung.

Mucha, V. and Daubner, I. (1971): Über die hydromikrobiologische Erforschung der Donau. *Schweiz. Zeitsch. f. Hydrologie* 33: 252–268.

Mucha, V. and Daubner, I. (1972): Die Bedeutung der hydromikrobiologischen Forschung für hygienische Massnahmen an der Donau. Symp. Biol. Hung. SIL Arbeitsgemeinschaft Donauforschung.

Mucha, V. and Daubner, I. (1973): Gewässerhygienie und Wasserversorgung. *Arch. f. Hydrobiol. Suppl.* 44: 162–176.

Mucha, V., Antonic, M., K. Balon, E., Daubner, I., Dub, O., Duba, D., Hanzlikova, G., Jacko, R., Konček, M., Mayer, J., Mucha, V., Rothschein, J. and Szolgay, J. (1966): Limnologia československého úseku Dunaja VSAV Bratislava.

Naidenov, W. (1972): Veränderungen des Donauzooplanktons durch natürliche und künstliche Einwirkungen. Symp. Biol. Hung. SIL Arbeitsgemeinschaft Donauforschung. 15. Arbeitstagung in Ungarn.

Némedy, L. (1972): A survey of the bacteriological investigations carried out by the Laboratory for water-microbiology of the Budapest Metropolitan KÖJÁL along the Budapest section of Danube since 1957 (in

Hungarian). SIL Donauforschung. 15. Arbeitstagung in Ungarn. Personal communications.

Némedy, L. and Pietrasko, G. (1972): Salmonella-Durchseuchung der Donaustrecke bei Budapest und der in seinem Anziehungskreis verweilenden Möven. SIL Donauforschung. 15. Arbeitstagung in Ungarn. Kurzreferat.

Nosek, J. N. and Bereczky, M. Cs. (1981): Untersuchungen des Bestandsstruktur des Ciliatenplanktons im Haupt- und in einem Nebenarm der Donau mit Hilfe der Produkt-Moment-Korrelations und der Pfadenanalyse. *Arch. f. Protistenk.* **124:** 173–192.

Obuskovic, L. (1975): Das Phytoplankton des mittleren Teils des "Djerdap" Stausees. International Arbeitsgemeinschaft Donauforschung der SIL. 18. Arbeitstagung 14–20. September, Regensburg, Wissenschaftliche Kurzreferate I. Teil.

OHV Vízkészletgazdálkodási Központ (1968): The water regime of Lake Balaton (in Hungarian). VIZDOK, Budapest.

Pásztó, P. (1974): *The effect of sewage discharges on the water quality of Lake Balaton* (in Hungarian). The Proceedings of the Session of the Balaton Vízvédelmi Bizottság, February 1974.

Petcu, M. (1974): Die Struktur der Cladozeren-Populationen des Stausees „Eisernes Tor" (rumänischer Abschnitt). 17. Arbeitstagung der Internationalen Arbeitsgemeinschaft Donauforschung 23–39. September, Galatz-Rumänien.

Pfeifer, Gy., Ponyi, J. E. and Nagy, Z. (1978): Pesticide residues in Lake Balaton. *Symp. Biol. Hung.* **19:** 21–26.

Ponyi, J. E. (1962): Zoologische Untersuchung der Röhrichte des Balaton I. Krebse (Crustacea). *Annal. Biol.* **29:** 129–163.

Ponyi, J. E. (1977): New results of the zooplankton studies in Lake Balaton. *Annal. Biol.* **44:** 199–214.

Ponyi, J. E., Csonti, F. and Baron, F. (1968): An investigation of the chlorinated hydrocarbon residues in the crustacean plankton in Lake Balaton. *Annal. Biol.* **35:** 183–189.

Ponyi, J. E., Tusnádi, Gy. and Wanger, É. (1975): An attempt to determine the feeding relationships of plankton organisms living in Lake Balaton by a CDC 3300 computer (in Hungarian). XVIIth Hydrobiological Days *Plankton and benthos, as well as fishing-biological investigations, with special respect to water protection,* 2–4. October 1975, Tihany.

Puskás, T. (1967): Waters of Hungary. (VITUKI) Budapest.

Ribiánszky, M. and Woynarovich, E. (1962): *Fish, fisheries and fish-farms.* Budapest.

Rodhe, W. (1969): Crystallization of eutrophication concepts in Northern Europe. In: *Eutrophication: causes, consequences, correctives.* National Academy of Science, Washington, D. C.

Rothschein, J. (1973): Über den Einfluss der geplanten Donaukraftwerke auf die Hydrofauna des Tschechoslowakischen Donaugebietes. *Ac. Rer. Nat. Mus. Slov.* **19:** 79–97.

Rudescu, L. (1972): Die Auswirkung der hydrotechnischen Arbeiten im Eisernen Tor und im Donaudelta auf die limnologische Charakteristik der Donau. Symp. Biol. Hung. SIL. Arbeitsgemeinschaft Donauforschung. **15.** Arbeitstagung in Ungarn.

Rudescu, L. and Banu, A. C. (1974): Produktionsbiologische Verhältnisse der Überschwemmungsgebiete des Deltas und des Vordeltas. 17. Arbeitstagung der Internationalen Arbeitsgemeinschaft Donauforschung 23–29. September.

Russev, B. and Kothé, P. (1972): Die Bedeutung des Zoobenthos für die Wasserwirtschaft im Donaubecken. Symp. Biol. Hung. SIL Arbeitsgemeinschaft Donauforschung. **15.** Arbeitstagung in Ungarn.

Schmidt, A. (1976): *Contribution to the knowledge of the algae in the Hungarian section of the Danube* (in Hungarian). Környezetvédelem és vízgazdálkodás, 1976. évi vándorgyűlése, Sopron.

Schmidt, A. and Vörös, L. (1981): Phytoplankton of the lower Hungarian reaches of the Danube in the 1970s (in Hungarian). *Hidrol. Közlem.* **7:** 330.

Sebestyén, O. (1963): *Introduction to lymnology. On the life of inland waters* (in Hungarian). Budapest.

Sennyikov, A. P. (1953): *Plant ecology* (in Hungarian). Budapest.

Soó, R. (1928, 1930, 1931, 1932): Data field records of the flora and vegetation of Lake Balaton (in Hungarian). *Magyar Biol. Int. Munkái* **2:** 132–136; **3:** 169–185; **4:** 293–319; **5:** 112–121.

Steemann-Nielsen, E. (1952): The use of radioactive carbon (C^{14}) for measuring organic production in the sea. *J. Cons. Explor. Mer.* **18:** 117–140.

Sylvester, R. O. (1961): Nutrient content of drainage water from forested, urban and agricultural areas. Algae and Metropolitan Waters, US Publ. Hlth. Serv., SEC TR W61-3, 80–87.

Szabó, I. (1973): Protection of Lake Balaton from water pollution caused by agriculture (in Hungarian). Personal communications.

Szabó, I. and Marton, M. (1956): Comments on the latest Hungarian theory on fruit biology (in Hungarian). *MTA Agrártud. Oszt. Közlem.* **14:** 49–63.

Szarvas, F. (1971): Hydrological biotechniques Part I. Considerations and principles. Vízügyi Műszaki Gazdasági Tájékoztató 35, VIZDOK, Budapest.

Szemes, G. (1964): Untersuchungen über das Phytoplankton der ungarischen Donaustrecke in Sommermonaten (Danubialia Hungarica XXV.) *Ann. Univ. Sci. Budapestiensis Sect. Biol.* 4: 169–199.

Szemes, G. (1967a): Systematisches Verzeichnis der Pflanzenwelt der Donau mit einer zusammenfassenden Erläuterung. *Limnologie der Donau* 3: 70–131.

Szemes, G. (1967b): Das Phytoplankton der Donau. *Limnologie der Donau* 3: 158–170.

Szemes, G. (1967c): Das Phytobenthos der Donau. *Limnologie der Donau* 3: 225–241.

Szemes, G. (1968): Zusammenhänge zwischen den Schwankungen der Wasserhöhe der Donau und der periodisch auftretenden Algenproduktion, mit besonderer Berücksichtigung der Beschaffenheit des aus dem Oberflächenwasser gewonnene Trinkwassers. Limnol. Berichte d. X. Jubileumstagung Donauforschung, Bulgarische Akademie d. Wissenschaften, Zool. Inst. Sofia.

Szemes, G. (1969a): Quantitative Charakteristik des Donauphytoplanktons. Bericht der XI. intern. Konf. der Donau, Kiev, *Limnologische Donauforschungen* 209–217.

Szemes, G. (1969b): The phytoplankton of the Hungarian reach of the Danube during the winter months (Danubialia Hungarica XLVI.) *Ann. Univ. Sci. Budapestiensis Sect. Biol.* 11: 75–117.

Szemes, G. (1970): The micro-flora of the Danube. Personal communications.

Szemes, G. (1971): Untersuchungen über das Phytoplankton des ungarischen Donauabschnittes in Frühjahrsmonaten (Danubialia Hungarica LX.) *Ann. Univ. Sci. Budapestiensis Sect. Biol.* 13: 173–252.

Szemes, G. (1973): Allgemeine limnologische Probleme sowie Verunreinigungen und ihre Auswirkungen auf die Donau. *Arch. f. Hydrobiol. Suppl.* 44: 149–161.

Szemes, G. and Bozzay, E. (1964): The chemical and microbiological quality of the Danube water under ice cover in the extremely cold winter of 1962/63 with reference to the water supply of Budapest. *Ann. Univ. Sci. Budapestiensis Sect. Biol.* 7: 201–212.

Szemes, G., Bozzay, E. and Bánáti, M. (1963): Donauwasser-Untersuchungen beim Budapester Grossen Oberflächenwasseraufbereitungswerk, mit Rücksicht auf die quantitativen Verhältnisse der pflanzlichen Mikroorga-

202

nismen, insbesondere der Bacillariophyceen. *Ann. Univ. Sci. Budapestiensis Sect. Biol.* **6:** 187–216.

Tamás, G. (1967): Horizontale Plankton-Untersuchungen im Balaton. V. Über das phytoplankton des Sees, auf Grund der im Jahre 1965 geschöpften und Netzfilterproben. *Annal. Biol.* **34:** 191–231.

Tamás, G. (1969): Horizontal plankton investigations in Lake Balaton, based on scooped samples and filtrates taken in 1966. *Annal. Biol.* **36:** 257–292.

Tamás, G. (1972): Horizontal plankton studies in Lake Balaton, based on scooped samples and filtrates taken in 1967. *Annal. Biol.* **39:** 151–188.

Tamás, G. (1974): The biomass changes of phytoplankton in Lake Balaton during the 1960s. *Annal. Biol.* **41:** 323–342.

Tamás, G. (1975): Horizontally quantitative phytoplankton investigations in Lake Balaton, 1974. *Annal. Biol.* **42:** 219–279.

Thienemann, A. (1926): Die Binnengewässer Mitteleuropas. Eine limnologische Einführung. Binnengewässer, 1, Stuttgart.

Tóth, J. (1960): Einige Veränderungen in der Fischfauna der ungarischen Donaustrecke in der vergangenen Dekade (Danubialia Hungarica VII.) *Ann. Univ. Sci. Budapestiensis Sect. Biol.* **3:** 411–414.

Tóth, J. (1969): The state of pike-perch stocks in the Hungarian reach of the Danube. (in Hungarian) *Halászat* **62:** 80–81.

Tóth, J. (1972): The fishery of the Hungarian Section of the Danube in 1971. (in Hungarian) *Halászat* **65:** 84–85.

Tóth, J. (1974): The distribution of the stock and the trend of the catches of carp in the Hungarian Danube section. (Danubialia Hungarica LXXI.) *Ann. Univ. Sci. Budapestiensis Sect. Biol.* **16:** 207–215.

Tóth, J. (1975): Some conclusions on the trend of the state of the pike-perch population (*Stizostedion lucioperca* L.) in the middle and lower sections of the Danube. (Relying on the data of fishery conducted there.) *Ann. Univ. Sci. Budapestiensis Sect. Biol.* **17:** 155–164.

Tóth, L. (1972a): On the present stand of the reedgrass vegetation of Lake Balaton (in Hungarian). VITUKI Tud. Napok IV. Kiadv. 1–16.

Tóth, L. (1972b): The study of the water quality of Lake Balaton with the aim of studying its phosporus regime (in Hungarian). Report on the hydrological study of standing waters VITUKI 69–72.

Tőry, K. (1952): *The flood control and regulation of the Danube* (in Hungarian). Budapest.

Uherkovich, G. (1966): Die Scenedesmus-Arten Ungarns. Budapest.

Uherkovich, G., Schmidt, A. and Vörös, L. (1978): Data on the algae in the Hungarian section of the Danube (in Hungarian). Personal communications.

Utermöhl, H. (1958): Zur Vervollkommung der quantitativen Phytoplankton-Methodik. *Mitt. Internat. Verein. Limnol.* **9**: 1–38.

Vadász, E. (1957): *Geohistory and development of the Earth* (in Hungarian). Budapest.

Velev, D., Abos, B., Bacalbasa, N. and Fekete, Gy. (1974): Wasserentnahme und ihre Auswirkungen auf die Wasserversorgung, den Gütenzustand, die Fischerei und Schiffahrt. SIL Arbeitsgemeinschaft Donauforschung.

Vogler, H. (1965): Beiträge zur Phosphatanalytik in der Limnologie II. Die Bestimmung des gelösten Orthophosphates. *Fortschr. Wasserchem.* **2**: 109–119.

Vogler, P. (1965): Beiträge zur Phosphatanalytik in der Limnologie. I. Probleme der Phosphatanalytik in der limnologischen Forschung. *Fortschr. Wasserchem.* **2**: 100–108.

Vörös, L. (1974): Die quantitativen und qualitativen Änderungen des Phytoplanktons im Donauabschnitt bei Mohács. 17. Arbeitstagung der Internationalen Arbeitsgemeinschaft Donauforschung 23–29. September 1974, Galatz–Rumänien. Kurzreferate.

Vörös, L. (1978): *The phytoplankton of Lake Balaton in 1976* (in Hungarian). Personal communications.

Vranovsky, M. (1972): Über die Bedeutung der Donaunebenarme im Stromkilometer 1820.5–1825.5 für das Zooplankton der Donau. SIL Arbeitsgemeinschaft Donauforschung. 15. Arbeitstagung in Ungarn. Kurzreferate.

Vranovsky, M. (1974): Zooplanktón Bacianskeho systému ramien pred vyústením do hlavného toku a jeho význam pre forovanie zooplanktonu v Dunaji. *Biol. Prace. Bratislava* **20**: (7), 1–107.

Weber, E. (1967): Stauregion. *Limnologie der Donau* **3**, Stuttgart, 272–283.

Weber, E. (1973): Auswirkungen der Stauhaltungen und sonstiger technischer Eingriffe auf den Gewässerhaushalt. *Arch. f. Hydrobiol. Suppl.* **44**: 184–198.

Weber, E., Brezeanu, G. and Jankovic, M. (1974): Limnologische Untersuchungen in Stauräumen-Donaustaufe. SIL Arbeitsgemeinschaft Donauforschung. 16. Arbeitstagung, 17–23. September 1973 in der ČSSR, II. Teil. 65–75.

Chapter 7

Soil destruction and soil pollution

The role of soil in the environment can be divided into two parts. Firstly, it forms part of the natural and artificial environment and by joining the spheres of air and water (atmosphere and hydrosphere) it is one of the ecosystem constituents along with the community of living organisms. On the other hand, it is merely a physical receptor of matter and energy flows reaching the Earth's surface, transforming and partly storing them (Stefanovits 1972).

Soil differs both from air and water in its functioning as it is localized and is of solid state. The danger that pollutants will accumulate and will have a permanent effect is especially acute in the case of soil. While, by air and water circulation, the dilution and purification of these two factors is rendered possible, in case of soil, these processes cannot reduce the danger of damage. By its fertility, soil, an important component of the habitat, contributes not only to the existence of the vegetation and of the fauna living on it but also to the welfare of humanity. The decrease in soil fertility is, therefore, an important indicator of environmental pollution. The aim of agricultural production is to maintain and increase soil fertility. However, intensive cultivation of crops, mechanization and the application of various chemicals carried out to achieve this aim, also works of irrigation and drainage may lead to the reduction of soil fertility. Due to inadvisable measures taken towards eliminating certain unfavourable characteristics, these may result in the appearance of other even more harmful factors.

SOIL DESTRUCTION

A certain proportion of cases of environmental damage appears in production due to an inappropriate process or misuse. Such a case is the rotting of flattened (lodged) wheat stalks, which can be the consequence of an overdosage of nitrogen fertilizers. Similarly, the ineffective pollination of fruit trees, caused by the misapplication of insecticides; the destruction of forests by the fluorine gas emission from aluminium works and the damage to shelter belts, the result of inefficient weed control carried out by spraying from aircraft, are examples of misuse. In these cases, one could say that the interests of environment control correspond to those of normal economic production and there is no conflict of interests between them.

The other groups of environmental damage do not manifest themselves in such a clear-cut correlation between cause and effect and a certain aspect of the relationship remains hidden. Those cases in which the birth of hairless calves, the bluish colour of hairs or the slow growth of calves are reported, caused by the low zinc-content of fodder, cannot immediately be traced back to the excessive application of phosphorus-containing fertilizers. However, this kind of damage is partly the result of the phosphate, applied as a fertilizer, precipitating the zinc content of soils and making it insoluble and partly the result of the excess phosphate, which hinders the zinc metabolism in plants. Neither can the toxic effect of algae multiplying in eutrophied watercourses or lakes, caused by the washing-in of nitrogen and phosphate fertilizers, be explicitly connected with the dying of ducks in duck-farms.

As there is no obvious connection between mistakes made in a production process and the harm caused within one and the same unit, it is more difficult to find out the cause, if its effect can also be felt in another unit. In an even less conspicuous case—and this can be classified as the third group of environmental damage—the damage and symptoms do not manifest themselves in production, but are revealed only in the course of comparative analyses. Such are the decrease in the number of rabbits or partridges and in other cases, the modification in the composition of the weed flora and the decrease in the number of its species.

Nevertheless, in all three cases, one is faced with environmental impairments of the same order. Therefore, environmental control has to cope with the following problems: (*i*) Preventing the erosion of the fertile soil layers. Control the deterioration of the physical soil properties; (*ii*) providing favourable conditions for the organisms living in the soil; (*iii*) preventing harmful pollutants from penetrating into water or into the air; (*iv*) eliminating all matters capable of causing damage to the food chain: soil–plant–animal–man or to any organism or association in the ecosystem.

In industrial regions, it is the deterioration of air and water quality that, in the first place, underlines the necessity for environmental control. In contrast to this, in agricultural regions, it is the changing soil quality and the decrease in soil fertility that exhibit large-scale modification of the environment. Consequently, in agricultural regions, measures taken regarding prevention, control and protection should be concentrated on the soil. This also implies that, in the majority of cases, both water and air pollution affects soil conditions. The impact of agricultural production on a landscape exerts an effect on the soil, which is quite different in scale and quality. As soil properties also influence both plant cultivation and stock-farming, this interaction may even increase the danger of harm to the environment. The modification of natural vegetation and the field cultivation of plants, in themselves change soil characteristics, this change being either favourable or detrimental to soil properties and thus affecting soil fertility.

Erosion

The simplest forms of damage can be traced back to physical movements, water or wind erosion and subsequent deposition of sediments to produce a new soil cover. It is known that inappropriate systems of ploughing largely increase soil erosion. While soil formation can keep pace with natural erosion and ensures permanent regeneration, increasing erosion brings about changes in soil properties and considerably and rapidly decreases soil fertility. In areas affected by urban development, erosion destroys not only the natural, but also the artificial environment, causing damage to transport systems and to urban infrastructure. Hungary is in a favourable position to establish the extent of water erosion, as the mapping work, launched in 1951, has established the areas affected and the degree of both superficial and linear erosion. Figures from this survey are summarized in Table 20 and illustrated by Figs 57 and 58. It can be seen that erosion is widespread.

When considering the impact of erosion on the environment, special attention should be paid to the role of the reduced thickness of soil, the result of surface layer erosion, the thinning of the soil layer bringing about a decrease in soil fertility. According to investigations carried out at experimental sites under various natural conditions, it has been observed

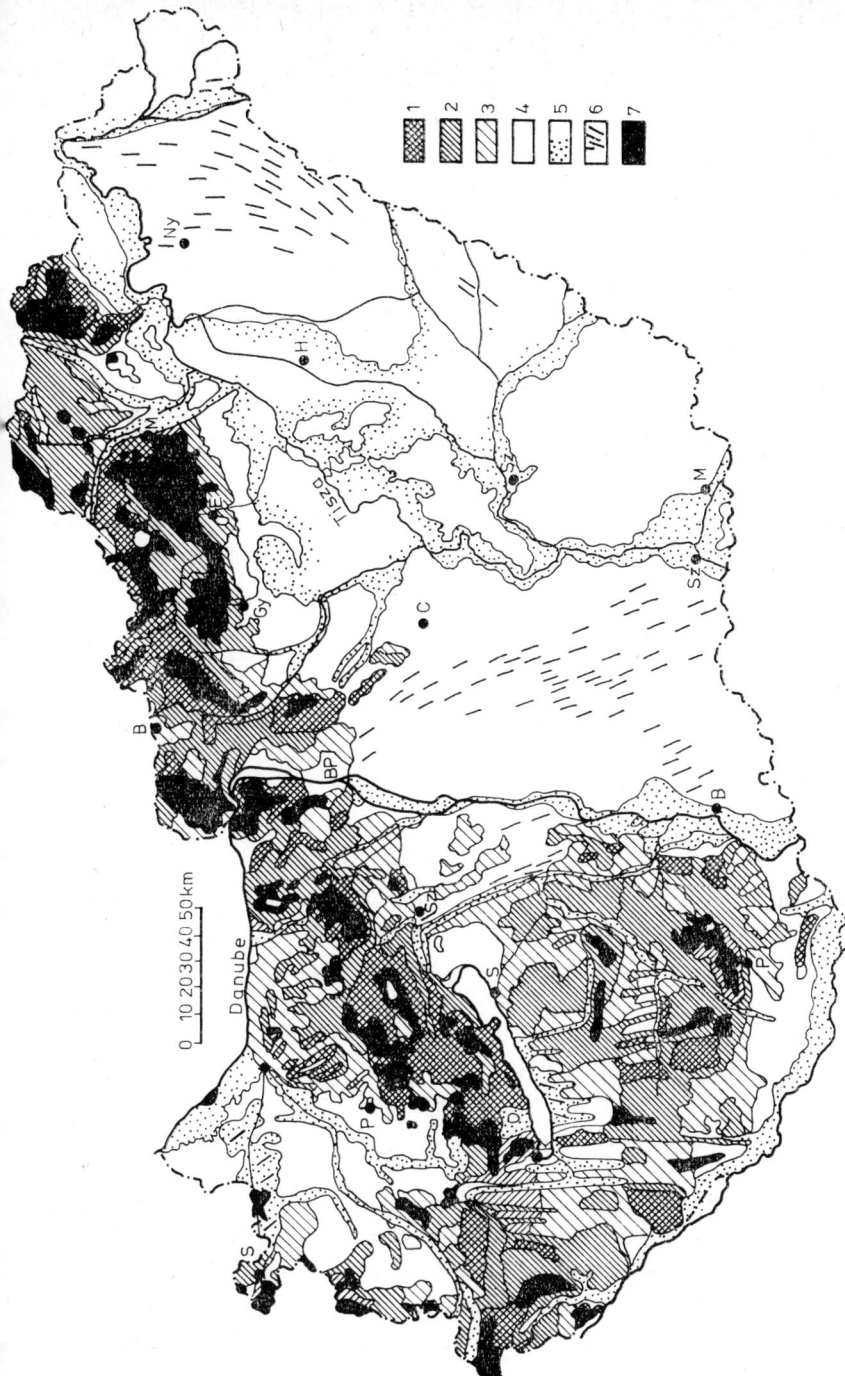

Fig. 57. Spread of the soil erosion in Hungary. (*1*) strongly eroded, (*2*) moderately eroded, (*3*) slightly eroded, (*4*) non-eroded, (*5*) areas with re-sedimentation, (*6*) areas frequently affected by deflation, (*7*) forests

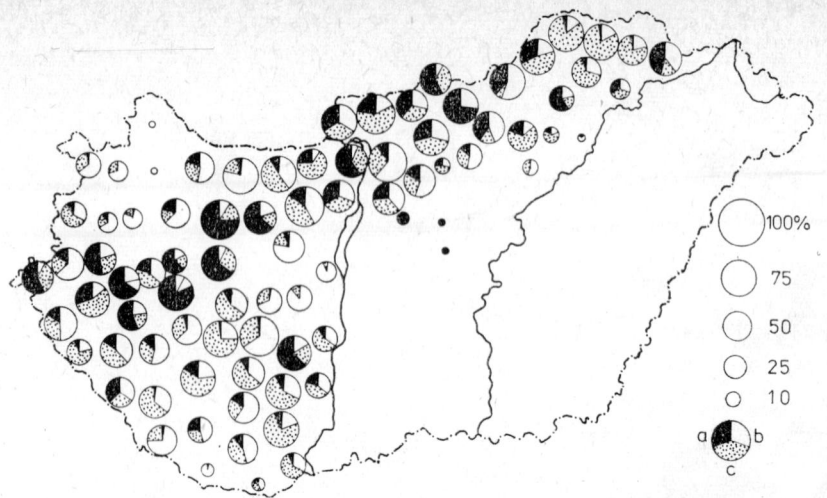

Fig. 58. Proportion of soil erosion and distribution of its intensity on the cultivated territories of Hungary. (*a*) strong, (*b*) weak, (*c*) moderate erosion

Table 20

Distribution of eroded soils in the Hungarian counties (in 1,000 ha)

Counties	Strongly eroded	Moderately eroded	Weakly eroded	Total
Vas	29	36	45	110
Zala	44	83	47	174
Somogy	37	162	121	320
Baranya	24	67	70	161
Veszprém	144	52	51	247
Győr-Sopron	12	26	59	97
Komárom	17	65	100	182
Fejér	28	46	130	204
Tolna	40	90	75	205
Nógrád	63	59	25	147
Pest	43	44	52	139
Heves	19	39	29	87
Borsod-Abaúj-Zemplén	54	116	54	224
Total				2,297

that compared with the fertility of non-eroded soils (taken as 100%) the value of weakly eroded soil is 80%, moderately eroded 60%, while that of the strongly eroded soil is 30%. Within these general values further distinctions can also be made, depending on the types of plants cultivated, the properties of the soil and the technology applied in cultivation.

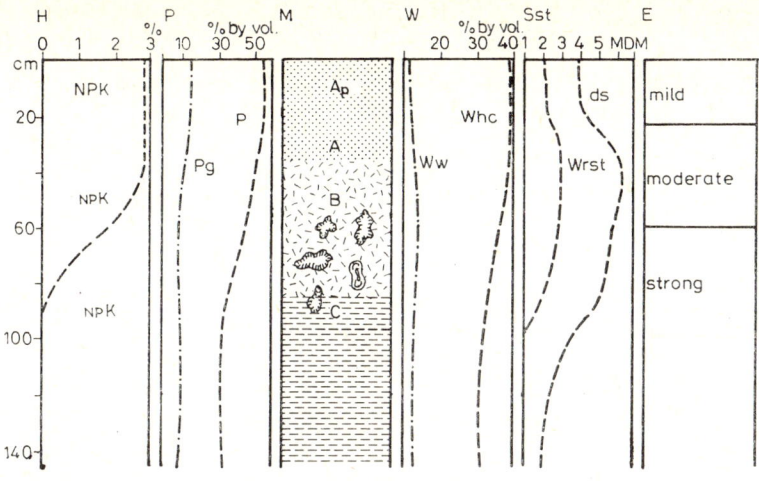

Fig. 59. Changes in the water and nutrient storage properties of a chernozem soil as a function of the degree of erosion. H: humus and nutrient content, (humus%, NPK = nitrogen, phosphorus, potassium. The size of symbols is proportional to the content). P: porosity (P = total porosity, in volume percentage, P_g = gravitational porosity as a volume percentage), M: morphological section, (A_{sz}, A, B, C = symbols of the soil layers), W: water balance (storage), (Whc; water holding capacity in volume percentage, Ww; non-available (bound) water value as a volume percentage). Sst: soil structure (ds = aggregates, MDM = medium diameter measured, Wrst = water stable-aggregates), E: degree of erosion

When studying the cause of decreasing fertility, one should start out from the nutrient and water balance of various soils. The possible differences among individual soil types are shown in Figs 59 and 60. It is obvious that the changes in the properties of a chernozem and a brown forest soil depend on the degree of erosion. Duck and Máté (1973) published remarkable data in this context. They studied interrelationships between the degree of erosion and the nutrient supply of soil and yields. These data verify the observation that, with advanced erosion, both yields and nutrient supply decrease (Fig. 61). As shown by differences between the calculated and empirical values of yield, this decrease is not, however, proportional to the degree of erosion, the latter being smaller on eroded soils. According to various authorities, this can be traced back to the differences in water transport and aspect (exposure) of soils, in which supplies of nutrients are not the only influence on fertility. In accordance with this, it is necessary to complete the elucidation of differences starting with the fact that these calculations are based on nutrient supply only. Consequently, the compati-

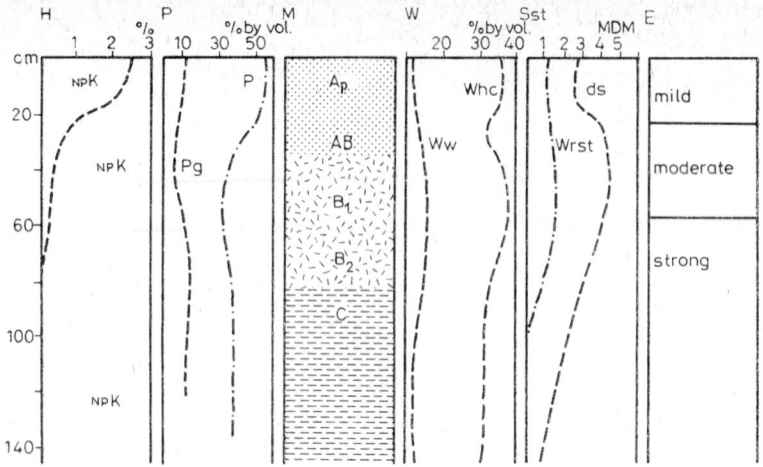

Fig. 60. Changes in water and stored nutrient proportions of clay-washed brown forest soil parallel to the degree of erosion. For symbols see Fig. 59

bility of nutrients, their solubility and the amount of non-investigated trace elements may also cause minor differences in the empirical values.

Pusztai (1975) studied the consequences of erosion on chernozem soils, in the Tambov-region of the USSR, stating that (*a*) As a result of erosion both the quality and quantity of the humus changes. (*b*) Nitrogen and phosphorus content of the upper soil layer decreases which results in the modification of the nutrient balance and of the relative concentration of nutrients in the soil. (*c*) The nitrogen content of the plants (barley, buck wheat) increases in proportion to the greater degree of erosion and decreasing yields, whilst the phosphorus and potassium content of the crop decreases. When studying the effect of erosion, in the case of afforested areas and on soils overlying solid rocks, an even more unfavourable picture will become apparent. In the latter case intensive erosion brings about the complete loss of fertility leaving only a bare, rocky surface in place of the soil. Water, however, causes damage not only by washing off soil from the slopes, thus thinning the fertile layer or washing away soil as a supporting medium, but also by depositing the washed-off soil at other places. This deposit may cover cultivated plants and suffocate them. In addition to this, major damage is also caused by deposits in water courses and on roads or railways.

Even in fields the effect of re-deposited soils could not counterbalance decreased fertility. It has been established that the fertility of newly formed soils, in general, is less than that of the soil to be found at the place of its

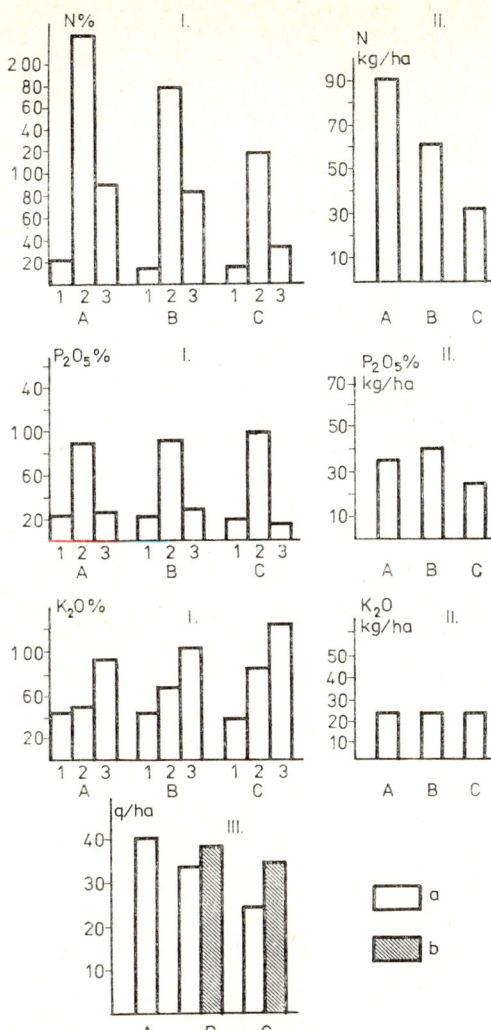

Fig. 61. Nutrient values of the chernozem soils of winter wheat areas, according to Duck and Máté. (A) non-eroded, (B) moderately eroded, (C) strongly eroded. Percentage of nutrients in the soil (*1*), in the grains (*2*) and in the straw (*3*). (I) Nutrient content of the soil, (II) amount of nutrients extracted by the grains, (III) proportion of effective and calculated amount of grains. (a) effective, (b) calculated yield

formation. The loss will be even greater if the deposited matter does not reach arable land and thus becomes lost to plant cultivation. How great an impact the latter process can exert on the environment, including not only the fate of the rainwater, but also damage caused by surface run off, has been illustrated in a book by Erődi and co-workers (1965). According to their investigations approx. 50 million m^3 of soil is washed away, yearly, by water erosion, in Hungary. Out of this total, approx. 1 mill. m^3 silts up channels and drainage ditches and 8–10 million m^3 of soil is washed into rivers and by accumulating on the river bed, increasing the danger of flooding and resulting in increased expenditure on dredging.

As cultivated plants on valley bottoms may become covered and either damaged or killed by deposited silt, the above-mentioned damage can be even greater. In the course of our investigations, we came across—on several occasions—cases, where an area equivalent to one-third or one-fourth of the area of the eroded slope became covered by silt. On the basis of data from countries with a well developed agricultural and fertilizer industry, Pusztai (1975) tried to assess nutrient losses caused by surface layer erosion. According to him, damage caused by erosion, amounts to $^1/_3$ to $^1/_4$ of the value of annual fertilizer production. However, one should take into account the fact that the same amount of nutrients also loads aquatic ecosystems causing their eutrophication and in the case of severe impacts, spoiling the quality of drinking water. The above-described effects of surface erosion are frequently connected with those of linear erosion. This results in the formation of gullies and channels which so reduce the fertility of the surface that, in most cases, it is the underlying basic bed rock that comes up to the surface. This cutting up of the surface leads to an even more severe damage to the environment. This is partly an aesthetic impact, although the resulting restrictions on the utilization of the land are even more important. Only to mention a few examples: they can influence the alignment of roads, the cultivation of fields and increase the spread of weeds.

Deflation

The other form of soil destruction, deflation (wind erosion) is caused by wind. Sandy soils and peat bogs are generally considered to be the only soils affected by it but this view was proved to be wrong, in the spring of 1973, when most sugar-beet sowings were blown away on the silty chernozems of the Great Hungarian Plain, so that sowing had to be repeated.

The assessment and mapping of damage caused by deflation, all over the country, is a much more difficult task than that of erosion (Table 21). The thinning of the soil layer can only be regarded as an indicator where, in a certain area, the blowing off process is predominant. In our sandy and boggy areas blowing off and deposition are alternative processes, even at the same location and therefore, newly formed soils are hard to distinguish from the original ones. In a broader sense, the present surface of sand-covered territories, in the Great Hungarian Plain, characteristic landscapes full of sand hills, have all been formed by deflation and the movement of sand. Nevertheless, only those lands are regarded as deflated, on which the movement of soil particles can be observed even today. Therefore, maps recording deflation in the whole country, or only in a particular

Table 21

Distribution of soils endangered by deflation in Hungary (1,000 ha)

Counties	Wind-blown sand	Brown forest soil with iron bands	Sand of cher-nozem charac-ter	Boggy meadow soil	Mead-ow bog	Drained meadow bog	Total
Baranya	—	—	—	11	—	—	
Fejér	1	—	10	22	7	—	
Győr-Sopron	—	—	—	37	—	37	
Somogy	14	143	—	18	5	17	
Tolna	3	—	8	38	—	—	
Veszprém	—	—	—	37	19	—	
Zala	—	—	—	10	17	—	
Transdanubia	18	143	18	173	48	54–454	
Bács-Kiskun	178	—	139	54	4	—	
Békés	—	—	—	—	—	10	
Csongrád	9	—	—	4	—	—	
Hajdú-Bihar	66	16	6	21	—	6	
Pest	23	—	47	42	—	—	
Szabolcs-Szatmár	64	180	—	51	24	5	
Szolnok	2	1	5	—	—	—	
Great Hungarian Plain	342	197	197	173	28	21–958	
Borsod-Abaúj-Zemplén	4	2	7	—	1	2	
Heves	—	14	—	—	—	—	
Nógrád	—	—	—	—	—	—	
Northern Mountains	4	16	7	—	1	2–30	
Total:							1,442

Fig. 62. General and possible areas of sand deflation in Hungary (*a*) wind blown sand, (*b*) sand covered by sandy loess, (*c*) low-lying silty areas. (on the basis of data by Z. Borsy)

territory, only give a preliminary indication of the possibility of deflation. However, this does not exclude the possibility of soil destruction in very windy years. In moderately windy years, with a high humidity, soil destruction can be observed in smaller areas. Our map (Fig. 62) prepared on the basis of this principle, gives only a rough outline of the general extent of deflation in Hungary. In the construction of the map we have made use of the valuable paper by Borsy (1971) on this topic. The impacts of deflation on the environment are various. The blowing off of soil causes direct damage, while the soil deposited at other places causes impairment through wind blown material. Additional damage is caused by sand storms. Drifting dust and sand are harmful to the respiratory organs of both man and animals. From among these factors, data by Király (1970) and Fekete and Király (1973) on wind-blown sand are quoted. According to them, in the dangerous spring period of a windy year, the loss of soil caused by wind, can amount to 10 cm. They also established that generally the coarser fraction of the blown-off sand damages plants only at a height of 60–70 cm above the soil surface. Finer sand may cause damage to fruit trees, already at a height of 1.5 m, even at a distance of several hundred metres from the place of its origin.

ENVIRONMENTAL IMPACTS OF SOIL CONSERVATION

The first step in achieving good results in the control of soil destruction—both surface and linear erosion—is to use soil for proper purposes and to apply the appropriate methods of ploughing and plant cultivation.

Before analysing the factors of soil conservation, attention should be paid to the harmfulness of the rationalisation of soil utilization in relation to soil destruction. It means large-scale farming itself may have unfavourable effect on the environment. They may have an influence both on the water cycle and on the nutrient balance of the landscape as well as on air purity together with its favourable composition; in short, these measures serve the cause of environment control.

The soil conservation effect of vegetation is a function of both soil coverage and the degree of soil coverage in different seasons. On the basis of this, Duck (1969) made the following assessment:

Efficient soil conservators: Forests where vegetation is enclosed and there is no grazing and their undergrowth is undisturbed. Perennial grasses giving a good soil coverage over the entire year, when they are not disturbed by carwheel tracks and no animals trample on them. (Mixtures of grass species are effective, generally, already in the first year of growth and will not thin out in the future). Other perennial species, belonging to the Papilionaceae (pea) family with a minimum yield of hay reaching a medium height and producing a dense cover of plants.

Plantations with a medium soil conservation effect: In the case of successful summer planting, crimson clover forms a continuous cover by the autumn. Autumn fodder mixtures and winter cereals, if they become well established before the onset of winter produce fertile fields and make it possible for the less fertile areas to be withdrawn from agricultural field and horticultural production, when their cultivation is not economical enough. Thus, a large proportion of arable land reverts to forest. As afforestation is not always economic on these less fertile soils, therefore, forestry authorities cannot take over them as operations would show a financial loss. These areas will thus lie fallow and it has not yet been decided, whose duty it is to be responsible for the conservation of soil in these areas. Therefore, measures should be taken to see that land areas withdrawn from under cultivation are preserved in a state which enables their further destruction to be prevented. Thus, they can become also aesthetically part of the landscape.

The conservation of economically cultivable land can be achieved by soil-protecting crop rotation, modern cultivation methods and by appropriate field management. Should all these prove ineffective, terraces should be built. These steps can exert their favourable effect only if carried out in harmony with each other; they make it possible to form such man-affected ecosystems, which themselves contribute to the success of soil conservation and which exert a favourable effect on the environment. They may also influence the water cycle and the nutrient balance.

Plants with a slight conservation effect: Plants sown in spring belong to this group, but at the time of spring showers and windy periods these do not yet give proper coverage. By the time of the summer showers, they will already have become stronger. Potatoes, well sown in rows and cultivated by an earthing-up hoe, can also be included in this category.

Plants having bad soil conservation effects: Hoed plants—maize, sunflower and tobacco—requiring wide and weedless inter-rows are in this group. Root crops also belong to this group, though they are not cultivated on sloping areas or on loose sand.

As can be seen from the above-mentioned cases, plant-cover plays an important role in soil conservation, therefore, in itself is an effective factor in the formation of environment. This can even be increased by technical implements used for soil conservation, securing and even strengthening the biological effect.

While on one hand the basic element in the control of deflation is to provide appropriate plant cover and to apply soil protective cultivation methods in the early stages of their growth, in the case of water, maximum protection—coverage—has to be achieved at the time of melting snow cover and of summer showers, the best wind control being achieved by plant crops already existing in the spring.

In addition to this, as the network of screening trees breaks and slows down winds and filters soil particles the afforestation of areas most exposed to wind forms an important part of the protection measures.

EXTERNAL SOURCES OF SOIL POLLUTION

Foreign substances can get on to the soil surface from sources independent of agricultural activity and from materials introduced into the soil in the course of agricultural production.

The polluting effect of industry on the environment may take different shapes. From among them, as far as soil pollution is concerned, the role of air-borne soil pollutants is the greatest. It is an already proved fact that industrial establishments can exert their effect within the range of some hundred kilometres, lying along the direction of the prevailing winds. Just to mention that parallel to the dynamic development of British industry the acidity of soils in Scandinavia has been increasing. The result of sulphur introduced into the air has reduced the soil pH by a half unit, though it is not only the amount of sulphur but through it also that of the sulphate and sulphuric acid, that increases. The air which passes over industrial regions is also enriched by increased concentrations of chlorine and nitrogen oxide. These gaseous substances are absorbed by rain water and thus they get on to the soil surface, where they accumulate in the upper layers.

Suspended ash and soot particles reach the surface, partly by way of sedimentation and partly by rain water. Soil pollution is especially striking in the vicinity of the cement works at Vác, Hejőcsaba and Beremend. In 1971, the amount of pollutants, at Vác, was approx. 100 t/km^2. The emission from other industrial plants also amounts to almost the same value. It is also known that, in the vicinity of aluminium works, soil contains a higher amount of fluorine. Similarly, spoil banks (tips) occupying large areas or the soil-destructive effect of open mining are considered to damage the environment. The dust of spoil banks frequently contains materials which decrease soil fertility in their surroundings. The destructive effect of mining on the environment manifests itself in the form of ground subsidence, accumulation of water, or in some cases damage to drainage systems.

In power stations and also in the field of ash disposal, significant Hungarian and also international results have been achieved as well as more recently, in the field of open mining and brown coal mining, in solving the problem of spoil bank utilization. As its utilization has proved successful in Hungary, the recultivation of the spoil banks produced by the open mines of Visonta has already been solved. In the German Democratic Republic, the utilization of areas remaining after the abandonment of open-strip mines of brown coal has given outstanding results.

Nevertheless, the problems of both the transport and the utilization of ash produced by power stations are still unsolved. At present there are processes in which valuable raw materials are extracted from the ash and the residue is utilized in building industry and in this way it becomes harmless for the soil. In other investigations, the applicability of the ash for soil improvement was studied. It has been established that depending on the composition of the coal or of the ash derived from it, the ash may be utilized for the improvement of either acidic or saline soils.

It would need a separate chapter to discuss the problem of domestic refuse (garbage) disposal which gives rise to an ever growing problem in environment control. It is not only rubbish dumps covering the soil surface, but also the rubbish blown or washed into soil by wind or water that is deleterious to soil. The waste content of organic manures, spread out on the fields, is a similar problem. Concerning their content of slowly decomposing matters, the wastes of today are much different from the ones produced some decades ago. While earlier the ploughed layer of soil contained only broken pottery fragments and pieces of unburnt coal as foreign matter, nowadays these have been replaced by different pieces of aluminium foils or plastics and of glass.

Parallel with urban development, it is not only the quality and quantity of solids which have changed but also the amount of sewage has increased. As sludge incineration installations are only rarely to be found, a substantial proportion of sludge produced by sewage irrigation or sewage purification, reaches the soil. It is at this point that the detoxification capacity of soils plays an important role, though this has not yet been properly evaluated at present.

In the earliest forms of society, the detoxification activity of soils had already been made use of. Solid toxic wastes were dug into the ground or liquid wastes were detoxified by making use of the purification capability of soil. However, the tolerance and thus the loading capacity of soils is also limited in this respect. Especially, sewage irrigation and liquid manure irrigation have indicated how much the soil can take.

When speaking of external sources of pollution, one has to mention the components of car exhaust gases. Considering the major rise in the number of vehicles that took place between 1965–1975 (cars: 5–times, lorries: 2.5–times, buses: 1.5–times), it is obvious that these vehicles greatly contribute to pollution. Pollutants emitted by petrol (gasoline) are different

Table 22

Polluting matters produced by internal combustion engines

Components	Petrol gasoline engines	Diesel-engines
Carbon dioxide	5.0–12.0 v%	1.0–6.0 v%
Carbon monoxide	0.5–10.0 v%	0.1–2.0 v%
Nitrogen oxides	0–3,000 ppm	200–5,000 ppm
Hydrocarbons	100–10,000 ppm	10–500 ppm
Aldehydes	0–200 ppm	0–50 ppm
Soot	0–0.002 g m^3	0.01–1.10 g m^3
Benzo-pyrene	10–20 μg m^3	0–10 μg m^3
Lead containing compounds	present	absent

from those of Diesel-engines, These materials are being emitted into the air and are only partly washed into the soil. Differences in the composition of exhaust gases are given in Table 22.

THE EFFECT OF FERTILIZERS ON THE SOIL

Parallel to the development of chemical industry the use of chemical fertilizers and sprays has assumed greater importance. It can be said that present-day modern agricultural production is inconceivable without the use of chemical fertilizers.

The long lasting dispute between the followers of traditional manuring and the use of chemical fertilizers has satisfactorily been settled with the result that, wherever there is a sufficient supply of manure, its application is necessary and justified. In cases where crop production has insufficient supplies of manure and the aim is to achieve higher yields then additional chemical fertilizers should be used to ensure the proper nutrient content. The available potential is limited by only the peak of the curve of yield or, in other words, the economic optimum. In the past, the application of chemical fertilizers was only restricted by the extra yields to be expected,

At present there must be an additional limit to the use of fertilizers, namely, an optimum which is such an effective and economic amount that is harmless to the environment. To analyse this principle in detail, we have to survey both favourable and unfavourable effects of chemical fertilizers from the viewpoint of environment control. It is only the knowledge of these factors that makes it possible to establish the idea of optimum use.

The most important beneficial effect of chemical fertilizers can be seen in the increase of yields. This primary effect, in itself, can be regarded as being favourable to man and his environment, as it contributes to the better exploitation of the environment and environmental conditions.

According to Kovda and Szabolcs (1971) the use of fertilizers brings about vital qualitative and quantitative changes within the whole of the soil and plant system. This favourable effect is so large that it far exceeds the concentration of nutrients originally present and introduced by chemical fertilizers into the soil. Nevertheless, in addition to this primary effect, mention should be made of other factors affecting the environment. First of all, it should be emphasized that a greater green mass produces a greater surface for assimilation, which in turn absorbs the carbon dioxide content of the air and at the same time increases its O_2 content. Owing to this function, vegetation can be considered the "lung of the landscape", which counterbalances both the carbon dioxide production (emission) of urban areas and of industrial plants and also their consumption of oxygen. By increasing the green mass of plants man also contributes to improving the air. According to an assessment by Smith (1971), on a maize field with an annual yield of 6,300 kg/ha, plants extract 18.5 t/ha CO_2 and emit 15 t/ha O_2 into the air. This means that 1 ha of maize can meet the annual oxygen demand of 30 men. It is interesting to compare this effect, with the air purifying role of our forests which, on an area of 1 ha, are capable of meeting the annual oxygen demand of two men. Further effects of the application of fertilizers are greater mass—denser plant cover—better soil coverage and consequently, better soil protection. Soil protection—as already mentioned—is a method of environment control. Greater yields achieved by the use of chemical fertilizers help to prevent the further determination of already eroded soils and results in a better utilization of soil fertility.

According to Pusztai (1975) and Tusz (1973), the effect of chemical fertilizers on eroded and non-eroded soils is different. Therefore, special attention should be paid to this fact. Tusz (1973) studied three soil types and their differently eroded varieties, in a pot experiment (Figs 63–65). These figures illustrate definite differences between the direct and long-term effect of chemical fertilizers. This applies also for individual plants. It can, however, be stated that owing to the application of chemical fertilizers,

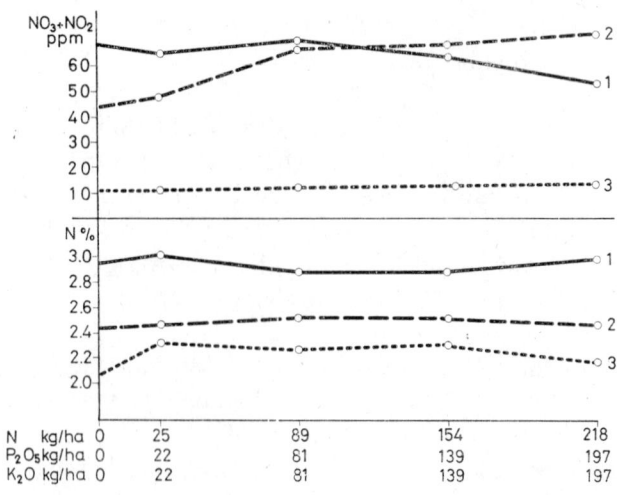

Fig. 63. Effect of different doses of chemical fertilizers on the amount of total nitrogen and nitrate+nitrite content. (1) bran, (2) fine bran, (3) flour. (Jerminecz 1978)

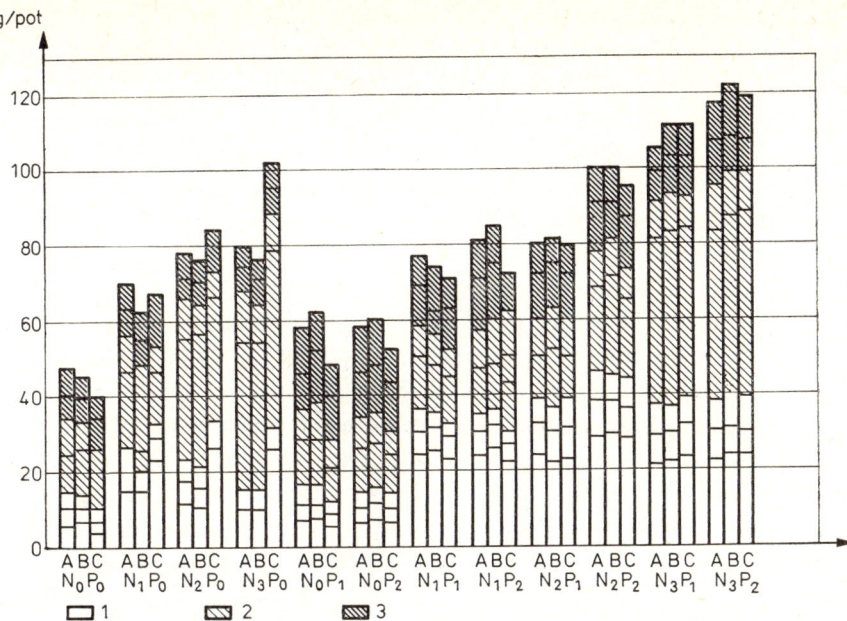

Fig. 64. Effect of a single chemical fertilizer on the subsequent crops of a pot experiment with loess-formed chernozem soil. A: non-eroded surface soil, B: ploughed layer of the moderately eroded soil, C: ploughed layer of a strongly eroded area: (*1*) sum of the wet-weight yields of three barely crops, (*2*) sum of three Sudan-grass yields, (*3*) three lucerne yields in 1971 and five yields in 1972. (Tusz 1973)

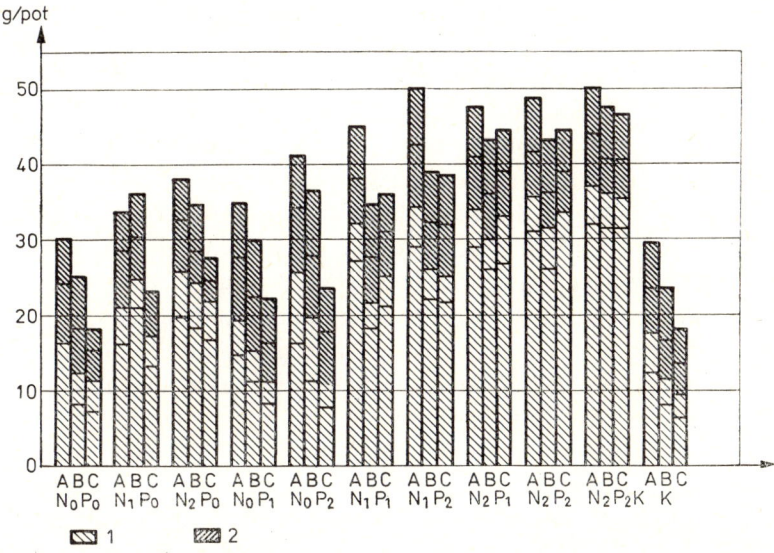

Fig. 65. Effect of a single chemical fertilizer on the subsequent yields of a pot experiment with a brown soil having formed on sand. A: non-eroded surface soil, B: ploughed layer of a moderately eroded surface, C: ploughed layer of a strongly eroded territory, (*1*) three Sudan-grass yields (1969–70), (*2*) three lucerne yields in 1971 and five yields in 1972. (Tusz 1973)

in at least certain years, the yield of crops on eroded soils is as high as that of the non-eroded soils. The figures also illustrate the accumulative nutrient uptake of plants grown in succession and demonstrate the rapid exhaustion of certain nutrients, in certain eroded varieties of soil. According to Pusztai (1975), owing to fertilizer application, eight times higher yields were achieved on the eroded varieties of chernozem soils. He established that, in highly eroded soils, nitrogen fertilizers gave good yields, but only if combined with phosphorus fertilizers. The latter also gave good results in the absence of nitrogen fertilizers.

Mention should also be made of the smaller specific water consumption of plants brought about by the balanced nutrient supply of manuring. It is known that plants supplied with a sufficient amount of nutrients of suitable composition require less water for the production of organic matter. These plants are also capable of better utilizing water resources in a given environment. Láng (1971) also referred to the connection between the application of chemical fertilizers and water utilization in dry years. In 1968, during a drought period, he observed that cooperative farms expertly applying fertilizers could harvest a good yield even in spite of the very dry weather. The average yield was also higher than in similar dry years, when chemical fertilizers had not been applied.

The next direct effect of the use of fertilizers manifests itself in a greater bulk of roots and of humus derived from it. Humification itself, the decay of organic matter placed on to or into the soil and its transformation can be considered the driving force of dynamic soil processes. Thus, it is a precondition of nutrient exposure and it helps the evolution of the soil, one of the important environmental factors (Timár 1975).

In the other main group of chemical fertilizers, it is not the active substance that is responsible for the effect but a certain accompanying substance or additive. In spite of the latest efforts of industry to produce chemical fertilizers containing more active substance and only small amounts of other matters, the majority of fertilizers applied presently also introduces—besides the main nutrients—other elements into the soil. It is enough to refer to the fact that a certain proportion of nitrogen fertilizers contains large amounts of calcium or magnesium, while others contain sulphur or carbon. The majority of phosphate fertilizers contains calcium and sulphur, while potassium fertilizers contain magnesium, calcium and sulphur among the main nutrients. These play an important role especially in plant nutrition by contributing to the improvement of environmental conditions. In certain cases they may be even more effective than the main active ingredients. Knowing this, agrochemical experts in some countries are already of the opinion that in areas where large amounts of calcium-containing fertilizers are regularly applied, soil amelioration schemes are unnecessary.

Among the additives of chemical fertilizers, their content of micro-elements (trace elements) should be mentioned. This content, depending on the quality of raw material and on the technology used can be most varied. The following group of effects comprises favourable changes in the nutritive value of plants. Cases in which manured plants contain higher amounts of certain nutrients than unmanured ones do should also be mentioned. This increases both the fodder and nutritive value of cultivated plants. In other cases nutrient uptake is accompanied by other favourable properties: higher protein content, more favourable distribution of amino acids, higher sugar content or better frost resistance, or stem-stability. Effects of nutrient addition on crop quality are also underlined by Láng (1971). In a fertilizer trial over a period of two years, N-fertilizers increased the dry aleurone (protein body) content of the wheat variety Bezosztaja 1 by 1.4%.

According to Olson (1972, 1974) in controlled farming experiments with 54 plots, over a period of 15 years, nitrogen manuring resulted in the following mean extra yield and protein content:

N kg/ha	0	23	45	68
extra yield 100 kg/ha	0	1.8	3.0	2.8
protein content %:	10.3	11.1	11.6	12.4

Similarly in the case of millet, using the mean results from 10 experimental plots over a period of 12 years:

N kg/ha	0	23	45	68	90	113
extra yield 100 kg/ha	0	5.5	9.0	10.0	9.8	10.2
protein content %:	7.5	8.0	9.5	10.2	10.4	10.5

As already seen in Fig. 61 and as verified by Duck and Máté (1973), it is the higher nitrogen content of soil that increases seed yield. Investigations by Jerminecz (1978) also give interesting information on the relationship between the use of nitrogen and the nitrogen content of wheat. As illustrated by Fig. 66, independently of the amounts of fertilizers applied, the nitrogen content of wheat grains undergoes only minor changes. The distribution of bran (husk), fine bran and flour showed smaller differences

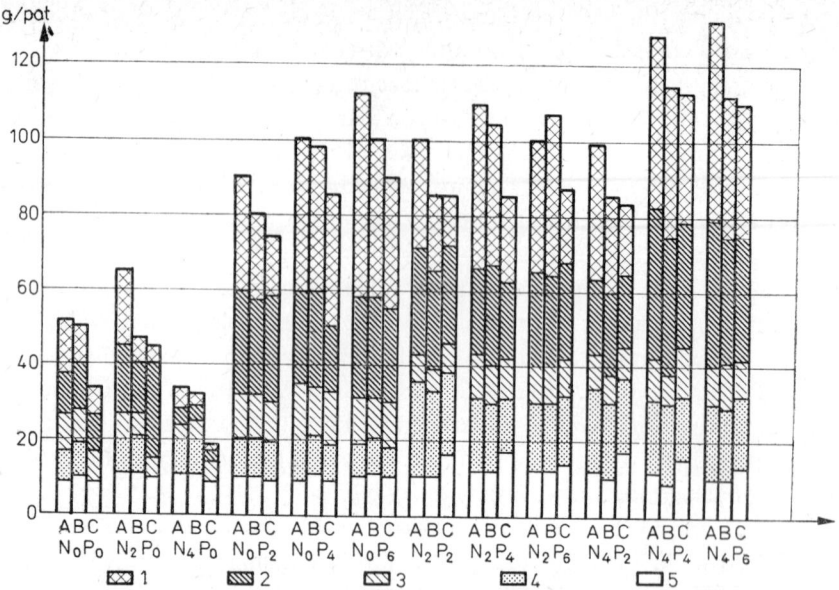

Fig. 66. Effect of a single chemical fertilizer on the subsequent yields of a pot experiment with Vertisol soil formed on tertiary sediment. *(1)* grain yield of winter wheat (1967–68), *(2)* straw yield of wheat (1967–68), *(3)* grain+straw yield of wheat (1968), *(4)* total of the three yields of Sudan-grass (1969), *(5)* total of three lucerne yields in 1970 and five yields in 1971. (Tusz 1973)

only in the case of either manured variants or of maximal doses. In each case, the bran contained the greatest and flour the smallest amount of nitrogen. Nevertheless, it was shown that even small amounts of nitrogen fertilizers increased the nitrogen content of flour by some 10% compared with controls, this being very favourable for nutrition. Changes in the nitrate-nitrite content, as brought about by the use of fertilizers, show a similarly favourable picture. While the nitrogen content of flour remained at the level of control in all cases, the nitrate-nitrite content of fine bran showed a significant increase in comparison with the control, in bran, the decrease observed being of the same order. This plays an important role in the application of certain grists for animal feeding.

Data on maize were published by Lásztity (1975). In a three years' experiment, he established that the application of nitrogen fertilizers increased the nitrogen content of seeds, while the phosphorus and potassium content did not show any significant changes. While these results are characteristic of only the calcium carbonate and humus-containing sandy soils of the area between the rivers Danube and Tisza, Latkovics (1975) furnished data on a further three soil types. On chernozem, sandy "Braunerde" and meadow-chernozem soils, saline at their lower horizons, the nitrogen content of maize grains cultivated on these soils had risen, on average, over 4 years, from 1.03 to 1.25%, from 1.17 to 1.39% and from 1.35 to 1.50% respectively. While phosphorus and potassium manuring did not change the nitrogen content, additions of phosphorus fertilizers increased the phosphorus content of the corn-cobs.

Firstly it can be concluded the main effect is that manuring increases the nitrogen content of maize on all soil types. Secondly, changes in the phosphorus content of corn-cobs are not uniform. In view of the fact that maize is one of our most important fodder plants, these effects are very important and they play an important role in the nutrient cycle of agricultural ecosystems.

Favourable changes caused by micro-element application can also be included in positive use of fertilizer. As in several cases, the effect of micronutrients, substances required by plants in only small amounts, is less well known, their evaluation cannot be complete. However, now it is obvious that they exert their effect not only on yields but also on plant metabolism and through this, on the acid content of fruits, their colouring and the formation of flavour-substances (Győri 1971).

Microelements are important environmental factors, not only in the plant kingdom, but they also have an effect on animal and human life. The role of fluorine in bone formation and the physiological effects of iron, cobalt, iodine are known examples. These elements can either form part of chemical fertilizers or are applied separately to field and horticultural crops.

As manuring means an external interference with the natural mineral balance, it implies the danger of environmental damage caused by its abuse. The impoverishment of nutrients, as a predictable consequence of the use of fertilizers, should be mentioned in the first place. It may seem a paradox, at first sight, to state that the introduction of nutrients into the soil may cause its impoverishment. It is merely the inexpert introduction that is to be blamed, the one-sided manuring, which by introducing one and the same nutrient into the soil brings about the rapid exhaustion of other nutrients. If the plant mass grown on a unit area is increased by nitrogen fertilization alone, this also involves a higher uptake of other nutrients and where the soil cannot meet the increased demand for nutrients, then the use of this fertilizer may then bring about the impoverishment of nutrient resources.

Data by Kozák and Mészáros (1971) also confirm the effects of unilateral, not the optimum mixed nutrient supply, on sandy soil. According to them, in contrast to a yield of 1,450 kg/ha gained by the use of NP and NPK fertilizers, on a sandy soil, with low humus content, N and NK application resulted in a rye yield of 980 kg/ha. On humus containing soils the following yields were realised: 1,170 kg/ha and 1,900 kg/ha. This also points to the fact that the impoverishment of phosphorus resources on sandy soils may become an obstacle to balanced production and the good utilization of environmental conditions, in cases where the use of fertilizers is not well balanced. Cserni (1971) also arrived at similar conclusions, when manuring monocultures of maize variety "Kecskeméti" and rye. In wheat manuring trials Bócz (1973) established the great significance of the appropriate ratio of nutrients. Averaged over a period of several years, 100 kg/ha N active ingredient, applied together with 100 kg/ha P_2O_5; gave a higher yield of 400 kg/ha, compared with the same amount of nitrogen fertilizer applied with 25 kg/ha of phosphorus fertilizer as P_2O_5, owing to the unsuitable ratio of elements, plants left more nutrients in the soil than they would otherwise have done in the case of a suitable nutrient ratio. The probability of detrimental environmental impacts, therefore, increased.

The upsetting of the nutrient balance of soils brings about changes in the active ingredients of plants cultivated on them, thus affecting the healthy feeding of the animal kingdom and also the nutrition of man. It is not only macronutrients that can bring about the above-mentioned imbalance. Moreover the inbalance in the lack of microelements can also increase. In such cases, although the addition of macroelements is carried out by experts, no attention is paid to the appropriate supply of micro-nutrients.

When further analysing the relation between the nutrient balance of soils and nutrients introduced into the soil, by the use of fertilizers, one has to take into account those interrelationships which exist between individual nutrients, which greatly influence also the extent of their uptake from the soil. Two groups of elements should be examined in this respect: (*i*) elements hindering the uptake of other elements; (*ii*) elements that increase the availability of others. The effects of unfavourable N:K, K:Mg, C:N ratios are already known. In addition to these, mention should be made of other observations demostrating further unfavourable effects. Fertilizers containing NH_4 and K-ions may decrease the availability of Ca in soil. By replacing calcium, on the absorptive surfaces in the upper soil layers, these ions decrease the amount of Ca both in the upper layers of soil and in the root zone.

It is also a known fact that nutrients, introduced into soil by fertilizers, are not entirely taken up by plants, or at least not in the first year (Table 23). Lathwell et al. (1970) established, on the basis of 21 experiments in

Table 23

Effect of nitrogen dosages

Year	Increasing N-dosages kg/ha	Yield kg/ha	Fertilizer uptake %
	0	3,300	0
First	56	6,300	80
Second	56	7,800	40
Third	56	8,280	15
Fourth	56	8,520	5

New York State, that the effect and availability of different doses of N-fertilizers is affected by the following factors.

Apart from the varying proportion of removed and residual nutrients the "fate" of the residue can follow only three paths: (*i*) they may remain in the soil, (*ii*) they may be leached out either through the soil or by run off and (*iii*) finally, in the gaseous state, they may be introduced into the air. Depending on the nutrients involved and their physico-chemical reactions and biological behaviour, the proportion following each of these pathways can be different. Just to mention a few examples, some data are quoted from Russel's survey (1972) with special emphasis on the major nutrients. Using labelled phosphorus-containing fertilizers it was established that where the phosphate content of the soil was low and the application of fertilizers was most favourable, plants had taken up approx. 20% of the phosphorus applied to soil. This rate of uptake can only be less where conditions are less favourable.

The remaining phosphate becomes immobilized on the soil colloids by adsorption and chemisorption. Therefore, each application of fertilizers increases the phosphorus supply of the soil, until it becomes saturated. The leaching out of phosphates is very rare. Should this be the case, it is connected with the destruction of the soil surface and the erosion of phosphate-binding colloids. Introduced into soil, potassium also becomes fixed. Firstly it is adsorbed by the surface of colloids, then it is partly bound to the lattices of clay minerals of the smectite and vermiculite types. In soils containing such clay minerals, potassium will therefore not be leached out. For example, a 1% increase in the potassium content of soil containing 20% active clay minerals may result in the absorption of 30,000 kg/ha K_2O in a layer one metre thick. This example also shows that it is only in the case of sandy soils that potassium can be leached out.

The nitrogen content of nitrogen fertilizers is much more easily removed from soil than the above elements. In lysimetric experiments a certain proportion of the nitrogen of the fertilizers was taken up by plants with the remainder absorbed in the soil by clay minerals and humus. The rest was leached from soil. Measuring and adding up these fractions, it was found that approx. $^1/_3$ of the nitrogen was missing. The loss was found to be caused by ammonia, elementary nitrogen and nitrogen oxides escaping into the atmosphere. On the basis of data by Kozák and Mészáros (1971) it can be seen that, in areas with alkaline soils, it is ammoniacal nitrogen that can be found at the highest concentration in rain water. This, in our opinion, is the result of ammonia released from fertilizers. Nitrogen oxides are a further source of danger for the environment. Being freed from soil they get into the upper layers of the atmosphere bringing about ozone decomposition. Thus, they reduce the efficiency of the ozone shield which filters out cosmic radiation.

It is mainly the leached-out nitrogen, migrating with soil water, that has the greatest effect on the environment. On the one hand it causes the eutrophication of surface waters, whilst on the other it increases the nitrate content of wells and of drinking water.

The connection between large-scale applications of fertilizers and the nitrogen content of waters is far from being merely a question of quantity. The amount of nitrates getting into water from the soil, is influenced both by the quantity and the quality of precipitation and the degree to which the vegetation of the area in question takes up nutrients. Should the uptake be proportional to the release of nitrates, it would mean that, even in the case of larger dosages, no nitrate would get into the soil or surface waters. In the period outside the growth season the potential danger of large fertilizer dosages and much rain can be considered to be real sources of damage.

According to Bacsó and Tusz (1977), below a vineyard, the nitrate content of land drainage water amounted to more than 40 mg/l, which is the direct result of large fertilizer dosages, applied at the time of planting. Under winter wheat, maize and lucerne they measured values around 20 mg/l. In each sample, phosphorus could only be detected in traces, while the potassium content amounted to 5 mg/l.

The direct effect of large fertilizer dosages on soil should be discussed separately. Firstly, we should mention the increased salt concentration of the soil solution, a phenomenon which can be brought about by the application of water-soluble fertilizers. In contrast with hot beds and greenhouses, under field conditions we have not observed this effect of high doses. According to Bui Dinh Dinh (1974) nitrogen fertilizers, such as ammonium nitrate, ammonium sulphate and urea cause plant damage at application rates of approx. 1 g/kg, i.e. 2,000 kg/ha N.

This direct saline effect is accompanied by two other factors, namely the effect of salts, which owing to the ion exchange of the fertilizer nutrient-ions are released either by substitution taking place on the surface of the soil colloids or by decomposition from soil components. Their composition depends not only on the amount and quality of the fertilizers applied, but also on the composition of the soil.

Until now, consideration has only been given to the effects of the main active ingredients of fertilizers and to that of nutrients. Nevertheless, apart from them, fertilizers also contain several other elements which are partly impurities and partly additives. When large fertilizer dosages are applied, their effect may be most significant. Just to mention the role of calcium-ion introduced to the soil in the form of superphosphate or calcium nitrate. In acidic soils, owing to leaching, the amount of available calcium is small therefore, the side effect of the use of fertilizers is capable of meeting the calcium demand of plants. The same goes for our latest fertilizers, in respect of magnesium, the absence of which may be harmful for plants growing on soils of high acidity. This damage can be prevented by the application of fertilizers with added magnesium. The sulphur content of fertilizers can be useful, either in the form of ammonium or potassium and calcium sulphate, to meet the sulphur requirement of plants. After the uptake of nutrients, these substances remain in the soil and are capable of exerting long-lasting effects.

On the other hand, the effect of chloride-containing fertilizers is unfavourable due to the sensitivity of several cultivated plants to chlorides. As long as chlorides are not leached out from the soil, these plants will be damaged. Fortunately this ion is not bound by soil therefore, in the case of adequate amounts of rainfall, it will be leached out from the root-zone.

However, fertilizer applications may bring about further changes. They change the natural dynamic chemical and biological processes in soils and as a result of these, they influence the composition of the soil solution, the adsorption conditions, the nature of the leaching processes, the redox conditions and the direction and speed of protolytic processes. By substituting calcium and magnesium ions bound to the surface of soil colloids, the cations of fertilizers not only restart the role of these ions in nutrient uptake but, by occupying the adsorption surface, the new cations also change the physico-chemical behaviour of the soil colloids. Thus, they also modify the structure, porosity, aeration and the water balance of soils. These changes are generally unfavourable, as the cations of nutrients substitute those calcium ions on the surfaces, which are most favourable for the physico-chemical aspect of the soil.

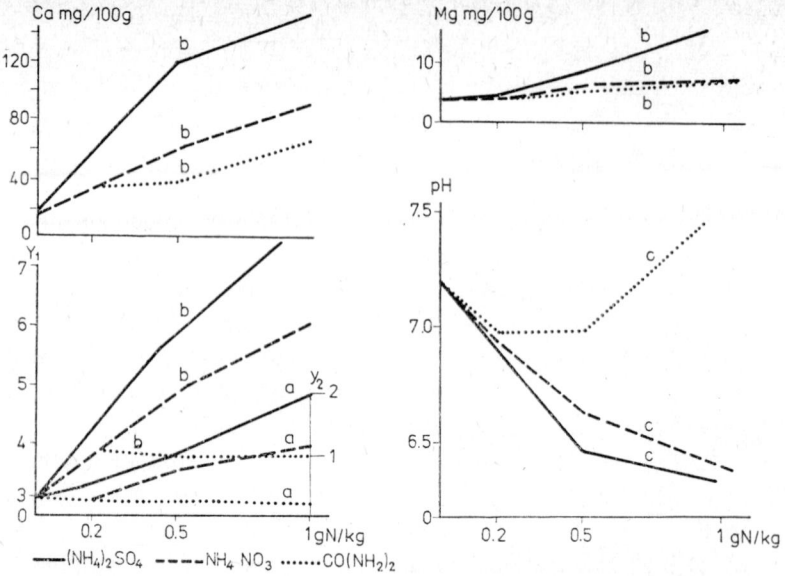

Fig. 67. Effect of different doses of N-fertilizers on the leaching out of Ca and Mg as well as on the acidification (y_1 and pH) of lessivated brown forest soil. Values measured in an aqueous solution (*a*), in the soil filtrate (*b*), in aqueous suspension (*c*). y_1: hydrolytic acidity, y_2: exchange acidity. (Bui Dinh Dinh 1974)

Bui Dinh Dinh (1974) published several sets of data on this phenomenon. Abstracts from this dissertation, on the acidity and leaching out of a brown forest soil type, are illustrated in Fig. 67. These data and also experiments by Sipos and Patócs (1975), indicate that especially soils lacking calcium carbonate undergo significant changes owing to the application of nitrogen fertilizers. Titratable acidity increases the possibilities for leaching out of calcium and magnesium—and because of this fundamental changes take place in the soil-dynamics. If not counterbalanced these changes will result in the reduction of soil fertility, sooner or later.

Should materials be introduced into soils by way of fertilizers, which are, under the given conditions, capable of taking part in the reduction and oxidation processes, similar significant changes will take place also in the redox-conditions of soils. It is primarily ammonium and nitrate-ions, the redox effect of which is to be expected in the first place. True enough, ions affecting the redox-potential will not alter the character of natural processes taking place in soils with a suitable microbiological activity. Nonetheless, ammonium ions may stimulate and nitrate ions counterbalance the effect of reduction processes in soils, in which the reducing processes are already dominant. This may alter the dynamics of the iron-related processes and the availability of other biologically active elements of the soil, such as manganese and molybdenum.

Changing redox-conditions may affect the fertilizer itself through the soil. For example, greater nitrogen losses or the formation and release forms of gaseous nitrogen into the air can be the consequence of modified redox-conditions, as well.

Changes in the ingredients of plants can also be brought about by environmental factors. Broadly speaking, smaller rates of fertilizer application do not change the composition of the cultivated plants, none the less, after the application of larger amounts, the enrichment of ingredients has been observed. This effect could be favourable, since on the whole, both in human and animal nutrition the higher concentration of ingredients is more favourable. There are also other cases in which plants receiving high amounts of fertilizers contain higher amounts of nutrients than those not manured or those receiving only small amounts, though the forms of incorporation are not identical. Nitrogen generally, but especially in the case of larger amounts, is incorporated into protein but only to the extent of a small proportion of the total. Among these amino acids, there are only a few of value. Owing to changes in the elemental composition of plants the commercial quality of the crop also decreases. This has long been a well known phenomenon in the case of barley, sugar-beet, tobacco and owing to the steadily increasing application rates, this is also becoming known in the context of other cultivated plants. Excessive application of nitrogen fertilizers increases the nitrate content of lettuce and spinach, which can exceed values of 150 ppm, the upper limit of marketability in certain countries. Lőrinc (1971) also referred to the possibility of unfavourable changes in ingredient composition. On the basis of fertilizer trials carried out with "Hybar" on the sandy-uplands between the Danube and Tisza, he established that as the rate of fertilizer application increased (from 50 to 300 kg/ha active element) the nitrogen content of both leaves and stem (expressed as %) also increased. Nevertheless, he did not recommend higher amounts than 200 kg/ha N in order to prevent nitrate accumulation in the leaves.

Changes in the chemical composition of plants also influence their anatomical features, changing stem stability, the duration of generative and vegetative phases in the course of development (growth), frost resistance, the resistance to certain diseases, factors that both separately and jointly determine the quality and the quantity of the yield.

In long-term experiments on winter wheat and maize Kramer and Latkovics (1971) established that while the application of fertilizers caused no significant changes in the proportion of NPK nutrients taken up by cereals; in the case of maize, however, grains contained almost twice as much available substance as the unmanured plants did.

According to Láng (1971) both intensive use of fertilizers and the spread of high yield varieties capable of benefiting from it, frequently brings about the spread of diseases. Although, according to experiments carried out in the county of Somogy (Hungary), potassium application increased potato-rot resistance. In addition to this, the latest experiments have shown in the case of other plants, that suitable manuring does not increase the spread of plant pests, on the contrary, it even increases the resistance of plants.

Referring to the experiments with rice carried out by a Japanese scientist Osada, Bálint (1973) concludes that the use of fertilizers for individual varieties had led to an almost linear increase in photosynthetic activity though, there are also varieties which react to larger nitrogen rates, by reducing their activity. Apart from this, the respiration loss of individual varieties also varies. Consequently, the favourable effects of the application of fertilizers can be achieved only by such varieties which, as a result of fertilizer use, increase their photosynthetic activity and their respiration remains constant or only slightly increases.

The amounts of fertilizers reaching the soil affect the weed and natural vegetation of the land. Under field conditions, both the quantity and quality of weeds show significant changes—this especially applies to the nitrophilous weed plants. Depending on the dominant nutrients, the use of fertilizers on pasture and meadow modifies the composition of the grass-communities. As the dominant nutrients change, ecological conditions become more favourable for some other species and varieties. It is known that depending on the ratio of nitrogen to phosphorus, the ratio of species belonging to the Papilionaceae-family (peas and vetches) and the dominant grasses will be changed within the community. Apart from this, changes in the chemical reaction or in the calcium supply of soils brought about by manuring may exert the same effects even if these are less well known.

Summarizing the evaluation of the effects detailed above, it can be concluded that the application of large amounts of fertilizers can influence the environment favourably or unfavourably. It is important, therefore to calculate the appropriate quantity and nutrient ratios, which are economic and favourable from the viewpoint of environment control.

THE EFFECTS OF SOIL IMPROVEMENT
ON THE ENVIRONMENT

When studying the effects of soil improvement on the environment, primary and secondary or main and side effects can be distinguished.

The liming of acidic soils brings about chemical and physical changes. The substances used for this purpose meet the calcium requirements of the plants and on the other hand, owing to its buffering effect, reduce acidity. The primary effect manifests itself in higher yields and the widening of plant variety though, side effects are no less important. These are displayed in the increasing solubility of nutrients, the transformation of microbiological processes and the changing of their character and intensity.

A comparative study by Bán (1967) records that the amount of material applied in liming corresponds to 10 to 20 t/ha as $CaCO_3$, of soil improvement material. This quantity is of such importance that its impact on the environment is not limited to the modification of the chemical characteristics but it also changes the physical properties of the soils. Both structure and water-drainage will change, after a shorter or longer period, making tillability also more favourable. The map showing the potential for soil improvement also outlines the areas of acid soils (Fig. 68). These can be divided into two groups: (i) the group of acid forest soils, (ii) the group of hydromorphic acid soils. In the first group it is mainly the chemical character of liming that is the most important whilst, in the case of the second group, the improvements can be traced back to the physical properties.

Both in the case of environmental influences and in that of manuring the emphasis is on higher yields and greater plant mass. When evaluating the environment modifying impacts of liming, air composition, soil coverage and the amount of organic matter introduced into the soil are of primary importance although, the effect of liming on water-balance should not be neglected as it has an influence on the water economy of a region.

Of the Hungarian contributions in this field, the investigations by Lamberger and Máté (1970) should be mentioned. They studied the effect of liming on the increase in biological activity measured on the basis of carbon dioxide production. Field experiments using half dosages of lime brought about an increase of 30%, complete dosages increased biological activity by 50%.

Papers describing land improvement schemes in Őrség also confirm the efficiency of liming. They underline the special role of pseudogleys in this region. According to Belák (1965), as neither of these methods are efficient enough on its own, it is not economical to apply liming without breaking

234

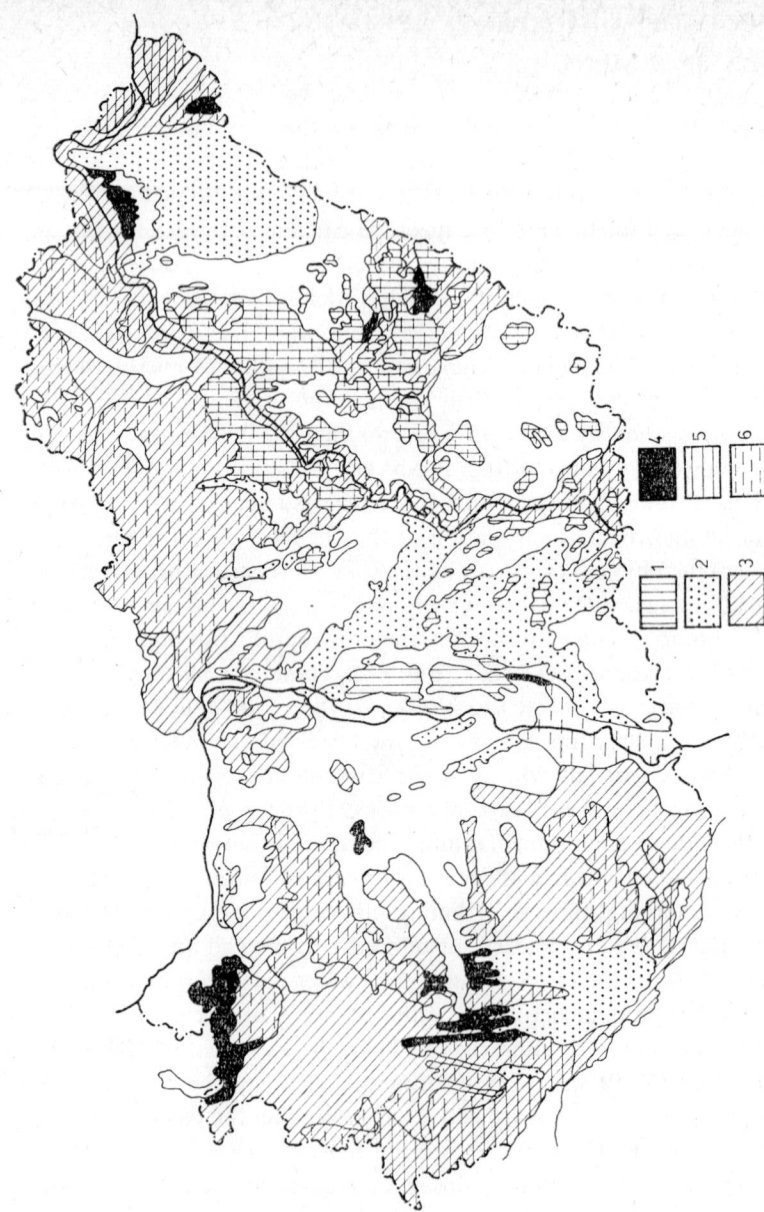

Fig. 68. Map showing the potential for soil improvement. (*1*) salt-affected soils by subsoil spreading of lime or gypsum, (*2*) by sand stratification, (*3*) acidic soils by liming, (*4*) hydro-ameliorated marsh areas, (*5*) areas by subsoil drainage, (*6*) areas by deep ploughing. (Stefanovits 1961)

up the subsoil and drainage. The exact effect on the environment, of these complex improvement processes can be measured mainly by the productivity of agricultural farms. Nonetheless it can be presumed, on the basis of facts mentioned in the context of manuring and liming, that soil improvement exerts a similarly great impact on the landscape and also on water and air conditions. Filep et al. (1973) indicate the complexity of the effect of liming materials. They established that the calcium carbonate containing materials of soil improvers also contains large amounts of micro-elements. Data by these authors are given in Table 24. It can be seen that the amount of trace elements introduced into the soil by means of liming materials exceeds that which reaches the soil through either organic manuring or use of artificial fertilizers.

In Hungary, the problem of salt-affected soils has a long history. The method of lime and gypsum containing subsoil application which is considered to have the greatest modifying effect on the environment has been known since Tessedik (1742–1820). The subsoil material is produced in the area to be reclaimed or in its vicinity, applying large-scale production methods. Material excavated at a depth of 3–5 m is spread out in a 7 cm thick layer over the surface. In contrast to the clay-pit remaining after mining operations, the surface of the reclaimed territory is thus levelled up. As seen, this method of soil improvement exerts its nature and thus environment-forming effect not only by its calcium carbonate and trace of gypsum content but also as a result of the breaking up of the subsoil.

Results of the last 20 years of improvement work on salt-affected soils have been recorded in books by Arany (1956), Herke (1959), Prettenhoffer (1969), nevertheless, this activity can be traced back to Sigmond, Treitz and Tessedik. All these confirm that, applied at a suitable place, either subsoil spreading, liming or gypsum spreading can be equally effective and efficient methods. Not only yields are increased but also the chemical and physical properties of the soil are permanently changed, tillability and drainage of soils is improved and cultivation becomes more reliable.

Table 24

Microelement content of manure, superphosphate and lime from a sugar factory (in g)

Material	Mn	Cu	Zn	Fe
10 t manure	275	25	200	
1 t superphosphate	150–200	15–40	20–60	2,000
10 t lime from sugar factory (50%)	750	100	200	3,000

The range of cultivated plants is widened and thus both higher yields and the more varied plant cover will lead to modification of the environment. Further, considering that on improved areas the yields are higher than on those not treated, it will be relevant to note that improvement also has an effect on animal husbandry, thus constituting a newer direction of environmental changes. As a consequence of soil reclamation, both the applicability and the effectiveness of the use of fertilizers and irrigation is modified. Briefly, the changing of one component of the environment also opens up the possibility for the greater effectiveness of other methods. In addition to soil reclamation, in several cases closely related to it, evidence shows the necessity and efficiency of physical soil improvement. Either drainage or subsoiling are separately applicable methods though, in extreme cases, they are only jointly effective. Both subsoiling and drainage of soils with excess water, change not only the water balance of those soils but also exert their influence on the water supply of the local landscape and of the environment. Apart from all these effects, they also increase the yields. Through modification of the water regime of soils, subsoiling and drainage also improve its aeration. By this means, they increase the availability of nutrients and result in increased microbiological activity.

The layering method of sand improvement combines both the physical and chemical effects of improvement techniques. By incorporating 1–2 cm thick coherent layers of organic and mineral colloids, or soils having a similar effect, into the deeper soil layers, this method also changes their water and nutrient balance. The substances applied, which consist of manure, turf, clay and fertilizers, will persist at a depth of 40–60 cm for a long time and moreover, together with appropriate agricultural practices, they constantly regenerate themselves through the decaying of the rich root systems. Its effects are shown by higher water capacity of the soil and the slowing of infiltration, the greater amount of nutrients in the root-zone and by increased microbiological activity. According to Egerszegi (1964) the method modifies even the formation of root systems. Roots penetrate deeper into the soil and, thus they build up a more extensive network. Therefore, the plant can utilize the water resources of deeper lying soil layers resulting in higher yields.

The sand improvement method increases yields primarily, although it simultaneously provides a better protection of the soil surface against deflation and also the better utilization of precipitation. All these factors jointly mean a significant modification of the environment. As soil improvement also makes it possible to cultivate plants which formerly could not be cultivated efficiently in the area, it is accompanied by a wider variety of plant species. Moreover, the greater plant mass provides a possibility to feed more animals, thus joint harmonious development of plant cultivation and animal husbandry can be realized.

The reclamation of bog-soils should also be mentioned amongst those methods of soil improvement that threaten imminent destruction of the environment. Water regulation, the first step in bog-soil reclamation, involves the lowering of the ground water level to such a depth, where there is no danger of the roots of cultivated plants suffocating. Should, however, the sinking of the ground water-table be large enough, so that the uncovered soil surface can dry out, it will lead to large-scale deflation. Particles of dried out soils are, namely, of such a low bulk density that even a breeze can suspend them and drift them far away. Wrongly adopted methods of reclamation may, therefore, lead to serious destruction of the environment. The self-ignition or the deliberate burning off of peat soils, already reclaimed, involves similar dangers. In such cases, the dry bog-layer gets burned off to the zone of capillar humidity and merely ash and glazed cakes of soil remain. This kind of environmental destruction is frequent in the vicinity of Little-Balaton and partly in the region of Sárrét, in Fejér county. On the basis of the above-mentioned facts it is very important that reclamation of bog-soils should be carried out with great care, simultaneously with the sinking of the ground water-table, means of applying spray-irrigation must be provided in order to secure the proper water requirements of the soil.

THE EFFECTS OF IRRIGATION ON THE ENVIRONMENT

The primary aim of irrigation is to secure for plants the required amount of water in due time. As far as environment control is concerned this goal is the most beneficial, if it secures greater yields and at the same time creates favourable conditions in the soil for both the plant and animal communities. Nevertheless, irrigation may have also side-effects, which are harmful for the environment. These include the deterioration of soil structure, the detrimental water excess and secondary alkalization of the soil.

Irrigation itself is capable of causing great changes in the environment either by the civil engineering works providing a water supply or by the effect of irrigation water on plants and soil which not only increase yields but also modify the processes of soil formation.

From among these factors, first let us mention excess of water, or more exactly waterlogging. This process starts when the soil is over-saturated for a long period not only for the hours of actual irrigation. As a result of saturation by water, air is expelled out of the soil-pores, in this way increasing the water–air ratio. As a consequence of decreased amount of oxygen the biological chain processes, taking place in the soil, diverts into a completely different direction. In general, waterlogging can be prevented by shorter irrigation periods and by soil aeration. Persistent or frequently repeated waterlogging—by initiating the formation of meadow-soils— influences both soil formation and the process of meadow formation. In addition to the alteration in humus quality it also affects cation exchange processes and the migration of iron. Only the systematic and regular application of relevant agricultural technics makes it possible to divert the formation of meadow soil into steppe soil. In the phase of swamp formation, the soil aerobic microorganisms may either temporarily or finally disappear. These microscopic organisms of the soil are responsible for the transformation of organic matter, the changing valency of certain elements, the soil acidity and through these mechanisms also affecting the processes of absorption and solution in the soil. Aquaphilous and water tolerating weeds appear, while the majority of cultivated plants die out. The same occurs when either the water-table temporarily rises up to the soil surface or large amounts of precipitation bring about the accumulation of water in surface depressions. The effects of swamp formation can only be eliminated if agronomical methods are combined with water regulation. In the following stage, of which water saturation is characteristic during the major part of the year, both the nature and direction of humus formation acquire a new character. Due to the interaction of anaerobic organisms with the aquaphilous vegetation and the slow accumulation of decay products, the anaerobic synthesis of humus takes place. Its final stage is peat formation, in which the submerged dead organic matter of sedge, rush and reed species decays. In this process, releasing a relatively small proportion of carbon, it is transformed into peat which has a high carbon and organic matter content. Irrigation and especially inexpert flooding forms the first stage of this process. Rice growing, where the soil is submerged during the greater part of the growth season is a good example. According to Ponnanperuma et al. (1961), and Rodrigo (1967) soil acidity, as a rule, decreases as a result of water coverage. Depending on the organic C and total N content of the soil, redox-values decrease at varying speeds. The more organic matter and nitrogen that the soil contains, the faster the redox-potential decreases and the lower its value is. In general, following a 20-day-flood period, a moderate increase can be experienced in the Eh-value (namely a redox potential value expressed in mV), so the tendency is reversed. During the first 20 days of the flood, the nitrogen content—in the form of ammonium ion—in soils containing high amounts of organic matter and having little clay content, first shows a sudden increase then stabilizes. In contrast to this, in soils containing little organic matter and high mineral colloids, following an initial increase, a slow reduction can be observed. The easily soluble organic matter content shows a similar tendency. These changes may initiate further processes. Among them the reduction of iron, manganese and other valency-changing elements should be mentioned in the first place as these may lead to phosphate-fixation, thus modifying the solubility of several trace elements.

All these changes in organic matter composition affect soil structure in the same way. As established by Nguyen Thi Dan et al. (1971), the flooded soils tend to compact and become clogged. Data on iron and manganese migration have been supplied by Hungarian soil science workers by e.g. Gerei and Máté (1957), and Gerei et al. (1960). Figure 69 illustrates changes taking place in the redox-potential and EDTA-soluble (easily soluble) iron content, as measured during a 40-day-flooding of a meadow soil.

Changes taking place in the soils at the bottom of fish-ponds and reservoirs should also be included as environmental effects. It has been believed for a long time that fish-ponds functioning in the same area, for a shorter or longer period, improved the quality of Hungarian soils, especially that of the salt affected-soils. The study of the soil of fish-ponds

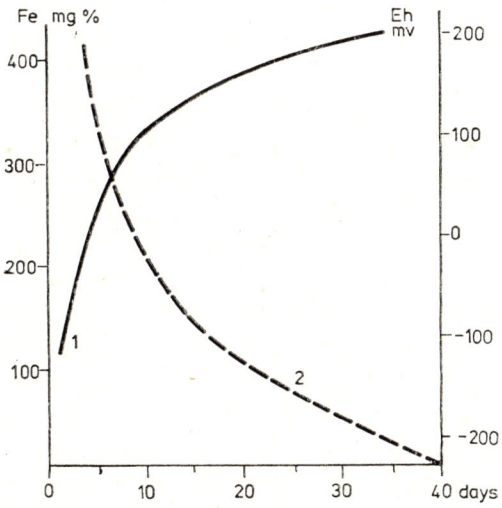

Fig. 69. Changes of redox-potential (*1*) and EDTA-soluble iron content (*2*) in flooded meadow-soil, (Gerei and Máté 1957)

by Ábrahám (1957) did not support these views. According to him there had been no significant changes that would have unambiguously indicated soil improvement. Neither did their nutrient economy improve significantly nor was soil salinity reduced.

Summarizing the effect of flooding it can be seen that it brings about great changes in the environment. It initiates waterlogging and so leads to significant chemical and physical changes in soil properties which are, in most cases, the precursor of environmental changes, mainly a deterioration of previous conditions. Spray irrigation is less harmful, although in the case of too large rates of application, it may also lead to long lasting water excess in the soil, especially in the low-lying areas of the fields. The inexpert application of both irrigation methods may initiate irrigation erosion, the horizontal shifting of soil particles. Another form of the impacts of irrigation is the raising of the underground water-table in the areas irrigated. This may lead to meadow, swamp or bog-formation, although the same environment destruction may also take place in the absence of the above-mentioned factors. In cases where the higher ground water-table is nearer than 60–100 cm below the soil surface, it will cause great damage to the natural and cultivated vegetation. It is generally observed that apricot trees and vine-stocks die or are seriously impaired if the water-table reaches the level of 60 cm in the spring or early summer. Therefore, independently of the method of irrigation, the initial rates of dosing should be chosen in such a way that the water which penetrates into the soil should not raise the water-table.

The above-mentioned cases occur when the quality of both irrigation and groundwater is suitable that is to say it does not contain much salt, especially sodium salts. The secondary alkalization of soils means a great danger for the environment it is the result of using irrigation water of bad quality or the impact of higher saline ground water. From the papers by Filep (1970), Darab (1958), Szabolcs (1961) and Várallyay (1967) much information has been gained as to the principles of these processes. It can be established that by knowing the depth of the water-table, its salt content, the degree of soil salinization and the quality and quantity of irrigation water, it is possible to forecast the degree of alkalization to be expected. Thus, as already applied by Szabolcs et al. (1968a,b, 1969) in the survey of the Tisza II irrigation system areas, the danger of secondary alkalization can be classified according to the above principles. This, at the same time, helps to reduce the danger of this process to a minimum and thus to prevent deterioration of the environment.

If quality requirements are strictly compiled with, the danger of environment deterioration, secondary alkalization can be avoided. This means that neither in the field irrigated nor in surroundings will there be soil salinization and moreover, among the cations of the soil and its adsorption-complexes by sodium will not be dominant.

THE EFFECT OF PLOUGHING AND CULTIVATION ON THE ENVIRONMENT

Apart from the previously mentioned effects of agricultural production on soil, compaction can also occur occasionally. It results from the combined effects of increasing mechanization and the use of unsuitable tillage techniques. Mechanised transport and ploughing equipment exert a certain pressure on the soil surface by moving across the ground. Should the water-content, structure and elasticity be unsuitable, the soil will become compacted, its weight per unit volume will increase. How important this can be from the point of view of yields is illustrated in Fig. 70 derived from Gál and Szirtes (1973). This compaction, which mainly occurs in wheel-tracks, also reduces yields in flat areas of land. When it occurs on sloping fields, especially in tracks which follow the slope, it can be even more harmful. Because of limited infiltration, drainage water collects in hollows and by running off the slope, speeds up to such an extent that it is capable of carrying soil particles. Thus, owing to soil compaction, wheel-

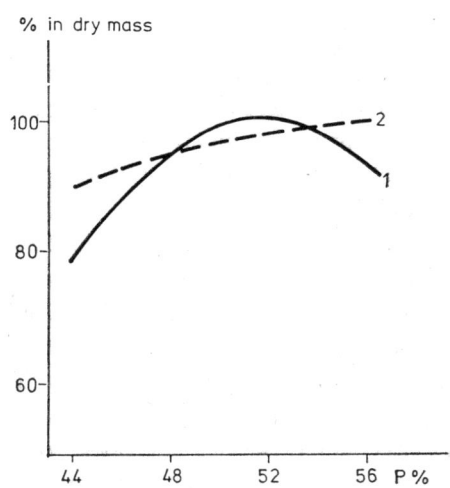

Fig. 70. Effect of chemical fertilizers and soil porosity on the yield of maize, (*1*) not manured, (*2*) manured. (according to Gál and Szirtes)

tracks develop into gullies. It is, however, not only wheel-tracks that can cause soil compaction, but also cultivation equipment, including ploughs. Pressure from these implements is no longer exerted on the surface but at the bottom of the furrow, which in consequence becomes compacted. At the same time both porosity and permeability decrease. By filtering out the silty, loamy particles from the soil solution percolating through the loosened layer above it, this layer becomes even more solid. Thus, evolves the plough share compaction at the bottom of the furrow, which both reduces permeability and hinders the development of the root-system of plants growing on it.

This problem in the control of water, changes not only the water regime of the whole landscape and through this, on sloping land, also the degree of soil-erosion but also affects the entire environment. As seen in Fig. 70 even in the case of identical porosity, the yields on manured and non-manured soils are different. It can be seen that the detrimental effect of compaction can be compensated for partly by the use of fertilizers and therefore a certain proportion of the environment destruction—the loss of yield —can be eliminated. (It should, however, be emphasized that it is only the loss of yield that can be reduced and not the deterioration of the water regime.)

INTERACTION BETWEEN HERBICIDES AND THE SOIL

As water flows through the soil several soil processes are changed such as the leaching of nutrients and herbicides. According to Tomkó (1973) the migration of herbicides, containing different active ingredients and so the formation of concentrations of active material are greatly dependent on soil properties. It is well known that the fixation of herbicides or leaching by water depend on the solubility of the given herbicide, the absorptive properties of the soil and on its chemical reaction. The absorptive properties are, however, dependent on the amount and quality of humus and clay. Moreover—as established by Tomkó—the calcium carbonate content of the soil significantly influences the leaching of various herbicides, too. It follows that, when choosing the appropriate application rates, it is necessary to know and take into account these characteristics, so that effective weed killing should be accompanied by the least possible amount of residues in the soil. In order to demonstrate the above processes, the leaching of Hungazin PK is shown on three soil types, based on the work of Tomkó (Fig.

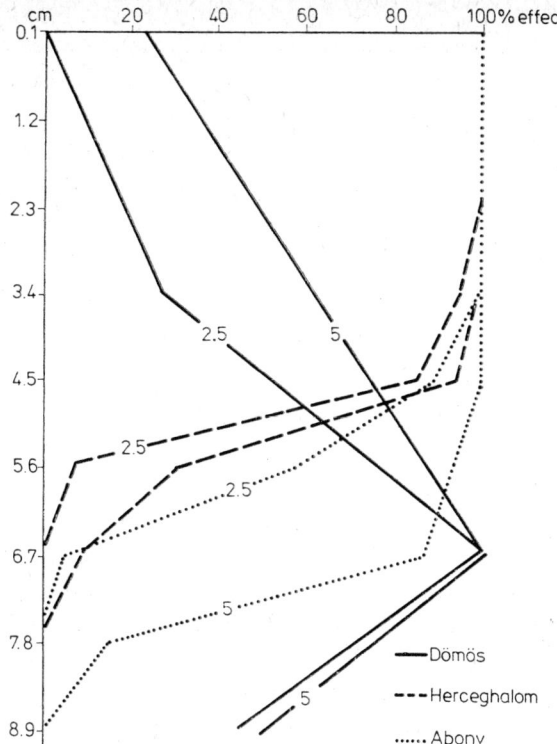

Fig. 71. Leaching in of Hungazin PK (doses 2.5 and 5 kg/ha) in the soil brought about by 40 mm of rainfall, Dömös: barren territory; Herceghalom: calcic chernozem; Abony: lime-layered chernozem of the Great Hungarian Plain. (Tomkó 1973)

71): A carbonate-containing eroded soil, at Dömös, a calcareous loamy chernozem, at Herceghalom and in the ploughed layer of a silty calcareous chernozem at Abony. As shown in the diagram, it is the 30% calcium carbonate-containing eroded soil which contains only traces of humus with only a little clay, that absorbs the smallest amount of Hungazin PK. As a result, it is also in this soil that the herbicide is leached into the soil and penetrates most deeply.

Heinisch et al. (1976) illustrate the migration of triazine herbicides in the upper and sub-surface layers of sandy soils (in the German Democratic Republic) as well as in loamy soils. Based on their own data and on the result of several hundred investigations carried out in the German Democratic Republic, it was established that, in sandy soils, the leaching of Simazin, Atrazin and Propazin were detectable (samples taken at the depth of 15–30 cm contained higher residues than those taken from the upper layers) whilst soils with a higher clay content showed an opposite trend. The higher clay content binds residues already in the upper layer and leaching was detected only in the case of Propazin. Similarly, it is also Heinisch and his co-workers who drew attention to the uptake of soil-borne residues by plants. According to investigations carried out with carrot and medicinal plants, he could detect Prometrin in carrot, while medicinal plants only contained residues in exceptional cases. Concerning environment control, it is the absorption of herbicides that regulates the quantity of residues in the root zone of plants, while leaching can cause pollution of the environment through surface run-off.

Not only physical and chemical reactions influence the fate of herbicides in soil, but also microorganisms which interact with them. Herbicides, with differing chemical structure, either affect the activity of soil-borne microorganisms, or contribute to their decomposition and their detoxification.

Changes in the living world of the soil are an important factor affecting the formation of the environment (Timár 1975). Both macroscopic and microscopic organisms in the soil are sensitive to changes in the physicochemical properties, as well as to quantitative changes in organic and inorganic matter which penetrate the soil and are of vital importance. Loss of even one link in the food chain, as a result of the appearance of a certain chemical substance may cause change in the living world of the soil. As both primary and secondary processes taking place in the soil are maintained by the energy of biological processes, any change in its living community or the modification of its activity, may greatly affect the soil population dynamics. How significant changes can be brought about by the activity of soil-borne microflora and microfauna, is illustrated by the table taken from a paper by Heinisch (1976) (Table 25). Concerning the interaction between herbicides and soil microflora, Heinisch (1976) makes the following general observations. The recommended application of herbicides does not affect the number of organisms (exceptions are Dinoseb and DNOC).

Table 25

Data characterizing the activity of the microflora and microfauna of soil
(kg/ha/yr) (Heinisch 1976)

Humus formation	3,000
Carbon dioxide formation	10,000
Ammonia and nitrate formation	800
Fixation of atmospheric N	250
Fixation of the mobile-N of soil	50
Phosphorus released	50
Potassium released	200

Species belonging to Actinomycetes are very tolerant to herbicide residues, while algae react sensitively and nitrogen fixing bacteria are the most sensitive.

Microbiological activity helps the decomposition and inactivation of herbicides which is very important. Ehwald (1976) calls attention to the danger that, in the course of herbicide decomposition, different aniline-derivatives and azocompounds may be formed.

It can be concluded that both chemical substances introduced into the soil and chemical and physical changes affecting it, can bring about changes in the properties of the soil and consequently may change its fertility. It cannot, however, be said that each interference, which increases soil fertility in a given growth season, is always favourable. Therefore in the case of all interference with the soil, even if the aim is to increase yields, then the side- and after-effects should be taken into account. Only in this way is it possible to prevent deterioration of the environment. Moreover, it should be added that changes in soil—as it is localized and of solid state—cannot be altered as easily as those which occur in air and water (Stefanovits 1978). Therefore, no interference, i.e. agricultural production and also in this context, environment control should fail to consider the ecological approach to the problem (Kormondy 1976; Duvigneaud and Kestemont 1977). Unless this is done neither the coordination of actions, nor the minimizing of material and energy consumption can be achieved.

References

Ábrahám, L. (1957): The impact of fish-ponds and storage lakes on the salt-affected soils of Hortobágy. *Agrokém. és Talajt.* **6**: 29–42.

Arany, S. (1956): *Salt-affected soils and their improvement.* Budapest.

Bacsó, A. and Tusz, Zs. (1977): The effect of the use of fertilizers on the extent of leaching, and the chemical composition of ground water in a drained vineyard. In: Stefanovits, P. (ed.): *Soil and environment control* (in Hungarian). Budapest.

Bálint, A. (1973): Some problems in the breeding of high yielding plant species (in Hungarian). *Magyar Mezőgazdaság* **28**: 6–7.

Bán, M. (1967): *Methods and results of soil improvement* (in Hungarian). Budapest.

Belák, S. (1965): Mechanical improvement of acid soils. *Agrártud. Közlem.* **24**: 361–371.

Bócz, E. (1973): The success of wheat cultivation (in Hungarian). *Magyar Mezőgazdaság* **28**: 10–11.

Borsy, Z. (1971): Studies in wind erosion in the windblown sand areas of Hungary. *Acta Geographica Debrecina* **10**: 123–132.

Bui Dinh Dinh (1974): The effect of nitrogen fertilizers on the chemical properties of soil. Personal communications.

Cserni, I. (1971): The dynamics of the annual seasonal changing of the soluble phosphorus content of the soil and the release of stored phosphorus fertilizers on the sand-covered soils of the Danube–Tisza Midregion. *Agrártud. Közlem.* **30**: 511–514.

Darab, K. (1958): Secondary alkalization of the irrigated meadow soils of the region East of the Tisza river. *Agrokém. és Talajt.* **4**: 53–69.

Duck, T. (1969): *Basic soil protection in Agricultural production Units.* Budapest.

Duck, T. and Máté, F. (1973): Correlation between nutrient content and soil fertility on eroded chernozems (in Hungarian). *Agrokém. és Talajt.* **22:** 65–82.

Duvigneaud, P. and Kestemont, P. (1977): *Productivité biologique en Belgique.* Paris–Gembloux.

Egerszegi, S. (1964): Plant physiological principles of efficient sandy soils improvement. *Agrokém. és Talajt. (Suppl.)* **13:** 209–218.

Ehwald, E. (1976): Boden und Umwelt. Sitzungberichte der Akademie der Wissenschaften der DDR. *Mat.–Nat.–Techn.* Nr. 12/N.

Erődi, B., Horváth, Z. and Kamarás, M. (1965): *The management of soil protection in mountainous and hilly regions* (in Hungarian). Budapest.

Fekete, Z. and Király, M. (1973): Special Aspects in the environment control of a sandy plain. *Agrártud. Közlem.* **32:** 105–114.

Filep, Gy. (1970): Changes in the chemical properties of irrigated soils in the region East of the river Tisza, brought about by using irrigation waters of different qualities. *Agrokém. és Talajt.* **19:** 213–230.

Filep, Gy., Loch, J. and Kutassy, Zs. (1973): Analysis of the macro- and micro-element content of some Ca-containing soil improvers by potentiometric and atomic absorption methods. *Agrokém. és Talajt.* **22:** 197–205.

Gál, J.-né and Szirtes, V. (1973): The effect of pore capacity and methods of fertilizer application on the nutrient uptake of maize. Talajművelési Kutató Intézet, Karcag. Jubileumi Tudományos Ülésszak.

Gerei, L. and Máté, F. (1957): Iron and manganese-containing nodules and segregations in some native soils (in Hungarian). *Agrokém. és Talajt.* **6:** 43–50.

Gerei, L., Máté, F. and Benedek, J. (1960): The study of the formation of iron concretions in soil in model trials using the Fe^{59} isotope. *Agrokém. és Talajt.* **9:** 491–494.

Győri, D. (1971): The role of micro-nutrients in the development of soil fertility (in Hungarian). Personal communications.

Heinisch, E., Paucke, H., Nagel, H. and Hansen, D. (1976): *Agrochemikalien in der Umwelt,* Jena.

Herke, S. (1959): *Agricultural management of affected soils* (in Hungarian). Budapest.

Jerminecz, V. (1978): The effect of fertilizer doses on the nitrogen-content of wheat. Personal communications.

Király, M. (1970): The protection of the soils of plantations in the Duna–Tisza Midregion (in Hungarian). Personal communications.

Kormondy, E. J. (1976): Concepts of ecology. New Jersey.

Kovda, V. A. and Szabolcs, I. (1971): Biosphere and the soils and their relation to the soils (in Hungarian). *Agrártud. Közlem.* **30:** 437–450.

Kozák, M. and Mészáros, E. (1971): Chemical composition of rainwater in Hungary and its agricultural importance (in Hungarian). *Agrokém. és Talajt.* **20**: 329-352.

Kramer, M. and Latkovics, Gy.-né (1971): Examination of the effect of manuring on winter wheat and maize in a longterm experiment, II. Evaluation of the experimental results by means of quadratic polynomial functions (in Hungarian). *Agrokém. és Talajt.* **20**: 303-322.

Lamberger, J. and Máté, F. (1970): Investigation on the correlation between the liming of acid soils and their biological activity (in Hungarian). *Agrokém. és Talajt.* **19**: 107-116.

Láng, G. (1971): Some crop production problems connected with intensive application of fertilizers (in Hungarian). *Agrártud. Közlem.* **30**: 1-15.

Lásztity, B. (1975): Change in the NPK-content of maize-grains and the recovery of fertilizers on a calcareous sandy soils (in Hungarian). *Agrokém. és Talajt.* **24**: 279-290.

Lathwell, D. J., Bouldin, D. R. and Reid, W. S. (1970): *Effects of nitrogen fertilizer applications in agriculture. Relationship of agriculture to soil and water pollution.* Proc. Cornell. Univ. Conf. in Agriculture Waste Management.

Latkovics, Gy.-né (1975): Effect of NPK-fertilizers on yield in maize monocultures, I. NPK content of grains as affected by the application of fertilizers (in Hungarian). *Agrokém. és Talajt.* **24**: 259-264.

Lőrinc, J. (1971): Possibilities of increasing production of crops on the sandy soils of the region between the rivers Danube and Tisza (in Hungarian). *Agrártud. Közlem.* **30**: 533-539.

Nguyen Thi Dan, Szabolcs, I. and Lesták, J.-né (1971): Effect of rice production on some physical characteristics of soils (in Hungarian). *Agrokém. és Talajt.* **20**: 231-260.

Olson, R. A. (1972): Effects of intensive fertilizer use in the human environment. *FAO Soil Bulletin* **16**: 15-33.

Ponnanperuma, F. N., Martinez, E. and Loy, T. (1961): Influence of redox potential and partial pressure of carbon dioxide on pH value and the suspension effect of flooded soils. *Soil. Sci.* **101**: 421-431.

Prettenhoffer, J. (1969): *Improvement and utilization of native salt-affected soils.* Budapest.

Pusztai, A. (1975): Study on the productivity and the application of fertilizers to an eroded chernozem soil (in Hungarian). *Agrokém. és Talajt.* **24**: 325-340.

Rodrigo, D. M. (1967): Dynamic nature of the chemical regime of flooded rice soils. *IRC. News Lett.* **16**: 7-13.

Russell, E. W. (1972): Summary of technical discussions. Effects of intensive fertilizer use on the human environment. *FAO Soil Bulletin* **16**: 1–14.

Sipos, S. and Patócs, I. (1975): Soil: chemical properties of and crop yields as affected by continuous application of fertilizers (in Hungarian). *Agrokém. és Talajt.* **24**: 303–312.

Smith, G. E. (1971): Statement at Senate subcommittee hearing on air and water pollution. Personal communications.

Stefanovits, P. (1972): Transforming, buffering and storing effect of soil in material- and energy-flow systems. In: Szádeczky–Kardos, R. and Pécsiné Donáth, É. (eds): *II. Conference on material and energy flow,* 189–197.

Stefanovits, P. (1978): Soil and the environment (in Hungarian). *Agrártud. Közlem.* **87**: 13–24.

Stefanovits, P. et al. (1977): *Soil protection and environment control.* Budapest.

Szabolcs, I. (1961): *The effect of water control works and irrigation on the soil formation processes in the Trans-Tisza region* (in Hungarian). Budapest.

Szabolcs, I., Darab, K. and Várallyay, Gy. (1968a): The Tisza irrigation systems and the fertility of the soils in the Hungarian Plain I. Soil conditions and the potential for use of irrigation in the counties of Szolnok, Hajdú-Bihar, Békés and Csongrád (in Hungarian). *Agrokém. és Talajt.* **17**: 453–464.

Szabolcs, I., Darab, K. and Várallyay, Gy. (1968b): II. The "critical" depth of the water table in the area within the irrigation system of Kisköre (in Hungarian). *Agrokém. és Talajt.* **18**: 211–220.

Szabolcs, I., Darab, K. and Várallyay, Gy. (1969): III. Methods used in the preparation of 1 : 25,000 scale maps indicating the potential and the existing state of irrigation (in Hungarian). *Agrokém. és Talajt.* **18**: 221–234.

Timár, M. É. (1975): The ecological view and its significance in soil science (in Hungarian). *Agrokém. és Talajt.* **24**: 437–444.

Tomkó, B. (1973): Investigations into the absorption and migration of herbicides with different active ingredients, on various soil types (in Hungarian). Personal communications.

Tusz, Zs. (1973): Data on the production of guidelines for the application of fertilizers (in Hungarian). *Kísérletügyi Közlem.* **66/A**: 61–76.

Várallyay, Gy. (1967): Salt balances of soils in the region between the Danube and the Tisza II. Salt balance under irrigated conditions (in Hungarian). *Agrokém. és Talajt.* **16**: 27–56.

Chapter 8

Environmental control and plant protection

According to Balogh (1974) there are three main types of ecosystems: (*i*) self-controlling, (*ii*) externally controlled, and (*iii*) surviving. In the field of plant protection, naturally, we are concerned with ecosystems of the second group, in which "the original equilibrium of self-control has ceased and has been replaced by external control applied by human activity". Before studying the basic types of ecosystems of external control from the point of view of plant protection, the tasks and methods of plant protection are outlined.

The main goal is to protect the source of food produced by photosynthesis and chemosynthesis. The quantity and quality of the production of cultivated plants and plant communities is endangered by living organisms: animals, plant pathogens and parasites and also the so-called weeds. Plant protection fights against this huge quantity of destructive organisms, food antagonists and field parasitic plants. Demographical problems, mechanization and subsequently the intensive usage of chemicals in plant cultivation have given rise to environmental control problems. Therefore, the different methods of protection will be first surveyed.

METHODS OF PROTECTION

Biological protection

Although its methods are the least dangerous for the environment, in practical plant protection, mainly large-scale farming, they are not important. As in biological protection the aim is to make use of the parasites, the predators of pests, and the antagonists of pathogens, it is successful only in the presence of pests in large numbers, that is to say, in the case of an explosive generation or an epidemic.

Only by reducing the abundance of pests in the initial rapid growth phase of development to such a degree that they could not reach mass propagation, could biological protection serve as an effective way of control. (The rapid growth stage is the initial phase of over-population. It is characterised by the large number of eggs and viable offsprings.) In the rapid growth phase, the microorganisms, the enteromorphous insects or insectivorous vertebrates cannot compete with the generally very vigorous pests even if only present in small density. Doubtlessly, in spite of this we have succeeded in reaching results against some pests by means of biological protection. However, these cases always require an exceedingly thorough preliminary study, an extraordinarily circumspect and rather expensive labour.

It is known that in the 1910s Vasiliev was successful in fighting against corn-bugs, but only when breeding them on a large-scale and setting them free, at the stage of egg-laying, on the Crimean peninsula. Reichart and Szalay–Marzsó (personal communication) have achieved some success against the autumn webworm by applying a suspension in the small worm stage, that is to say when they were in the first and second larval phases. The apparently good result of biological protection is often only superficial. Thus, when Löffler killed off field-voles in Greece by means of *Salmonella typhi murium,* the development of their stock had already peaked and was in a declining stage. Manninger had a similar case with pine wasps, when he applied a polyeder virus against them (this method was described by Ubrizsy 1968) when these had reached a declining stage of regression. Jeszenszky, in the 1930s, introduced the ichneumon-fly *Aphelinus mali* from Italy to combat a large-scale woolly aphid infestation. We expect that the latest trends in biological protection will result in better solutions.

Parasites, with island-like or isolated locations, that can easily be bred in large quantities, can be sterilized by ionising radiation or by chemicals. In cases where we can ensure a tenfold distribution of sterilized males against the normal males, the number of parasites can be reduced most effectively in the course of several generations and they could even be killed off. In this way, by means of this self-destructive method we have succeeded in greatly reducing and even killing off the melon fly, the eastern fruit-fly and the American blow-fly on some islands and peninsulas.

From among the biotechnical methods, experiments with physical stimuli also show promising results in plant protection. Such are the light, especially the photoperiodicity and the acoustic-repellent effects. Attention to the former was called by Sáringer (personal communication) in Hungary.

Investigations into chemical stimuli are even more interesting. In this respect, success is expected from the application of systemic hormones and the sex-attractant odours of pheromones. Substances restricting feeding and ovulation are even of greater importance. These were investigated in detail by Jermy (1957).

Mechanical protection

It can be considered as an environment conservation method comprising two main groups: (*i*) keeping off of parasites; (*ii*) killing of parasites. The enclosure of plantations is a well-established method which is still used. By the application of electrically charged wires this expensive and labour-intensive method of protection can still be perfected mainly against rabbits. Roadside trees and individual trees can effectively be saved by wirenets or plastic covers. In case of fruit trees sticky bands can be used against certain insects. Wiremesh on the windows of barns and straw cover on the ground keep pests out of a building. Recently, by applying bright aluminium foils aphids could be kept off from paprika, tomato and lettuce fields (Kuroli 1970). The foil cover prevents both the growth of weed plants and the excessive evaporation of soil moisture. Against vertebrates different repellent chemicals have been used for a long time. By varying them frequently (with 2–3 days' intervals) this method is highly effective.

The collection and killing of insects means, in the majority of cases, a drastic intervention. The surrounding of fields with ditches is regarded nowadays as an obsolete method. Nevertheless, the combined method of using shallow furrows containing insecticides is even today frequently applied. These—mainly in spring—prevent insects from passing over from one plot to another. Doubtlessly, among the migrating herbivorous insect predators, mainly capsid bug predators, can also be found.

Before the mass development of chemical protection, growers made attempts to reduce the damage caused by insects killing cultivated plants by collecting them in different ways. At the beginning of 1930s, the 4–5 m wide pulling net was in usage. It was dragged over the surface of field crops by two men and was especially useful in the collection of flower and seed pests located mainly in the upper parts of the plants. The pulling net was very soon hauled by the wheel barrow and not much later, at the beginning of the 1950s, by tractor. Instead of the net on the tractor only one trough was mounted in which the insecticide content killed the insects collected in it.

The parasites can also be collected by light and sexual traps, though these serve mainly as forecasting purposes. Nevertheless, the trapping of rodents has been effectively used until recently. In orchards the pupating and overwintering insects are collected and burnt together with the straw of corrugated paper bands fixed to the trunks. In early spring, by the cleaning of the trees, the collection and burning of caterpillars' nests and pupae, the fruit trees can also be freed from quite a number of parasites. Caterpillars' nests of autumn webworm and cobweb-moths are also burnt during the growth season. In arable farming the different grass and grain driers, using warm and hot air, also kill the parasites of fodder plants. In glasshouses soil disinfection is carried out by fumigation. The removal of diseased plant parts is also an effective control method used in horticultural establishments and in household gardens. However, mechanical weed killing with rakes, harrows or other machines, can also be included as protective methods in the case of many crop plants. When using harvesters, the stem-crushing and stem-tearing mechanisms devitalized the majority of parasitic insects living on the plants. Finally, flooding can also kill quite a number of pests

Agronomical protection

As a result of human activity the fields under agricultural cultivation have become covered by a secondary plant-cover. The aim is to grow a plant-cover which can ensure the greatest possible quantity of raw material for both food and industry. In the cultivation of these plants we try to introduce appropriate growing methods so that the competing weed plants as well as animal and plant parasites should cause the least damage.

The appropriately applied methods of cultivation are also, therefore, means of protection. On large areas of arable land crops to be harvested within one year should be grown. The sequence of these crops should be carefully considered so that in the next growing season the parasites can only find the most susceptible plants with the greatest difficulty. Previously, the well-planned crop rotation and later the so-called changing of the crops served this purpose. Recently, the large-scale monoculture of maize can be observed a cropping system in which maize is grown repeatedly on the same land over many years. Although, from a financial point of view, such a production may be the most economical, even our sophisticated modern technical and chemical facilities do not make it possible to maintain such a monoculture over a very long period.

The urbanization of land and move of labour to the cities tend to wipe out or greatly reduce manual plant cultivation. Mechanical cultivation that was to kill competing plants and the weeds, has also decreased in importance. The ploughing and inter-row cultivation of field crops, the fast and deep-working modern machines, combined with disc cultivators, combine-harvesters and rotary-hoes also cause the death of certain soil parasites. The crop rotation of only a few species and the monoculture themselves also impoverish the fauna of arable land. This, in the presence of favourable abiotic factors, may lead to a number of variations of certain species.

The new agronomical methods such as early mowing, the introduction into culture of uncultivated plots, the improvement of soil quality, these all make living conditions for several parasites unfavourable, thus hindering their mass reproduction. The selection of adequately resistant varieties can also be looked upon as an agronomical method. Although there are already plant varieties resistant to certain pests, this method plays an important part in the protection against fungi, bacteria and virus damage to our crops. Thus, by choosing resistant varieties we can effectively control sun- flower moth and phylloxeras (*Homoptera*). Plant breeders have also achieved partial success with several other crops. In the transformation of nature, therefore, agronomical methods can mean already substantial inter- ventions.

Chemical control

Although its methods are more dangerous for the environment, modern agriculture can no longer fulfil its task of plant cultivation without it.

Chemical plant protection—mainly by the application of herbicides— has brought about a change of a qualitative character in agriculture. While in the past weeds were removed from among the crop plants by manual and mechanical methods, in the specialised plant production systems of today already the vastness of arable land excludes the employment of manual labour. The application of herbicides resulted in the sudden development of weedkilling, not to mention the savings. The pelletized seed has ceased the tiresome work of singling. At the same time, in the intensive plant produc- tion systems insecticides and herbicides are also needed. "The lack of crop hygiene due to isolation and catch-crops also increases the danger of epidemics. All the more so, as the host organisms stand in direct contact with each other on a large surface and they might reproduce and form a mass, which, according to the basic law of epidemiology, leads inevitably to the quick proliferation of diseases and parasites" (Nagy 1973). Truly enough the use of chemicals in plant protection has been increasing from year to year. However, it should be mentioned that the Department for Plant Protection of the Ministry for Agriculture and Food—with the involvement of experts—does its best to prevent the contamination of the environment. "For health reasons, the use of outdated active substances, like arsenic and chlorinated hydrocarbons, which accumulate in the organism, was banned in agricultural production first in the world" (Nagy 1971). Chemicals with the so-called persistent active substances, that is to say, substances which are preserved unchanged in the organism for a long time, have been gradually withdrawn from circulation. Thus, chemicals belonging to the cyclodiene group of chlorinated hydrocarbons (aldrin and dieldrin) were also banned. But very soon they were followed by DDT, which had, for a long time, been looked upon as entirely harmless. Though DDT is even today an important chemical against the vectors of malaria, in widespread use, Hungary was the first to ban its use. The next goal is to minimize the usage of chemicals labelled "very poisonous" in favour of the "poisonous" and "moderately poisonous" herbicides.

The other aim of the leaders of natural plant protection is to decrease as much as possible the danger of "drifting over" i.e. the whole amount of the chemical should reach its intended site which also directly helps to preserve the environment. The most damaging sources of over-drift are chemicals applied in mist or vaporised aerosol form. The use of dusts with a particle size of 10–40 µm has been declining due to the danger of "drifting-over" and the application of sprays and particularly the spraying at a lower pressure means much less danger.

From the point of view of environmental control, the application of pelletized powders and the use of seed-dressings is of great importance. By means of caustics the quantity of poison getting to a unit area is the smallest and the pellet reaches the appropriate place. This applies, especially, to the drill distributors of industrial-scale production systems of maize. The probability of environment pollution varies depending on the distributors. Powder spreading aircraft, evidently, work with less danger than those distributing aerosols and dusts. The aircraft distribution of herbicides is regulated by rather strict precautions. From among the distributors working on the ground, granulate spreaders cause the least concern.

Plant protection chemicals, with natural active ingredients, are only rarely used. The number of synthetic products on the market, however, exceeds 1,000. Organic compounds in use can be grouped into the following categories (Hargitai 1972):

Fungicides: dithiocarbamates, disulphides and phthalic amide derivatives.

Insecticides: chlorinated hydrocarbons, esters of phosphoric acid.

Herbicides: phenol, phenoxy, triazine, urea, toluidine and aniline derivatives, including anilides etc.

Generally speaking, fungicides destroy the reproductive organs of fungi on the plant surface. Insecticides act in several ways. The following groups can be distinguished: stomach poisons, contact sprays and poisons which affect breathing (inhalation) processes. The herbicides exert their action by causing scorching or by resorption.

As far as long term prospects are concerned, both Hungarian and worldwide research aim at finding selective (specific) poisons and chemicals. As already stated by Jermy (1957), it is not mechanical and scent, but chemical stimuli that play an important part in the specific mechanisms of the feeding processes. The new development and probable advantages of appetite inhibitors had been first indicated by Jermy (1957). By means of these specific substances, it is possible to prevent contact between the insect and hostplant, in other words, the damage. Chemicals thus distributed would be neither phytotoxic for the plant, nor toxic for human beings, their domestic animals or for the plant and animal communities.

The insecticide Dimilin named Midox powder, containing a specific compound 1-(4-chlorophenyl), 3-(2,6 fluorbenzoyl)urea: Iupac or[[(N-)]]4-chlorophenyl[amino/carbonyl]-2,6difluorobenzamide: CA /Diflubenzuron/ should also be mentioned in this context. This stomach poison affects only the chitin synthesis. It can, therefore, be applied against young caterpillars or leaf-feeding larvae and gives good results in the control of turnip-moth caterpillars Agrotis segetum and the larvae of the turnip flea beetles (*Phyllotreta spp.*).

The categories concerning the toxic character of pesticides have been worked out by Bordás (1972). According to this classification, instead of an assessment based only on the poison-labelling, the toxicity of chemicals is determined from three aspects: (*a*) labour hygiene, (*b*) food hygiene, (*c*) environmental hygiene. On the basis of this assessment there are four degrees of toxicity for pesticides: (*i*) highly poisonous, (*ii*) medium poisonous, (*iii*) moderately poisonous, (*iv*) practically non-poisonous.

Concerning the environment it is most important that the poisonous chemical should not reach the surrounding, especially inhabited areas. Neither should it accumulate or get into surface and underground waters. The application of Thiodan containing endosulfan-organochlorine insecticide and acaricide, Melipax (Camphecor, U.K.) toxaphene (U.S.A.) and copper-containing pesticides—which are dangerous to fish and for aquatic fauna within a 200 m distance from open water surfaces—is subject to special authorisation.

Beside the already described general measures, mention should also be made of some specific regulations. There are a specific number of legal provisions regulating the application of chemicals. For domestic use, the application is legalised for only those chemicals which are approved by the Plant Protection Service of the Ministry for Agriculture and Food, the Research Institute for Plant Protection and other public health authorities. These supervise the chemicals (pesticides) from the production stage up to their application and work-out regulations taking into account the side-effects. Accordingly, there are pesticides which can be applied without any special regulations in the smallholdings or in scattered isolated fields. The field distribution of others is permitted only on big farms and under the supervision of properly qualified experts. The concessions for the insecticides are published in the official publications of the Ministry of Agriculture and Food and are also simultaneously announced in the weeklies "Hungarian Agriculture" and "Horticulture and Viticulture". For certain chemicals, used for experimental purposes temporary concessions can also be issued. These are restricted to applications on a maximum area of 57.5 ha. The list of licensed plant protection chemicals is issued yearly in which it determines (a) the days of storage for food hygiene, i.e. the number of days that should elapse from the time of application until the harvest, (b) the possible amount of residues, i.e. the maximum amount of active ingredients expressed in mg/kg to be found in the crop at the time of putting it on the market, and (c) the days of storage for labour hygiene, i.e. the number of days that should pass before workers are allowed on the treated land without the use of protective equipment.

Furthermore, the list contains the value of the acute toxicity index or LD_{50}, on the basis of which information is given on the oral toxicity of the insecticide. (This number expresses the amount of pesticide in mg per kg body weight of the experimental animal—most frequently a rat—which when administered orally, causes a 50% mortality of the animals.) Finally, the list also contains the degree of toxicity of the insecticide for fishes and bees, so that those who apply them, can follow the regulations.

It is also an important safety measure that the insecticides must be stored in a store-room under the control of a qualified storekeeper. Further supervision is exercised by toxicologists, the Service for Public Health and Epidemiology, as well as by plant protection stations. Plant protection chemicals can be applied only by using protective equipment. Information on them is also given in the list mentioned above.

The stations for plant protection function in each county as a public authority. By the help of modern equipments they can make an accurate determination of the residues and where the application is not according to the rules, they initiate proceedings. The same procedure takes place in case of herbicides, as the improper application of triazine derivatives may cause substantial damage. There are special regulations providing for the safe disposal of packing materials, spray remnants and equipment wash-water.

It can be stated that, without plant protection chemicals, large-scale farming could no longer be carried out today. Though formerly being auxiliaries, pesticides have become one of the main elements of production. The responsible authorities do their best to promote the application of chemicals so as to preserve nature to the highest degree and to ensure at the same time their most efficient application.

INTEGRATED AND COMPLEX
PLANT PROTECTION

The complex or integrated protection means the joint application of the previously mentioned methods in such a way that they complement each other. Integrated protection always includes biological protection, which is hard to match the efficiency of chemical control. Integrated plant protection aims at controlling the interactions of ecosystems in such a way that the pest, possibly, should not or may not reach the stage of mass reproduction. In Fig. 72 the weaker or stronger interactions of the elements of a cultivated ecosystem are illustrated according to Schwerdtfeger (1950), Manninger (1960). The objective of integrated plant protection is to increase the effects against the pests in the best possible way while to reduce those hindering the growth of cultivated plants to a minimum (Table 26). Perennial plant crops are more suitable for integrated protection than annual plants, and also the insects are more suitable than diseases (Franz and Krieg 1972). The objectives of integrated protection are summarized in Table 27 (Franz and Krieg 1972).

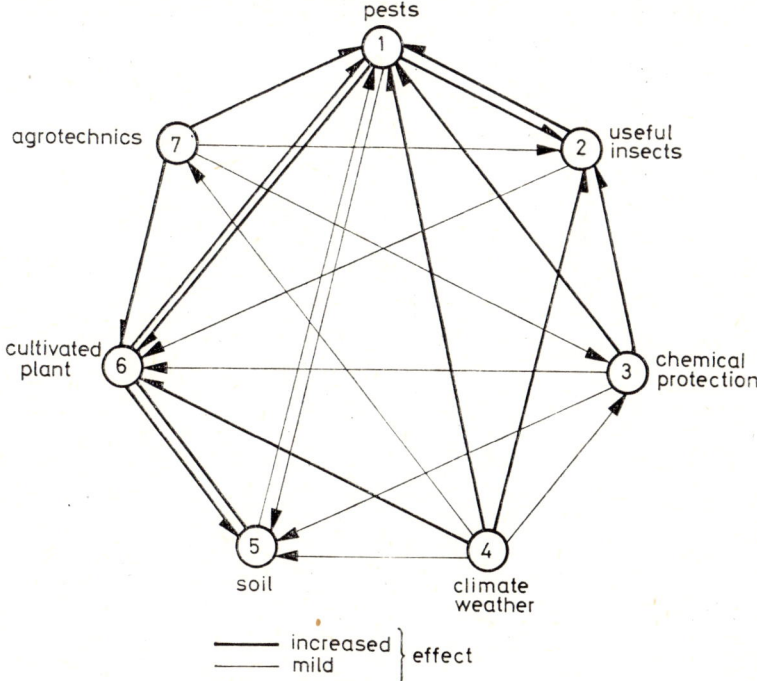

Fig. 72. Interaction between the ecosystem components

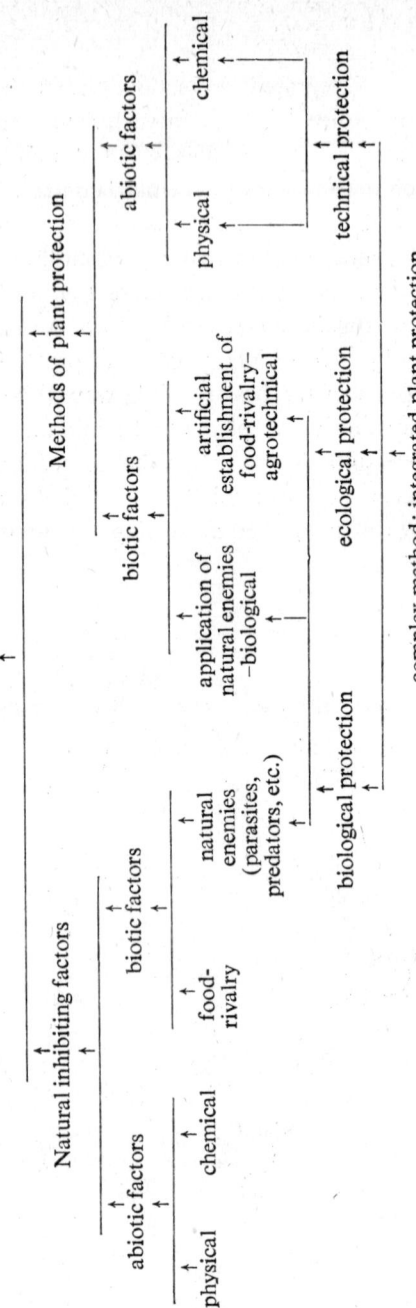

260

Table 26

Integrated plant protection

Aim: to keep the number of pests under the danger limit

mortality factor

Natural inhibiting factors

abiotic factors

physical — chemical

biotic factors

food-rivalry

natural enemies (parasites, predators, etc.)

Methods of plant protection

biotic factors

application of natural enemies –biological

artificial establishment of food-rivalry–agrotechnical

biological protection

ecological protection

abiotic factors

physical — chemical

technical protection

complex method: integrated plant protection

Table 27

Methods of integrated plant protection

Methods	
In connection with plant cultivation	choice of the soil manuring selection of species mowing-time
Physical	mechanical methods heat-treatment
Biotechnical	sound light hormones pheromones repellents attractants phagodeterrents phagostimulants
Biological	protection of useful organisms focal development from useful organisms introduction of useful insects self-destruction microbiological protection biological weed control
Chemical	insecticides acaricides rodenticides nematicides fungicides

COMPLEMENTARY METHODS FOR THE PRESERVATION OF THE ENVIRONMENT

Methods which are less dangerous for the human being, for domestic animals and for the already formed or just evolving agro-biocoenosis than those used until recently are called environment conservation complex methods. Although these mainly include methods using chemicals the term also implies modified or less "drastic" physical or agronomical techniques. The following example illustrates these particular conservation methods.

Two and a half decades ago, the technical HCH and DDT dusts were used against the pests of lucerne in all possible cases, from spring until the appearance of green flowering shoots. When it became probable that DDT and BHC were far more toxic than had been previously thought and were accumulated in the human body, all efforts were made to replace them. In protection the aim is to prevent the chemicals from getting on to the plant, and also to prevent soil and air pollution. The modernization of harvesting and cultivation methods has come to our assistance in achieving this aim. The chief requirement for making silage and for hot air drying is the early mowing and immediate collection of lucerne. In Hungary this work is done either in the last ten days of April or in the first ten days of May. At this time, the characteristic spring pests of lucerne (*Phytodecta fornicata, Subcoccinella* 24 *punctata, Phytonomus variabilis*) are still in the egg or young larval phase. The early harvest and conservation of lucerne kill the eggs and young larvae of these parasites. The small, susceptible larvae remaining in the field, will lack food and protection (Manninger 1972). This agricultural technology prevents the mass reproduction of the insects mentioned and consequently, the damage they cause. In exceptional cases, the diazinon (organophosphorus insecticide and acaricide) containing granules of Basudin can also be applied on the lucerne stubble. It must be worked into the soil by the harrow. Consequently, in this case the toxic substance does not get on to the plant.

In seed growing, besides the application of either the above-mentioned or of conventional methods, attractant strips can also reduce the degree of chemical protection needed. When starting with seed growing of lucerne (as we usually leave second growth for seed) non-mown attractant edges or strips are left. These will then attract the insects to themselves, especially when the budding and flowering phases appear. Apart from the stubble application, plant protection can be restricted to the strips. Even at the time of flowering, hand or mechanical insect collectors are to be applied only in the strips; insecticides which do not affect the pollinating insects can also be used.

It is a pity that Phosdrin (containing mevinphos, a systemic organophosphorous insecticide of short persistence) has proved to be phytotoxic (Benedek et al. 1971). Manninger and his co-workers, however, apply pesticides in the flowering phenophase, when they are not toxic to bees, but kill the majority of pests. Thus, although the climate of Transdanubia (at Alsópáhok) is not at all favourable for growing lucerne seed, following an evening spraying with Phosdrin, the employment of lucerne leaf-cutter bees (*Megachile rotundata*) led to a seed yield of 31.2 q/ha in 1973.

The so-called soil sterilization, generally used against soil pests, means the placing of insecticides into the soil. By aboveground application of pesticides the organisms living in the soil can be preserved. According to this objective a successful protection was carried out in 1966 and 1969 against the imagos (flying insect stage) of the forest maybeetle, when their development had been forecast. A Yugoslavian example shows that the control of the imagos of corn-beetles (*carabidae*) is working also in stubbles.

POSSIBLE ALTERNATIVE METHODS OF PROTECTION

In the case of a negative forecast for the number of pests to be expected all protection may be abandoned. If the pest infestation is low then the amount of damage is likely to be minimal. In this way substantial quantities of material and labour can be saved and the poisoning of the biosphere can also be greatly reduced (Manninger 1971). From among the insects, those developing only one annual generation offer the best opportunity for negative forecasting. In 1951, on the basis of forecasting, in the control of *Bothynoderes punctiventris,* and *Psalidium maxillosum,* large quantities of chemicals could be saved in several districts of the country.

A computerized study of 640 maize fields in 1971 proposed to abandon protection in 73% of these sites. In 1973 the survey of 120,000 ha of industrial maize production system at Bábolna resulted in the saving of large amounts in costs.

CLASSIFICATION OF ECOSYSTEMS FROM THE PLANT PROTECTION POINT OF VIEW

In nature conservation areas there is no place for the use of plant protection chemicals. Pesticides should only be applied in surrounding areas with the greatest care and steps should be taken to prevent their drifting over to these areas.

In the national park forests only bird protection and in some cases well-proved special biological control, may be done (Plant Protection Code § 47–53). The potential use of integrated plant protection is possible only in large forests, with special emphasis on the biological, and if required, chemical method of preserving useful organisms.

In household and small-scale farming or in isolated scattered agricultural areas, minimal chemical protection may also be sponsored, together with the mechanical, biological and modern agronomical methods. This is another case where integrated protection is being applied. In large-scale farming with crop rotation the isolation of fields plays an important role in the protection system. Here the complex protection, using agronomical and chemical methods is applied. In intensive plant production systems, isolation is not such an important factor as the application of chemical protection. The aim is to ensure nature conservation and rational control at all stages, together with the help of modern forecasting of the incidence of pests.

References

Balogh, J. (1974): Ecological regulating systems and environment control (in Hungarian). *Búvár* **29**: 3–9.

Benedek, P., Gaál, S., Horák, E., Komlódi, J. and Manninger, S. (1971): Possibilities of use of insecticides in flowering lucerne crops (in Hungarian). *Növényvédelem* **7**: 241–248.

Bordás, S. (1972): Recent systems for the evaluation of the public health risks of plant protection chemicals (in Hungarian). *Növényvédelem* **8**: 496–500.

Franz, J. M. and Krieg, A. (1972): *Biologische Schädlingsbekämpfung*. Paul Parey Berlin–Hamburg.

Hargitai, F. (1972): Chemical plant protection. In: *Manual of Agricultural Chemistry* (in Hungarian) Magyar Vegyipari Egyesülés. Budapest.

Jermy, T. (1957): The importance of the food specific of herbivorous insects in relation to plant protection (in Hungarian). Növényvédelmi Kutató Intézet Évkönyve 4: 45–51.

Kuroli, G. (1970): Repellent action of aluminium foil against aphids in tomato and paprika crops (in Hungarian). *Növényvédelem* **6**: 499–503.

Manninger, G. A. (1960): *Animal pests of agricultural crops, with special reference to protection on large scale farms*. Budapest.

Manninger, G. A. (1971): Possibilities to reduce the poisoning of the biosphere by plant protection by forecasting pest intensities (in Hungarian). *Agrártud. Közlem.* **30**: 271–274.

Manninger, G. A. (1972): The modern harvesting of lucerne and the reduction of the danger of poisoning the biosphere (in Hungarian). *Agrártud Közlem.* **31**: 173–176.

Nagy, B. (1971): Plant protection economy and technology (in Hungarian). Personal communications.

Nagy, B. (1973): The role of chemical processing in recycling technological sytems. II. *Magyar Mezőgazdaság* **28**: 8.

Schwerdtfeger, F. (1950): *Grundriss der Forstpathologie*. Berlin–Hamburg.

Steiner, H. (1966): Proc. FAO Symp. *Integr. Pest. Contr. Rome, 1965*. **3**: 13–20.

Ubrizsy, G. (1968): Biological plant protection In: Ubrizsy, G. et al.: (eds): *Encyclopedia of plant protection* (in Hungarian). Budapest.

Chapter 9

The effects of urbanization on landscape elements and woodland cover

THE EFFECT OF HUMAN ACTIVITY ON THE BIOSPHERE

Modern man has applied ever more sophisticated methods to investigate the Earth's life history. He is interested in its past and wants to find out and to have proofs on the great question as to when the Earth was formed and what happened to it in its "youth". According to the latest investigations the predecessors of the present man had existed in Africa already 3 million years before us. 400,000 years ago he probably lived together with 1 million of his fellow-"men" on the Earth. Homo sapiens appeared some 80,000 years ago. In order to secure his food he needed approx. 4 km^2 of gathering and hunting areas. Following the domestication of some animal species, the first revolution in the production of material goods had taken place: it was the tillage of land. With the glaciers receding in the last ice-age, the territory between the latitudes 20 and 40 had been gradually becoming warmer and drier. People, who until then had lived sporadically, were moving in the direction of the river valleys where they built settlements and acquired the knowledge of irrigation of the plants. With the introduction of farming, the number of inhabitants on a given territory could quadruple, as already 1 km^2 territory was needed for the sustenance of one man. It is relevant to note that farming was confined to only a small proportion of such a huge territory, the greatest proportion being used for grazing and hunting for a long time.

In the Middle Ages, in Europe, 3–4 ha of cultivated area was sufficient to cover the needs of one man, whilst today, in the economically developed countries, 1 ha of land would be enough to nourish 5–6 individuals if the demand for animal protein—in comparison to the Middle Ages—had not multiplied.

To illustrate the length of the ages of development in relation to each other, it has become customary to condense the events into the 24 h of a day. To do this, in the case of the history of Archeothropus, 1 h would equal approx. 125,00 years and it was only at the beginning of the 24th h that Archeothropus became Homo sapiens. The idea of farming occurred to man at "3–4 min" to midnight only; towns had been built only for some "2–3 min" and it was not until "20 s" that an area of 3–4 ha nourished one man, and only "2–3 s" that 1 ha could supply food for 2–3 men. No wonder that man has not thought as to what could be the consequence of his environment-forming activity, the urbanization of vast areas.

The "demographical explosion" has been giving much concern lately. The rapid increase in the population of the Earth and its consequences are, however, mainly dealt with only in general terms.

At the time when one man needed 4 km^2 area to secure his food, approx. 23–25 thousand men could live on the 93,000 km^2 territory of Hungary. (At present this is the number of inhabitants in a smaller Hungarian town.) At the beginning of our era 100,000 people could have lived in the territory of the country but, in contrast to the present 100, only 1 person lived on 1 km^2. With their primitive tools they could not do any great harm to their surroundings. In the Middle Ages, when our agricultural territory amounted to 6 million ha, the population may have numbered between 2–3 million. As a rough estimate, this meant a population density of 25 capita/km^2 this being higher than the average population density of the Earth at present. Today, in Hungary the population density exceeds 100 capita/km^2, with nearly 7,000 m^2 agriculturally utilized and 9,000 m^2 total area occupied by one inhabitant. Should around the year 2000 the number of the population of the Earth amount to 6 billion and only half of the dry land be considered inhabitable, the population density could be as high as it is in Hungary today. The present population density in North and Central America amounts to 12.7, while in South America it is 10 and in Africa 11.

Until the introduction of farming the biosphere had not changed substantially. Archeothropus has, however, changed all the more. He remained part of nature, acquiring, however, only the characteristic features of his life style, the use of tools and agricultural production. From his evolution, condensed into 24 h, man needed more than 23 h to become Homo sapiens. It had taken a very long time until he separated from the biosphere, and became a social being. This separation, lasting until "5 min" to midnight was however, a relative one, similarly to the period to come in which he had definitely to adapt himself to his environment. As a sentient being he transposed the powers of nature governing his everyday life into supernatural ones and by offering sacrifices he tried to find their favours.

According to a dramatized parable in the peoples' epos, the Bible, God preferred the sacrifice of Abel, the hunter, to the burning products of Cain, the farmer. Cain kills Abel, destroys the old, so that the development of the new be unharmed. His offsprings, the farmers being bound to one place were more dependent on the "blind powers of nature" than the hunters had been. Therefore, they had created such new gods, who demanded already human-sacrifices. Many a man had been put on the sacrificial altar before sufficient knowledge and experience secured the continuous food supply.

Originally, the fertile territories suitable for agriculture had been woody, afforested river valleys. With the increasing population newer and newer agricultural areas were needed, as the development of the majority of production tools was slower than that of the increase in population. Forests had to be felled in order to start food production in their place. Marshes and water-covered meadows were drained and pastures ploughed. The number of settlements was growing. With the exception of the water of rivers everything disappeared that had made the Earth fertile earlier, and wind and water erosion became widespread.

Owing to the wish to live in the accustomed surroundings and man's inventiveness, the skills of irrigation were invented. Looking back in time, the size and efficiency of barrage and other irrigation systems are fascinating. As the increase in fertility due to the effect of forest, marsh and other water surfaces—as well as effects due to climatic factors—had ceased, the production of sufficient amounts of food became possible only by the application of artificially regulated water. Where the conditions for irrigation had ceased for a particular reason, vast areas became deserts within a short period of time. If wars were not aimed at the occupation of new territories, the primary goal of the invading armies was to destroy the irrigation works and to kill all those who had the knowledge to rebuild them.

Although the afore-mentioned episodes lasted only for "seconds" before "3–4 min" to midnight, the ruins of settlements of cultures having existed 5–6 thousand years ago, have been found mainly under the mounds of the sand deserts.

Presumably, in the area of the "fertile half-moon"—in the valleys of the Nile, Tigris, Euphrates as well as the Indus—the climate had not been as hot as today although, in the course of some thousands of years, it had become already similar to the present climate.

The metabolism of a naked, inactive man—depending on the humidity and motion of the air—is at its minimum when the temperature of his environment is 29–35° C. With the temperature rising, especially in the course of heavy physical work the oxygen consumption and the intensity of the metabolism increase. The amount of blood flowing through the hand thus transporting heat to the surface of the body frequently increases to thirty times the normal value, while that of the water transpired within a given interval, becomes 100-times greater. Workers in heated workplaces transpire some 12 l water during 8 h. The temperature-regulating mechanism of those working at high temperatures or of those doing heavy physical labour, regulates the inner temperature of the body not infrequently permanently above 38° C.

As the feeding of draught animals would have required too large areas of land, in societies with high population densities, using irrigation, their breeding did not become widespread. Thus, irrigation made slave labour cheaper than animal rearing. Slaves did not need expensive robes and accommodation. Beyond the 35–40 latitudes of the northern hemisphere no slave state existed. The "living-tool" of ancient Mediterranean societies, the man working hard under the blazing sun "burned out" soon. His muscles produced 70% of the heat of his body. In comparison with this, the share of his brain was very small. His owner lived in conditioned environment protected against light radiation and heat.

Desert dwellers wore white robes reflecting light radiation. They lived in settlements reflecting light, which were characterized by narrow, shaded passages, smooth white walls and gates facing the direction of air currents. This was nothing else but instinctive, developing later on towards a conscious energy storehouse, based on physical phenomena. The palaces of monarchs were built in gardens rich in transpiring plants and evaporating water surfaces. High fences and walls provided protection not only against invaders, but also prevented cooled air from drifting away. This was the initially instinctive, later on consciously established energy-household based on biophysical processes. The Mediterranean slave societies had invented techniques, working methods and knowledge, by which it was possible to exploit the favourable natural potentials more effectively. These were also employed by the inhabitants of the sub-Mediterranean area and later on by people living in the temperate zone.

In the sub-Mediterranean, later on in the temperate zone, the formation of more developed societies—both in the economic and cultural sense—became only possible when the instruments of production had developed enough not only to produce sufficient quantities of food and clothing but rendered it possible to build appropriate abodes with heating as well. It is easier to protect the human body and the skin against cold than against heat. Heating is cheaper than cooling and it is also easier to obstruct air currents than to start them. The Roman Empire, with its centre in the sub-Mediterranean, became the greatest and at the same time, the last slave-keeping society of the world at the beginning of the last "minute" to midnight.

Owing to the highly developed standard of tools and the means of production, the relationship between man and his environment had greatly changed. Inhabitants of the Apennine-peninsula were no longer afraid of nature, but enjoyed it. Also the character of the gods had significantly changed by then.

Forests were no longer cleared merely in order to gain newer areas of land for cultivation. Besides the building of towns, commercial vessels and warships, heating and pearl-ash (potash) production especially consumed large quantities of wood.

Rich Roman citizens preferred spending their time in baths, the water of which had to be clear and warm. Mainly charcoal was used for the warming up of water. This was preferable for several reasons. It did not pollute the town and could be easily transported even on long distances. In addition to this charcoal was easy to handle. As a result of this, charcoal and potash production (the latter was used for washing) had eaten up the forests of the peninsula, later on also those of the surrounding territories. Owing to geological reasons, this has not been followed by desert formation but by the formation of karsts. The Roman Empire had the greatest proportion of its food grown in its colonies. With the exception of the Po valley, which could be irrigated, there had remained scarcely a fertile area on the peninsula. As nothing had remained to prevent rainwater from running down on the karstic limestone surfaces, great floods were frequent. These were followed by the formation of swamps and marshes. Although these were effective as climatic factors and water-table regulators in soil, scientists of the age believed them to be the "hot-bed" of miasma. As in the drained state they were utilizable for plant cultivation, most of them were done away with in the course of river regulation.

Gradually, the local climate of vast areas on the peninsula was becoming more unfavourable, the fertile land surfaces barren and infertile. Roman citizens, statesmen, otherwise "focussing on infinity", owing to their local short-sightedness, had spoiled one of the basic preconditions of their existence, the fertility of their land. Rome was canalized. Aqueducts working on the principle of gravity spanned valleys. They supplied Rome with 1 million m^3 of water daily. (The water consumption of Budapest is less even in our days.) When the slums of the inner-town had already become intolerable, Nero set fire to them and public parks were built in their place in order to improve environmental conditions. Although rich Roman citizens lived in towns, in houses surrounded by gardens, in villas, they built also "villa suburbana" and "villa rustica" for themselves. The emperors established extensive resort units either in the vicinity of Rome or at distant places with favourable environmental conditions. Parallel to the increasing deterioration and barrenness of the agricultural areas, there was a growing demand for these. However, this method had not been invented by the Romans. Although on the territory of the "fertile half-moon" there had been ample examples for this, the Romans aimed at an, until then, unknown perfection in this field.

The transformation of the biosphere into the noosphere, a territory conquered by man, started 8,000 years ago. Around 5,000 years ago the formation of dwelling-regions started from the already existing scattered abodes. With the rapid extension of settlements, town regions with artificial vegetation had evolved which served for recreational purposes. Thus, in the territory of the Roman Empire the resort-region developed nearly 2,000 years ago.

According to certain theories almost during the entire Middle Ages one corn of wheat yielded three corns. One corn was used for sowing-seed, the second for different purposes and only an ear of corn remained for consumption. The daily energy need of a man is a constant value of about 3,000 kcal. In the early Middle Ages there was no potato, maize and sugar-beet in Europe. Animal protein and fats were almost treasures. As cultivation methods had not seen any significant development for centuries, there was only one way to increase the amount of food by extending the cultivated territory. Forest felling, pasture ploughing spread all over Europe. In countries, where wars, epidemics and other reasons slowed down the population increase, mainly nomadic stock-raising remained as a custom alongside farming. Naturally, such countries had remained backward in economic development.

By the time of the industrial revolution almost all forests had been cleared in Western and Central Europe and in their place partly food production started. It is relevant to note that this resulted in the decrease in fertility. The nutrient resources of clearings giving temporarily great yields became rapidly exhausted, with the soil washed off from the slopes. Ploughing even accelerated erosion, as frequently it was perpendicular to contour lines. As there was no forest litter to hold back rainwater, the danger of great floods causing a loss in the value of the fertile plains along the rivers was always imminent.

In those parts of Europe where there was no ashlar (square-hewn stones), bricks had to be burned for building purposes. The demand for wood was therefore great. With the expansion of the towns the demand for heating material was also steadily increasing. For the washing of underwear lye was made at home by diluting and filtering woodash. This, however, was not able to meet demands. Consequently, in order to produce potash forests were being cleared and burned continuously.

In the Middle Ages European towns were not generally of such a size that they could have affected their environment. By the time trees and gardens appeared in towns surrounded by city walls between the official and residential buildings confined to a limited area, the local climate had deteriorated to such an extent that it was already detrimental for plant and man alike. Therefore trees and plants had to be cultivated.

In the Middle Ages people living in towns generally had a vineyard, an orchard and a vegetable garden outside the city walls where they could overcome the harmful effects of town life. The town-meadow, outside the town walls (the Pratum, Prado, Prater), the predecessor of today's public parks was a favourable place for the "sport activity of the masses". Private parks of larger extent were established only in the Renaissance and the Baroque era. In the Middle Ages the resort regions for mass relaxation were unknown.

After the discovery of America, merchant shipping had become a vital economic factor. The spread of food crops of American origin—potato and maize—had become an important basis for the growth of population. Simultaneously with the emergence of a new social class, the connection between man and nature had also changed significantly. One of the characteristic features of this change was the general spread of the idea and slogan "back to Nature". Nevertheless a long time had passed before town's folk started to think of forests as part of the "peaceful and idyllic nature".

By the time of the industrial revolution, about 80% of the population of European countries was engaged in agriculture. Therefore, in the present sense of the word there were really not many urban dwellers. However, with the start of coal-mining and industrial production the ratio of farmers and industrial workers has changed. The standard of economic development of a certain country is to be determined on the basis of different characteristics. One of these is the employment and professional structure. Developed agriculture can rise on developed industry, while both of them require a high level of education, research, organization, planning, in general, the basic structure of the services.

More than 80% of the population in economically undeveloped countries or in those just starting development produce food, though rarely the amount and quality that would meet the minimal demands. In highly developed countries the ratio of the food-producing population is under 10%. The latter, however, produces generally much more than required by the entire population.

With a high ratio of animal products, forced vegetables and fruits, only those countries are capable of satisfying the requirement of their own population in which at least 15–20% of the population is employed in food production. According to statistics, in 1970, some countries could be characterized by the following values of agricultural employment: England 4, Belgium 6, Sweden 12, GDR 19, Italy 25, Poland 43, Greece 53, Romania 59, India 70, Nepal 92%. In Hungary, approx. 18% of the population is concerned with food production directly. (In 1945 the proportion of farmers was nearly 60%.)

In the 19th century the towns of industrially developed countries saw a rapid development. The majority of them had far outgrown the medieval city walls and at the beginning of the 20th century towns numbering millions of inhabitants were not uncommon. During the period of rapid expansion little attention was paid to how much mines, factories or the towns themselves harmed the public interest, or affected local facilities. Apart from apathy, the neglect of the public interest and short-sighted optimism caused much damage, especially in water regulation on a regional basis and in river regulation. Water that had been considered superfluous and detrimental in the 19th century gave much concern to the farmers and water-regulators in the 20th century. The largest part of agricultural land was in private ownership. In areas of reduced fertility and in hilly eroded regions only poor farmers were generally farming. It had not occurred to anyone that by expropriating and afforesting these territories the cause of floods could be eliminated. It seemed to be a realistic solution to speed up the water flow by cutting off river bends, to secure defence from floods by building dikes and to gain new fertile areas by the draining of marshy and boggy areas. No matter how economic and advantageous this method may have seemed at first sight, in reality it was not, even in those times when the extension of fertile land was almost the only possibility of increasing yields. The rapid conveyance of surface waters into rivers and then into the sea may endanger the energy-balance of a territory. As a result of drainage, yields of great regions decrease to a greater extent than the surplus yield gained on the extended cultivated area. On the Great Hungarian Plain several of the agricultural drains are called "evil-drain".

THE ROLE OF VEGETATION IN THE NOOSPHERE

In the course of their interactions, during millions of years, solar energy, water, vegetation and soil have created a state of equilibrium. Any disturbance done to it may have fatal consequences.

Since a plant is a living organism, with a heat and water regime of its own, it exerts a certain reaction on the climate of its habitat. As in the course of their development, plants change their form, increase in size, their effect on the light, heat and water economy of the surrounding air-layer and soil also increase. There will be an interaction between plant and the climate of its habitat—on which its existence depends—which results in the changing of the climate of the habitat.

The ability of plants to modify the micro- and local climate depends mainly on the extent to which they can affect the energy-economy of their own as well as that of their environment. Even the simplest, most primitive and physically lowest (forming the thinnest layer) vegetation changes the light, heat and water economy of soil by raising the active level (surface) of insolation and emission—depending on crop density—to its own level. Due to this the most varied climatic phenomena occur within the atmosphere of the plant cover, either on its surface or in the soil coating and soil near the air levels. Vegetation is, therefore, a climatic factor the effect of which is displayed mainly in the changing of the material quality of the Earth's surface.

Within the plant cover or microclimatic modifications having an effect on layers nearest to the soil, these soil layers can exert their "remote-effect" only in those cases, where they are capable of modifying significantly the characteristic phenomena of their natural habitat. This ability depends on several factors, the amount of light energy consumed by the plant community in photosynthesis, the amount of light and heat reflected towards upper air layers or its environment (albedo), the amount of heat it is capable of storing temporarily by raising the temperature of its body, in the course of insolation, or the amount of heat fixed in the process of transpiration and evaporation.

Apart from the albedo-effect and the possibility of raising the temperature, the degree of light and "heat-consumption" in photosynthesis and transpiration, under given environmental conditions, also depends on the water-factor.

It is the deciduous and certain coniferous forests that exhibit the most perfect water-economy of natural precipitation. In forests, the run-off factor is minimal, on grasslands however especially in the case of sloping land it always plays a major role.

In enclosed deciduous forests, the active layer of insolation and emission is high above the soil surface, in the tree canopy or on its surface. Since the mechanical and physiological drying effects of wind are of lesser effect within the stand, therefore the climate of forests extends, in contrast to grassy surfaces, to a very significant air-layer. Moreover, as forests are capable of utilizing water, they absorb more light energy in photosynthesis, though their transpiration is also greater than that of the non-irrigated grass surfaces. Consequently, their effect on climate can be felt much more in remote regions.

Let us assume a case in which the intensity of solar irradiation amounts to 0.7 cal/cm²/min (1 cal = 4.1868 J.). 50% of this energy is photosynthetically active (400–750 nm) and the other 50% belongs to the infrared region. In the case of a favourable stand density, leaves absorb 85% of the photosynthetically active and 25% of the infrared rays, approx. 55% of the total energy. This amounts to 235 kcal/m²/h. In the case of the usual light intensity (average) 1.5 to 2% of the solar energy absorbed is utilized in the form of photochemical bonds. This will equal 3.5–4.5 kcal/m²/h. which, as a mean value, corresponds to the production of 1 g organic matter. The maximum photosynthetic capacity of plants is dependent on the relative optimum of factors in the habitat, among others, the optimum of the body temperature, which varies within relatively narrow limits. In windless weather, especially when the temperature of air exceeds that of the leaves required for optimal photosynthetic activity, long wave emission, heat-conduction and concention reduce the temperature of the leaves to a small extent. Roughly 400 g water has to be evaporated to counterbalance the circa 230 kcal/m²/h. heat energy. This is 400–600-times the organic matter produced and not utilized in respiration. This, expressed as the height of a water-column, amounts to 4–5 mm, i.e. 4–5 lm⁻², as a mean for summer days.

Should radiation intensity exceed the value of 0.7 cal/cm²/min. more than 5 1/m² water would be required to neutralize it.

Plants cannot live on those surfaces where there is no available water to regulate and cool the body temperature. Intermolecular movement which takes place at a body temperature of 45–50° C kills the sensitive proteins and plants at the same time. In summer, the temperature of sand frequently exceeds 50° C, even in the temperate zone.

While in the eternal-snow-covered parts of the world solar energy is not capable of inducing thermal-agitation needed to initiate plant life and in deserts it is the extreme of thermal agitation that limits plant life.

The daily and seasonal fluctuation of the energy of solar radiation would make plant life impossible except only on a little part of dry-land, if water by its high specific heat and especially by the uptake of energy required for transpiration, did not reduce the intermolecular agitation within the body of the plant.

By the evaporation of a 5 mm high water column, which corresponds to the evaporation of 5 l water per m^2, nearly 3,000 kcal thermal energy becomes latent heat. This is as much as the thermal value of 1 kg of brown-coal and would be sufficient to heat 1 m^2 area of glasshouse daily, in winter, in spite of the fact that the efficiency of heating installations is very small.

Water transpired in the course of the day reduces the temperature of plants, soil and plant cover, while the relative humidity increases. Should this humidity not be removed from the local climatic units by air currents or the humidity of other areas drift into a given space then, during nights that promote emission, it will precipitate, in the form of dew, on surfaces and then cool down to a large extent. When assuming that the amount of dew measured by the conventional methods does not exceed 1 mm occasionally, this would correspond to the burning of 1 kg coal of 3,000 kcal heating value on an area of 5 m^2. Concepts as to the form in which dew is utilized by plants are rather diverse. It is, however, a fact that condensed water implies further potentialities for evaporation and transpiration, it contributes to the reduction of the body temperature during the morning hours. This makes it unnecessary for the plant to transport this amount of water from the soil to the surfaces of transpiration, thus consuming its own energy.

It is worth considering two main aspects of the previously discussed, well-known complex phenomenon.

Deserts are characterized by an energy utilization regulated by physical principles. Day and night temperatures vary greatly. The main reason for this is that water does not take part in energy utilization. The energy utilization of surfaces covered by vegetation is regulated not only by physical but also by biological principles. Water and sun energy regulation is realised by the physiological mechanisms of vegetation. During the day a greater proportion of solar energy is transformed into latent heat by the help of transpiration thus reducing the air temperature and the thermal agitation of the matters involved. The vapour thus formed absorbs a certain proportion of infrared irradiation and reduces the warming up of the soil surface. At night, according to similar principles, long-wave emission as well as the reduction of thermal agitation are limited. At dawn, a certain proportion of the vapour precipitates in the form of dew, thus giving off the energy stored since the previous day. In this way it limits the fall in the air temperature and also the decrease in the intermolecular agitation of plants and thus plants are capable of better utilization of the radiation of the rising sun. Should the body temperature of plants rise to an undesirable extent, the evaporation of dew would reduce the temperature of the body and also that of the air. This sequence of phenomena is the most favourable, especially in the summer months. Vineyards with an eastern or south-eastern aspect along Lake Balaton or the River Rhine are in an especially favourable position, in this respect, as they are capable of utilizing the reflected irradiation from water surfaces.

Another important factor is—in order to improve the energy utilization of areas poor in precipitation in relation to their solar energy uptake—to secure such climatic conditions under which the physical state of the total rainfall, or a certain proportion of it can be changed within the local or mesoclimatic region several times. Thus, local climatic elements will become more balanced and more favourable for plant life. The most effective climatic factor of this type is the multi-levelled forest with a large volume stand.

ECOLOGICAL PROBLEMS OF LARGE TOWNS

The controlling balance, influencing the physical and physiological process-sequences, characteristic of landscape areas dominated by natural elements, are also characteristic of those dominated by artificial elements, i.e. of towns, residential areas. The formation of deserts, barren areas in vast regions of the Earth is, generally, the aftermath of human activity. While in the initial phase, the destruction of biocoenoses having evolved under the influence of local climate is gradually building up, the upsetting of the equilibrium, beyond a certain limit, results in a rapid deterioration. It is town building, that has damaged nature to the greatest degree. The local climate of large towns, the microclimate of small areas, is always less favourable for human and plant life than the original, natural climate of the same area. Large towns change almost all climatic factors characteristic and determinant of their area prior to their establishment and they spoil not only the local natural climate of their territory, but they also exert harmful effects on areas lying on their permanent lee side—frequently within the range of 30–50 km.

At present, in the urban area of large towns almost every square metre of area is covered by either building or solid cover. As a consequence of this, 60–90% of rain water falling on this area is conducted outside the town through the sewage system. This water is not evaporated or transpired within the town, therefore there is no latent heat to limit the amount of heat of solar origin. The humidity deficiency of urban air is generally higher—its relative humidity is, generally, lower—than values measured in their natural environment. In spite of this, owing to air pollution, fogs are more frequent than in the surrounding areas of towns, therefore—especially in the early morning hours—the annual mean of irradiation is generally much lower.

Towns develop a characteristic wind-system of their own. They generally limit wind velocity previously characteristic of its original area, though in "wind-tunnels" it is detrimentally increased. With the exception of winter, towns produce permanent ascending air currents, the intensity of which changes diurnally. The characteristic wind system evolving within different parts of the city, differs from any kind of natural wind-systems. Concerning light and heat, the building and covering materials used in towns behave in the same way as rocks devoid of water and they absorb and store large amounts of heat. As the emission intensity of vertical surfaces is very small, owing to the heat emission taking place during the night, towns cannot get rid of this heat easily, in the summer. On the other hand air-borne pollutants absorb and re-emit heat.

In towns it takes generally a shorter time for the snow to melt than in the natural environment and similarly, the interval between the last frost in spring and the first one in autumn is also significantly longer. The growing season sets in and the blossoming of plants generally begins earlier. Owing to factors roughly outlined previously, large towns are detrimental for human life for several reasons.

In Hungary several new towns and residential districts have been built and some old towns have been rebuilt, however, various factors make it difficult to secure optimal living conditions. Typical faults are scheduling carelessness in both planning and execution, insufficient knowledge or neglect of biological and climatic factors, unimaginative planning of green open spaces and their proper irrigation, the failure to secure favourable soil conditions for establishment of parks and gardens as well as the ill-considered saving of sums required for their maintenance. The individual units of a coherent verdure, situated within the town, are capable of exerting a local effect on their wider environment only in those cases, where their extent is at least a relatively unbroken expanse of 2–4 ha in area. Other plots of smaller extent and gardens exert a local or microclimatic effect only on their immediate environment and offer a climatic advantage mainly for those taking a walk, or having a rest. They are, mainly, of aesthetic or psychological value.

The establishment of "air-tunnels" connecting the town centre with the natural environment should be preceeded by detailed long-term climatic studies, which may last for years if it is necessary. Naturally, only the study of the interactions of numerous factors or the preliminary consideration of effects to be expected may succeed.

In the Federal Republic of Germany aerial serial photographs have been taken recording the infrared irradiation of towns and their environments. The direction and extent of local air currents are determined on the basis of these. Factors that hinder favourable currents are eliminated. By establishing new climatic factors, the intensity of the current will be increased.

It may seem unnecessary to emphasize that no industrial plant or other sources of air pollution should be established or tolerated on the windward side of towns, as such establishments may cause, in certain situations, greater damage than the suburban forests and the individual units of greenery are capable of counterbalancing.

When establishing new towns and suburbs it is a primary task to analyse both the macro- and local climatic phenomena of the areas in question. In a given case, the favourable or unfavourable local climate of a settlement may have a long-lasting influence on the town to be built predetermining the living conditions of its inhabitants in a biological sense. Where the local climate is favourable for town-building, special attention should be paid to preserve these benefits during possible urbanization. The artificial changing of an unfavourable environmental climate may prove very expensive in any given case. Although, at the present stage of our economic development, it is not possible to create all the necessary conditions at once, the possibility of implementing climate improving factors—afforestation—should always be ensured.

In the windless weather, towns built on flat agricultural areas cannot get rid of their air-borne pollutants, because wheat fields and stubble having lost their soil-humidity during the vegetation season warm up in the course of the day—especially at noon—at least to the same degree as towns, i.e. the environment of the town not being able to supply ascending currents (convection) of towns with cooler air, a more or less stable state evolves, which is most unfavourable for the town. By establishing a large area of forest belt around the town its local climate could be improved.

In areas where permanent macro- or local climate winds are characteristic—the velocity of these winds not exceeding 3–4 degrees on the Beaufort scale—the town to be built can make use of the purifying effect of wind. In such a case, it should be built with its longitudinal extension at right angles to the direction of the prevailing wind. It is advisable to establish forest-belts on the weather side in order to purify occasional winds of laminar character generally carrying much polluting matter, and to induce their slight turbulence before they could enter the town. Plans should be drawn up so that streets, beyond satisfying the requirements for sunlight, could serve their task of airing—they should be built in a direction, so as not to slow down the climate improving artificial or natural air currents, or not to reduce the effect of air currents reaching the most remote areas.

When planning the direction and width of streets, special attention should be paid to the fact that long and narrow streets, running parallel to the wind direction, functioning like wind-tunnels speed up light winds blowing over the town and make them a nuisance. In streets exposed to the danger of wind-tunnel formation, more trees should be planted, so that they could prevent the creation of high wind speeds, and induce the turbulence of winds that would otherwise be merely blowing straight through the street. In suburban areas, it is always possible to plant narrow, longitudinally wind breaking and wind-filtering protecting belts of trees. Moreover, such tree-planting is often advisable within the city itself, too, especially in those cases where the sources of air pollution are situated on the windward side of the town or if they are meant to separate industrial from residential areas. It is necessary to plant screening trees always on the lee-side of polluting sources; the air-filtering effect of these is common knowledge.

Summarising, it is only on the basis of the most cautious, mainly biotic activity that the mesoclimate of already existing or new towns can be modified. A relatively favourable town climate can be achieved by the most complete exploitation of the climatic factors of the environment, in case of necessity, by the deliberate establishment of favourable climatic factors. When establishing new towns, it is the selection of the most advantageous settlement areas and the adaptation of the methods applied, which are the main factors by which appropriate local climate is to be achieved.

Plant species and tree stocks used in the planting of mesoclimate-improving forests, should be selected with full regard to ecological principles, as the effect of ecological factors—mainly that of the water—can only rarely be modified significantly. In extreme cases residential areas must be built on land with unfavourable soil properties. This is generally the case, when the given town has already occupied land with favourable characteristics. In general, the extension of such towns is necessitated by major requirements of the national economy. The modification of soil properties, the sinking of the groundwater table, the improvement of salt-affected soils by means of substances used in land improvement or top-soiling with soil imported from outside, are technically feasible processes. Although these processes are seemingly expensive, they are, in general, economically much more favourable than the reconstruction of already existing residential areas. This applies especially to cases where the costs of transport and of public utility services are not too high.

TASKS OF TOWN AND COUNTRY PLANNING

Changes in the landscape and environmental damage taking place in the last "3 s" of the history of mankind, condensed into 24 h, have accelerated and multiplied compared with earlier times.

The industrial revolution—the initiating vastly developing forces of production—created a machinery and processing technologies, which entirely opened up new possibilities to interfere with the laws of nature. The situation of those who applied these new techniques and technologies, was similar to that of a little boy who, playing with matches, knowing what they are used for but the only thing he does not know, is what he is allowed to light with them, how the fire spreads and how it can be put out. Although the "fire" that menaces the foundations of mankind has been burning already for a long time, it is possible for man, the controller of the scientific-technological revolution, to keep it under control. This can be achieved by a more circumspect, cautious conservation of the natural elements than previously.

The elimination of air, water and soil pollution is mainly an economic-technical question and only secondarily, a problem of workshop discipline. Although the damage caused by pollution cannot be entirely eliminated, complete elimination is not altogether necessary. The amount of pollution that is tolerable is the function of the national economy to decide and—in a broader sense—the responsibility of world-wide political decisions and agreements.

The technical equipments and technological methods for the elimination and neutralization of pollutants have been developed and solved in the case of almost all substances.

No doubt the products of certain factories are less valuable than the damage caused directly or indirectly, therefore, these should be closed. Presumably, however, if certain countries compelled investors and industrial undertakings to act, it would be possible to work out complex economical technologies and processing methods to solve the problems. To keep alive the sense of responsibility of authorized persons and the consciousness of mankind, it is worth while and also necessary to deal with the aftermath of pollution incidents and the wasteful exploitation of natural resources. The solution to this problem lies with the practical application of control and not with science itself. More exactly, the natural science aspects can be considered to be solved. There is a somewhat different situation as regards the elimination of environmental damage which is primarily of biological and climatological character having been caused or having evolved in the past. The preparatory work to do so is, temporarily, at an early stage. Up till now specialists have dealt with only certain details of this complex task. Towards the end of the 1960s and the beginning of the 1970s the international alarm bells of environment control authorities called attention to this topic which became very fashionable. In the economically more developed countries, where the output of industrial production and related to this also the degree of pollution, far exceeds that of Hungary, there is an antagonistic contrast between the private group and the communal interest which creates a much more serious situation. Governments and administrative authorities of capitalist states can, therefore, only attempt to reduce the damage done to nature. They are aware of the fact that both pollution and any harm done to natural elements and to man are consequences of the geographical distribution of the means and methods of production.

As in socialist countries, the means of production are in social ownership, it is the State that is responsible for damages and harm done to nature, more specifically the bodies commissioned by society to lead production and the authorities. Therefore, in socialist states only such harm can be done to the environment, the prevention of which is impossible owing to economic and production political reasons. The emphasis is on prevention; in Hungary environmental protection is to be considered a sub-discipline of territorial development, land and environmental planning. Environment control is a sectorial, territorial development and environment legislative arrangements, an intersectional and interdisciplinary task, a task at governmental level.

THE SIGNIFICANCE OF WOODLAND COVER, PARKS AND GARDENS

Owing to its impact on the climate, vegetation by modifying its environment effectively increases fertility. Shelter-belt, screening and landscaping tree plantations to be made in poor agricultural areas with limited potential will also increase the fertility of the areas *ab ovo* more favourable for cultivation. The utilization of vegetation and other natural elements with an impact on the climate, among them mainly water, for environment modifying objectives, is not a new idea. Complexes based on the interaction of biologically active and inactive surfaces, with other elements, were established as early as the ancient world. Castle complexes built by the Arabic caliphs on the Iberian peninsula in the Middle Ages, can be considered as masterpieces in this context.

Biologically inactive surfaces can either be natural or artificial ones. Natural inactive surfaces are sand, stone and snow deserts, artificial ones are surfaces covered by inert materials. Surfaces covered by water and vegetation are biologically active. In contrast to the inactive surfaces, the energy regime of which is determined by physical principles, the active ones have an energy regime regulated by physiological principles. By transforming the electromagnetic irradiation of the sun, the energy of photons into the energy of chemical bonds, surfaces covered by vegetation and trees partly produce organic matter and partly regulate and stabilize the composition of the atmosphere through their processes of metabolism, and as living climatic elements they modify the sequence of atmospheric phenomena determined by physical laws and by exerting modifying effects on their own vital conditions or on those of other living organisms, they contribute to their improvement. Man, in the course of his cultivating and environment-forming activities, making use of the double role and function of vegetation, has been planting and cultivating plants either for their yield or for their landscaping effect.

The conditioning effect of plants is of a physiological, psychological and aesthetic character. Wind breaking shelter-belts are useful because, by modifying physical phenomena, they produce more favourable physiological conditions. Plantations alongside highways, in addition to providing optical guidelines, offering the feeling of security, exert a landscaping effect in a mainly psychological sense. Parks and decorative gardens of holiday resort places and of towns are meant to produce a mainly aesthetic impression. Nevertheless, it is relevant to note that trees in decorative gardens, in addition to their wood material, used in heating, also have a conditioning effect in a physiological and psychological sense. Forests cultivated to produce timber, water surfaces established for water storage and energy production have also the most significant landscaping effect.

At the time of its conquest, nearly 30,000 km^2 of the 93,000 km^2 territory of Hungary was covered by forests. The extent of water surfaces was also significant. At present more than half of the forests existing in those times is missing, especially in the plain regions. As far as the ratio of forests is concerned Hungary ranks as one of the smallest countries in Europe.

Owing to the afforestation activity, the ratio of forests has been raised from 12.1% to 16.3% during the last two decades. Should this value reach 25% by the year 2000, it would be still less than the 28% of the world ratio and 31% of that of Europe.

The previously described temperature-regulating, evaporating and water-table modifying effects of storage lakes and of water surfaces generally justify their construction. As marshes have also a similar impact, their draining should be considered thoroughly. (As to the future, their function is likely to become broader, as wells built in or besides them can supply pure water to the regional waterworks.) In Hungary, open water surfaces evaporate nearly 1 m of water per year. (Annually approx. one third of the water content of Lake Balaton undergoes physical change.) In the case of storage lakes, specialists consider this as an unambiguous and unavoidable loss. As its role in the regulation of air temperature cannot be measured, it must be looked upon in this way. The amount of heat energy bound in the form of latent heat energy, in the course of evaporation, is a multiple of the equivalent energy content of energy carriers such as coal, crude oil and natural gas explored annually in Hungary.

The National Building Regulations ordains that the green space system of settlements, which consists of shelter forests, public parks and open gardens must be laid down in development plans, although the effect of this regulation applies only to approx. 600,000 ha of settlement land, a relatively small area of the country. The landscaping verdure system—to these belong water surfaces with similar aims—should be extended to the entire country. It is hoped that the new draft of the "forest-law", which will need modifications sooner or later, will provide an opportunity for this to be done.

Chapter 10

The role of forests in environmental protection

FOREST AS A NATURAL COMPONENT OF THE LANDSCAPE

In the eyes of the traveller, landscape is reflected as the complex of forests, agricultural areas, relief and artificial environment (settlements, industrial and agricultural units, mines, energy-producing and -distributing stations, transport, energy-conveying and telecommunication lines and also other establishments). Forests lend a specific feature to the landscape; its aesthetic impact and atmosphere create a special effect, particularly on town dwellers.

The unlimited richness, the closed or scattered distribution of trees, avenues, isolated stands of trees and forests, the colour, light and shade variations, make fleeting or lasting impression, or even pleasure for those who long for relaxation. The depressing lifelessness of a barren area, the scorching summer heat, the unceasing whirling of wind and dust, the tedium of monotony are discouraging and tiresome for man, almost driving him away from the area.

A tree-lined horizon evokes different impressions than does a sky-line created by barren hill contours or by various kinds of buildings sited on ridges and cutting into the blue sky.

The artist uses dead material to create his masterpiece. There are glowing colours on the palette of the painter, in his hand there is the canvas and he is talented, too. The landscape architect however—whose mission is to form or to maintain a natural environment around the artificial one— deals with living organisms, which beyond their individual lives, depend both on themselves and on their environment. It is often the responsibility for some-thousand-year-old remains, invisible tiny little life communities and measures having an influence for decades, that directs, limits and influences the creativeness of specialists. Therefore, we have to explore the basic rules of the life of forests, the limits of their adaptability, their role in the scenery so that they should permanently serve the development of the landscape.

THE ROLE OF WOODLAND AND FOREST VEGETATION
IN A PARTICULAR ECOLOGICAL SYSTEM

The forest itself is a life community (biocoenosis, ecosystem), which consists of interdependent elements: trees, shrubs and plants (phytocoenosis) and animals (zoocoenosis) and which directly influences its environment and also the climate and soil (biogeocoenosis). Taking into account the presence of man in the life of the forest, it can be considered an ecological system (ecosystem). Consequently, the forest is an organic unit, the parts of which are not to be separated, as they cannot exist on their own. Nevertheless, it is also impossible to build up a forest from its elements, as it is a unit which is simultaneously developing with its elements.

The "eternity" of a forest does not imply that its organisms live for ever, but it means that by maintaining a state of dynamic equilibrium, it is always capable of renewal. The special character of forests is imparted by the trees, which play a leading role in it. Trees standing beside each other will form a forest only in the case where they act on each other permanently and consequently, acquiring special inner (physiological) and outer (morphological) characteristics. These characteristics are quite different from those of solitary trees standing in the open.

A forest is, however, more than merely a group of interrelated trees. The forest is the most developed plant association with the highest organization in which, in addition to trees, also the shrubs, mosses and plants of the undergrowth play the major role. The vegetation of the lower levels—the herbaceous vegetation—manifests important features and gives a clue to its original state. It combines the activity of the upper soil level, reflecting the effect of heat and light energy as well as that of the water and nutrient regime of the forest.

The equilibrium of the life community (biocoenosis) can be sustained only at the price of constant changes—opposing forces and their resolution —therefore, it can be called a dynamic state of equilibrium. The forest itself is changing both in space (zonation) and in time (succession). The spring, summer, autumn and winter aspects of the forest, the seasonal changes in the appearance of the forest of the bioceonosis are the results of climatic changes. The picture of the forest changes also in the course of the life of one tree, from its youth to its old age and these changes are characterized by certain phases of development. Such phases are: revival, youth, juvenile, mature, old and senile ages; or according to the tree-size: virgate (thin shoots), sticky, roddy (coppice), linear and mature forests and their tree-stock.

Forests have been changing for thousands of years. This is called successional development. If this development results from a changing of the macroclimate, owing to which very large areas of forests were transformed, it is called a secular succession. If the cause of the change lies with the life-community, it is called a biotic succession. This change also has several stages. These are: initial transitional stage and a stable forest-association (climax or terminal stage) which is in harmony with the prevailing climate. It is an essential characteristic of a forest that, at a given time, it shows a definite stage of development. The above-mentioned stages are regarded as natural (endogenetic) ones.

Changes are, however, frequently caused by man (exogenetic change), who through his economic and other objectives, directs and controls the life of the forest. The gathering and hunting activities of man had done almost no harm to forests. Later on, in order to gain pastures and arable land, he began cutting down forests, thus initiating rapid changes in certain components (e.g. soil) of the biotope. Now as a result of intensive agricultural activity, the natural landscape is being transformed and the native, so-called semi-agricultural landscape is evolving. Although the forest still plays a leading role in it, its area is receding and there is a slow change in the indigenous community. In the industrial revolution, man created such equipments and discovered such resources, by which he had almost unlimited possibilities to transform the natural and semi-natural landscape on a huge area of the Earth's surface and to create and maintain a cultural landscape alien to nature.

The large-scale loading and polluting of natural resources can be ascribed to this. Several plant and animal species disappeared and in the course of the process of urbanization, man "created" that way of life, from which he—though only temporarily—already wishes to seek relaxation. In the meantime, the highly efficient (productive), intensive agricultural production systems—in contrast to the already existing way of production using areas of land—are capable of satisfying the ever increasing demands of society on a significantly smaller area of land. Owing to rational land exploitation, several hundred thousands of hectares of agricultural land, of reduced fertility, revert to the sphere of semi-wild ecosystems. In the course of his forestry activities, man leaves the development of the forest either to the forces of nature or, by using different techniques, he interferes intensively in order to realise his objectives. Accordingly, forest economies can be divided into two groups: (*i*) natural and (*ii*) artificial (plantation) forests. Tree plantations, the timber producing afforested areas are extreme forms of artificial forests.

The biocoenoses of higher fungi growing on the soil and in the so-called "root-zone" of the soil and also those of the microorganisms form an organic and important part of forest life communities. It is bacteria, microscopic fungi and algae that establish the connection between the organic and inorganic components of the forest.

Burrowing animals, as well as those living on the soil surface play a significant role in the maintenance of the unharmed metabolic circulation of materials. They accelerate the decomposition of organic debris. Plant and animal organisms passing through the digestive system also undergo chemical changes, thus preparing them for decomposing by bacteria, algae and fungi. Their lifeless body also contributes to the enrichment of the organic matter content of the soil (Pántos 1966).

The common name of soil flora and fauna is edaphon (Francé 1913), and the terricolous animals jointly represent the zoodaphon. Terricolous animals are classified according to their size. Animals of the size 0.001–0.2 mm belong to microfauna. Such are the Protozoa, Nematoda, Rotifera and Tardigrada (water bears). The mesofauna (0.2–2 mm) comprises Collembola (springtails), Acarina (mites and ticks). Members of the macrofauna (2–20 mm) are Myriapoda.

Animals larger than 20 mm form the megafauna. The terricolous protozoa living in the forest litter are, as a rule, hydrophilic, or active only in water. While the drying out of litter makes them encapsulate they revive on the onset of humidity. Hygrophilous, though dry-land terricolous animals living in the soil of the forest are earthworms, slugs, certain insects, centipedes and crabs.

The xerophilous animal community, which lives and proliferates generally on the soil surface, uses soil only as a living place. Such animals are the arthropods, asselids, snails, vertebrates, etc.

Insects play an important role in forest biocoenosis. By eating the leaves, seeds, buds, roots, bark of the tree and even the tree itself, many forest insects cause damage. Frequently, the larvae, sometimes the insect itself or both of them, cause damage. Depending on the plants—healthy or unhealthy—they can be either primary or secondary pests. Trees growing in unsuitable habitats, or those of weak development are especially at risk. Certain insects are capable of explosive proliferation, thus upsetting the existing biological state of equilibrium (*Lymantria dispar, Thaumetapoea processionea, Aphids*). A denuded forest, especially when affected in the spring, can regain its original state only with difficulty and with great losses. The mass development of insects is a gradual process: incubation period, development, and the stage of breakdown. Freshly fallen green leaves and shoots, browning tree-crowns, finely-divided wood falling from standing and fallen trees, the more frequent appearance of eggs on bushes are signs of the onset of an outbreak. In addition to pests, there are also several useful insects in the community of forests playing an important role in the maintenance of equilibrium. Such are the ichnemonfly, the different predatory insects, and ants. Many plant species are pollinated by insects.

Avifauna is also a member of the forest ecosystem that limits the excessive proliferation of insects and certain plant species. Birds generally eat those insects feeding on plants. There are only a few seed- and bark- eating bird species. Owing to their ever decreasing number, birds of prey forming the top of the consumers (macroconsumers) in the forest ecosystems of Hungary, cannot play the same role that they had been playing for decades. Their death may upset the dynamic equilibrium. A large part of the life of birds, as nesting, reproduction and protection, is generally connected with a particular forest association.

The different big and small game, such as the roe-deer, moufflon, rabbit and the large number of predatory animals have mostly a direct connection with the plant associations. Herbivores generally consume a great amount of plant material. The daily green-fodder requirement of one deer is approx. 10% of its body weight.

According to their game-keeping potential, forest associations can be grouped into the following four classes (Bencze 1964). Class I comprises excellent game-grazing areas, young forests of *Populus alba* (white poplar), with a coppice comprising *Rubus* (blackberry), *Fraxinus* (ash) and *Cornus mas* (cherry). Grassy, bushy old stands can be classified as Class II. Class III comprises forests with thin undergrowth, while open forests, without undergrowth, can be classified as Class IV.

The extinction of large predators (wolf, bear, lynx, wild cat) further deteriorates the equilibrium of the forest ecosystem. Man himself is compelled to fill the gap with more or less success. Though deer, roe and wild-hog if occurring in great number cause irreparable damage, and owing to receding selection are gradually degenerated.

The recognition of the forest as a plant association of a high order has led to the formation of forest typology. In the following section the principles and system of forest typology used in Hungarian sylvicultural practice, according to Majer (1968) will be discussed.

The forest typology is founded on the basic sciences—the science relating to habitat and that of plant association—and pays the utmost attention to the specialized branches of the science of forestry. The resulting system is in harmony with both Hungarian and foreign systems of plant coenology. In the nature-like forests this system distinguishes natural forest types, while in the plantation-like forest it includes the cultivated forest types. The basic units are the forest types. In order to clarify the system used, the forest types have been assorted into forest-type groups.

When determining the forest types in Hungary, the following four factors were regarded as a basis: (i) The forest-type group or growing-stock type, which more or less corresponds to the association-groups or the associations of plant coenology. (ii) The chemical reaction of the soil, on the basis of which acidophilic (poor in bases) and basophilic (rich in bases) forest associations were distinguished. (iii) The water supply of the habitat, according to which the availability of water supply was distinguished. (iv) The underwood (sub-association or facies), by which the forest type was characterized.

In Hungary, there are two kinds of forests; coniferous and deciduous. They belong to one of the 5 forest belts. These are (a) pinewoods (alpine oak forests), (b) oak forests, (c) oak forests with hornbeam, (d) closed oak forests, and (e) stunted oak or scrub forests found in the belt of woody steppes.

In Hungary, approx. 75 forest and scrub-type associations are known. To clarify and amplify associations of nearly identical composition and more or less similar ecology, their dominant layer have been ranked into association-groups, so that they would correspond to the living stock types. These forest association-groups are shown in Table 28.

The forestry classification which is used in practice in Hungary was determined by Babos (1954). He distinguished 50 forestry regions. These were grouped into the following six large forestry regions (Majer 1968; Danszky 1963): (i) West-Transdanubian forestry region group, (ii) South-Transdanubian forestry region group, (iii) The Plain of Northwestern Hungary (Little Plain of Hungary), (iv) Transdanubian Central Mountain Ranges, (v) North Central Mountain Ranges, (vi) The forestry region of the Great Hungarian Plain.

The use of the forest typology leads to the thorough knowledge of the forest, the exploration of the complex life-forms and their relation to forest composition. With this knowledge, however, sylvicultural interventions may be carried out with greater safety.

The forest typology gives a simple and clear survey of the great variety of Hungarian forests enabling a comparison to be made of forests of different regions and the various sylvicultural operations.

When determining forest type, attempts are always made to reconstruct

Table 28

Forest association-groups and main stock-types in Hungary

Forest belt (local forest association-group)	Forest associations
1. Spruce stand (Piceetea-Pinetea)	I. Picea (spruce)
	II. Pinus silvestris (scots pine)
2. Beech stand (Fagetea)	III. Pinus nigra (Austrian pine)
	IV. Fagus (beech)
	V. Tilia-Fraxinus-Acer (lime-ash-maple)
3. Hornbeam-oak stand (Carpino-Querceata)	VI. Quercus-Carpinus (oak-hornbeam)
	VII. Fraxinus-Alnus (ash-alder)
4. Oak stand (Querceata)	VIII. Quercus petraea (durmast oak)
	Quercus pubescens (downy oak)
	Quercus cerris (Turkey oak)
5. Forest steppe (Corno-Querceata)	IX. Cotino-Quercus (dogwood-oak)
	Acer-Quercus (sycamore maple)
	Populus-Quercus (poplar-oak)
	Festuco-Quercus (fescue grass)
	X. Salix (willow)
	Fraxinus-Ulmus (ash-elm)
	XI. Alnus (alder)
	XII. Betula (birch)
(Cultured forests)	XIII. Populetea
	XIV. Robinia locust trees e.g. false acacia

the natural forest type, the knowledge of which secures the determination of the native forest-management. By forest identification the demands of trees can be gauged towards the habitat and consequently, the selection of tree species becomes more positive. The most important achievement of forest typology is that it makes both the assessment and the selection of the potential means of natural regeneration more definite.

In the forest, the correlation between renewal and the lower layers (shrub, herb and moss) is very close. Seeds falling from trees onto the ground germinate and grow in the very same environment as the undergrowth. If herbaceous species and their life conditions are known, it is possible to assess the chances of the emergence and survival of the regeneration process. The knowledge of a forest type gives reliable information on the role of the main tree species in the course of afforestation, and provides a good chance of developing a favourable stock-structure and of managing operations. Today, sylviculture practice is based on the uniform and firm basis of the forest and habitat typology.

MULTIFUNCTIONAL UTILIZATION OF FORESTS BY
SOCIO-ECONOMIC FOREST MANAGEMENT

The basic functions of forests determined at the VIIth World Congress of Sylviculture (1971) were production, protection and public recreational functions. The Congress clearly stated that, in determining the aims of economic development, the basic functions should be considered jointly. Consequently, a forest has to satisfy several requirements. At the same time it has to be a means of production and a source of income, a landscape protection area and also a large-sized park. Modern forest management can coordinate the practicalities of the biological factors of cultivation, economic results and a relatively high standard of landscaping.

It is absolutely clear that, in practice, management has to resolve rather serious contradictions in order to be able to satisfy the above-mentioned requirements of society.

Socio-economic sylviculture means both the rational exploitation of natural resources and a management of forest utilization and sylviculture by which the possibilities of forests to serve the public welfare are permanent and the forests should reproduce themselves on an increasing scale (Tóth 1973). It has been convincingly proved that one and the same forest ecosystem cannot comply with all the three basic functions (production, protection and public recreation). One of them must be favoured at the expense of the others. In practice, the function which makes the best use of existing conditions, from the viewpoint of society, will play the leading role and, depending on whether the main task is to satisfy the production, protection or public-recreation function, entails a spatial order for the forest-covered regions of the country.

According to forecasts, by the year 2000, production will be the main task on 75% of the afforested region of Hungary, while 10% will be required to satisfy public-recreation demands and 15% the requirements of protective functions (Gáspár and Hantos 1974). Nevertheless, priority must not lead to the under-exploitation or even waste of the other resources of the forests. Hungarian sylviculture is in such a favourable position that it works on the basis of management plans, the realisation of which is subject to supervision. Public welfare sylviculture will become a reality only when its principles and regulations will be included in management plans. It is a further task of the Hungarian sylviculture management that development should not be governed by the changing demands but should be controlled scientifically.

TASKS OF FOREST PROTECTION

Nature and landscape protection

It is the healthy ecological system in a state of equilibrium that secures those essential conditions, which are also indispensable for man. Therefore, our main task is to protect and maintain the integrity of the natural environment. Modern sylviculture, which is based on forest typology, makes it already possible to maintain natural forest types and to restore them where they have disappeared. Further, it also secures the widespread application of technologies for natural regeneration. Thus, it has become possible to avoid earlier mistakes in practice, such as the elimination of native grasses or the selection of inappropriate tree species.

Special attention must be paid to each important dying plant and animal member of the forest ecosystem and they must be saved for the biocoenosis. The primary requirement for this to be achieved is to improve the biological knowledge of specialist staff in this respect and to promote an effective publicity campaign leading to public awareness of the problem.

As the forest is one of the characteristic components of the landscape, its external changes have an influence on the entire landscape. The renewing of the forest—when the old tree-stock is replaced by young ones—in most cases creates a critical situation. On such occasions the familiar landscape also changes—in general, sharp, linear walls emerge which are even accentuated by the shade-effect. Years will pass until a new biological community evolves to the same extent. The removal of trees, the so-called "caps" from the ridges, aggravates the situation further. A barren horizon already from afar reveals the unsuitable operation. A "composed" end-cutting, in so far as it is practicable having regard to the relief, together with the aesthetic selection of forms and proportions, does not spoil but increases the beauty of the landscape and by emphasizing variedness and the contrasting effects, the natural regeneration even secures the continuity of the biocoenosis.

The white walls of quarries worked on hillsides, can already be seen from a long way indicate a conspicuous deterioration of the landscape. Public opinion reacts disapprovingly to the frequently unreasonable open mining and community efforts aimed at closing down these conspicuous mines are commonly successful. In landscape protection, however, a satisfactory situation can be created only by the cooperation of the authorities.

The reduction of water erosion and the improvement of the water regime

It is a much disputed, though not yet definitely settled question, whether woodlands influence the amount of precipitation of a given area. Nevertheless, it is known that the so-called horizontal precipitation (from fog and dew) is considerably greater in forests than on treeless land. According to observations in Poland and Germany (Keresztesi 1971), in alpine regions the amount of horizontal precipitation "combed out" from fogs can exceed by a factor of 2–4 the amount of the vertical precipitation.

When analyzing the water balance, particular attention should be paid to the impact of the forest on the surface run-off. Forests build up litter, which is of great importance for the water regime. The network of roots contributes to the formation and maintenance of favourable soil conditions. The decaying litter mingles with the mineral soil particles; by means of the root-textures the soil becomes loose and porous; the falling precipitation can more readily penetrate into it. Owing to this, in the forest in comparison with treeless areas the fluctuation of surface run-off is greatly reduced. It is especially evident at the time of showers and melting snow, when the quantity of water is more evenly distributed when entering the rivers. By considerably decreasing the maxima of surface run-off, forests reduce the danger of floods or reduce the rise in water level to a large extent. Afforestation serving the soil protection of sloping agricultural land is also based upon the great water-holding capacity of the forest soil: the afforestation of watersheds and ridges, as well as the planting of soil-protecting forest-belts along the contour lines.

Keszler (1950) has divided the role of forests in the water regime into a "passive" and an "active" part. He describes the role forests play in the struggle against the detrimental impacts of water (floods, soil erosion, the creation of ravines) as passive while, the useful exploitation of available water resources—for the national economy—is an active part. Observations show that the transpiration of vegetation is greater in forests than in open areas, while the evaporation from the soil surface is, in the treeless (open) areas, much higher. Summarising, in a forest 74% of the annual amount of precipitation is consumed usefully for the benefit of the national economy and in treeless areas however, the amount of utilized water is only approx. 50%.

The reduction of deflation

Owing to its bulk and the structure of the natural tree-stock, forests break the impact of winds. In the case of a well-formed (developed) margin, with tree branches down to the ground, the wind-speed measured in the open area will rapidly decrease towards the centre of the forest and after 150–200 metres, the wind will have almost totally died away. Nevertheless, above the tree canopy, wind will be blowing unabated. This effect of forests is utilized by man to protect settlements, roads, agricultural crops and sandy soils against the wind. The velocity of winds can be successfully broken by only two rows of trees, though a 20–50 m wide forest belt will afford greater protection. In an open area, the effect of a protecting forest belt can be observed up to a distance equal to approx. 25 times the height of the trees. In sloping areas, the effect of forest belts is less clear cut, as the relief-factors considerably influence their efficiency.

Protecting forest belts consist of most varied tree species. All the species classed as suitable for planting on the basis of soil analyses can be used. When choosing the proper ones neither their aesthetic, landscape-forming effect, nor the wish to provide protection and shadow for grazing animals and to promote the nesting and propagation of birds and encouraging small game, should be neglected.

The planning of forest belts has had a long tradition in Hungary. It was started in 1818, by Bachofen a sylvicultural manager in the frontier area, who accomplished the binding of the drifting sand area of Deliblát—the "European Sahara"—with success. In 1827, forest belts were established in the vicinity of Pusztavacs, their length being nearly 56 kms. The Afforestation Act of the Great Hungarian Plain, in 1923, gave a great impetus to the planting of forest belts and resulted in the planting of approx. 18,205 ha of forest belts and tree groups. Between 1950 and 1961, their extent amounted to some 106,737 ha.

The reduction of air pollution

Air can be polluted either by solid particles, in the form of dust, or by poisonous gaseous substances. Forest and green areas play an important part in the purification of air. Dense and high tree crowns filter out dust and soot penetrating through them. This natural filter is then purified by each succeeding rainfall thus regaining its original filtering capacity. In addition to this, trees renew their foliage annually. High forest belts consisting of several layers and well-spread forests are especially efficient. Because of the downward current above forests, the dust sediments sooner than in the surrounding area. Stocks of spruce and pine are capable of adsorbing 30–35 t/ha of dust annually, while beech forests absorb twice as much. The almost dust-free air in the depths of forests can be ascribed to the outstanding filtering capacity of the canopy of trees.

The forest is in great danger where air is poisoned by chimney smoke, exhaust gases of motors or by poisonous gases from chemical factories. It is not so much the individual gases, but the complex effect of various sulphur-, fluorine- and chlorine-containing mixtures and carbon monoxide, that is dangerous. Only instruments installed at the sources of emission (smoke and gas) are capable of ensuring clean air. Forests can also suffer from penetration by heavily polluted air and they suffer more from this pollution than they are capable of improving it.

Until recently, the emphasis has been mainly on the discussion of the dust and gaseous pollution problems of the air, but problems concerning the oxygen balance of the atmosphere are also coming to the fore. Oxygen, is however, essential for life. One adult consumes annually one-third of a ton of molecular oxygen and 350 kg of oxygen is required by a motorcar to burn 100 1 petrol. One motorcar owner, who drives 10,000 km annually, consumes the oxygen demand of 10 men. The 6 million inhabitants of Switzerland consume 2 million t of oxygen in the process of breathing (Krebs 1970). As combustion in industrial furnaces alone requires 28 million t of oxygen, this amount is equal to the oxygen demand of 84 million men. Apart from this, approx. 1.4 times this amount, 42 million t of carbon monoxide, pollutes the air and owing to her industrial development, Switzerland will soon double her oxygen consumption. Apart from air pollution, it will shortly become an especially serious task to satisfy the demand for oxygen. Only green plants, mainly within the canopy of forests are capable of decomposing carbon monoxide in the process of assimilation, with the help of solar energy and of producing free oxygen. A tree with a projected area of 150 m^2, in 100 years produces as much oxygen as is consumed by one man in the course of 20 years. Each tree is a small air-purifying, dust-adsorbing device and at the same time a small oxygen factory, as well. Algae in the oceans also play an important part in the oxygen economy of the Earth. No other significant oxygen sources are known yet.

The USA consume one and half times more oxygen than the amount produced by their vegetation. Although at present, we do not observe the decrease in the amount of oxygen and there will be no danger in the following decades in this respect, the fact itself that the CO_2 content of the atmosphere is increasing indicates that the vegetation of the Earth is no longer sufficient to decompose the carbon dioxide produced.

The reduction of noise damage

Trees reduce noise either by absorbing or suppressing it. The wood of deciduous trees, being of laminar structure, rather absorbs and transmits sonic waves, though in the meantime, by adsorption, they also reduce their intensity. The cylindrical needles of conifers rather distribute sonic waves and these by mutual interference are reduced. A 30 m wide, mixed deciduous and coniferous, dense forest belt reduces noise from 80 to 60 phons (Meister 1959).

The wind constantly moves the leaves of trees and bushes, brushing them against each other thus, depending on the wind speed, a more or less loud noise with a constant intensity is produced. Man's nervous system is capable of not only well tolerating this kind of natural noise but, similarly to the tinkling of a brook, its natural living rhythm, this noise even soothes him. The relative noise-reducing (absorbing) effect of arboreous vegetation is achieved in such a way that its soothing, even murmuring motion drowns the irregular irritating and harmful noises.

Afforestation in order to protect civil engineering works

In this category afforestations are included in those cases, where defensive works made out of inert material, are either not sufficiently effective, or are too expensive, spoil the natural landscape or where their maintenance and repair is too difficult to organize. Tree avenues and forest belts planted for the protection of roads and railways against snow are examples of this.

Frequently, civil engineering works are to be protected by the planting of trees and plants against stones falling, rock falls or snow avalanches, earth or mud flows and land slides.

The forest is clearly capable of reducing the harmful effects of technology and of industry to a large extent. Socio-economic forest management, therefore, entails environmental control and the protection of man, in the literal sense of the word.

SOCIAL AND RECREATIONAL FUNCTIONS
OF FORESTS

Sooner or later it will not be their capacity to produce raw material, but rather their usefulness for the public welfare that will determine and ensure the social significance of forests. The main purpose of traditional sylviculture is raw material production. In the course of processes of production it produces plant, animal and mineral products. These are put into circulation and the income constitutes the main financial basis of the management. Under present conditions of production and marketing, this system is self-supporting. However, in park forest management the exploitation of the social and resort advantages of forests is being manifestly pursued. This kind of management exerts its effect on man and his environment, its value being immaterial, with almost no direct profit. Its indirect results will be of almost no avail for sylviculture also in the future. A park forest of large area is a complex, multifunctional green area. Its special feature is that—apart from the traditional ones—it also requires architectural, sanitary and cultural implementation. Its main function is to give an opportunity for the masses to relax and enrich with impressions in a forest environment made suitable for this purpose. The massive need for relaxation is periodical, generally on days of public holidays (Roditchkin 1973).

The costs of park forest management can be ranked according to the following four groups: (*i*) costs of a capital investment character required for the establishment of new recreational forests and the provision of services in existing ones; such establishments as resort forests, game-reserves and aesthetic afforestation promenades, tracks for tourists, cyclists, horse riders, motorists and car-parking places, camping, scenic viewpoints, resting and picnic areas, play and sports grounds, as well as their services; educational trails and gymnastics paths, rain shelters, tables, benches, places for fire-laying, rubbish deposits, signboards, water-regulating and water drainage and associated buildings serving the aims of park forests and of permanent exhibitions; (*ii*) costs of a maintenance character which are required for a proper use of establishments and of the tree-stock of the recreational forest; (*iii*) operating costs of the recreational refuse (garbage) collection, various services and information; (*iv*) indirect costs which, in order to enable the forests to be exploited for the public welfare, arise from the limitation of felling and the application of more costly methods of felling and forestry.

The expenses of park forest management cannot reliably be covered by the income of conventional sylviculture and from raw material production and one has to look for other financial resources. Only a state subsidy can mean a final solution. In Hungary the number and kind of specialised jobs in park forestry have also been included in the sphere of government investment groups with special objectives. This is an extremely important fact.

The most suitable way of following leisure pursuits is to do exercises, in accordance with one's age, in a forest environment. When comparing the different territories from the point of view of microclimate, oxygen-production, dust, noise and radiation protection, the following sequence of values emerges:

plain, treeless area (basis of comparison)	1.0
city park with flowers and bushes	4.2
forest	8.8

It has to be mentioned that a park forest is capable of serving the recreation of the human organism most effectively when, not more than 50 people stay on a unit area (1 ha) at its most crowded site.

Park forests have to satisfy the following requirements: (a) the regular, leisure activities of the majority of workers, (b) it should be within easy reach of the means of public transport and of cars, (c) its structure and installations should be suitable to serve the cultural recreation and relaxation of various age groups, (d) it has to secure the preservation of both the historical and revolutionary traditions of the country, (e) it should promote the exploration of the flora and fauna of the country, (f) the chain of servicing establishments suitable to meet the modern, as well as sanitary, social requirements should be available for large numbers of people.

The establishment of a park forest has both sylvicultural and technical preconditions. The coordinated and cultural application of these guarantees, in addition to the preservation of the atmosphere of the landscape, the fulfilment of tourists' requirements for comfort. Park forests should be impressive and full of beauty. The sylviculturist, who makes use of the rules of forest aesthetics, explores all those elements of the landscape which can be the source of beauty, and can give pleasure and happiness to man and help his spiritual revival and bodily relaxation. A sylviculturist who artistically deals with the living trees, can attain the wished-for psychological and aesthetic effect. In a park forest the estimation of stocks, as well as the number of trees, require quite a different view from that in a commercial forest. When assessing trees, it is not their raw material-producing value that matters, but rather their aesthetic and functional value. In order to achieve varied species composition, the tree mixtures, wild-growing fruit-trees and bushes are preserved. Apart from the formal diversity of various tree species, the colour effect, the multicolouredness of the bark of trees and coppices, their canopy, flowers and fruits means a refreshing variety. The natural charm and romantic beauty of the forests must be preserved.

The establishing of park forests requires also technical aids. Urban people need comfort and to a certain extent, prepared situations in nature, too. A city-dweller can endure solitude only, when he or she is sure to find their way back to his or her habitual environment.

Roads with differing functions form the backbone of resort forests. In a park forest, surrounding the tourist centres, it is possible to build a road network, along which long walks can be taken, and which sets out from and returns to the public transport stops.

The so-called educational paths are aimed at serving the cultural benefit of the forest, the acquisition of botanical and geological knowledge, historical associations and the cause of nature conservation. Their main function is to communicate both professional and other interesting information, even in the absence of guides.

Paths for gymnastics also serve as active relaxation. They have a springy soil and alongside them, simple gymnastic equipment is sited, which is suitable for doing varied exercises.

Owing to their relief and climatic conditions, forest-covered areas of hilly, mountainous regions, generally, offer excellent sporting facilities. In winter skiing and sledging, in spring and autumn excursions, forest tours, rock-climbing. In the open green areas, clearings surrounded by forest, that the large-scale benefits of forest air and sunlight can best be ensured. Weather-proof oak benches and tables, rain shelters, places for fire-laying built of stones surrounded by seats and benches are all important furnishings of park forests. The latter, besides the pleasure of roasting and cooking (barbecues), also offer the ancient pleasure of looking at a flaming fire and blazing logs. Peaks with especially beautiful panoramas are crowned by lookout towers. It is considered that the task of park forests is that they should uncover the historical forest remains and display them for tourists.

THE DEVELOPMENT OF FOREST LANDSCAPES

Landscape planning is somewhere half way between town and regional planning. While city planning determines the basic categories of land use within the internal area of towns, landscape planning must deal with the entire outer area, even crossing the administrative boundaries and it must relate to administrative centres functioning—to some extent—isolated from one another. In this case the aim is no longer the selection of areas merely suitable for building, but also the requirements of agriculture, sylviculture and water management, to which equal weight should be given. Planning is becoming more and more complex. In order to select the most rational plan for development of areas, a great number of variations are to be considered. The selection of the most favourable one requires a comprehensive view of the whole country. Today, we possess no properly summarized planning and environment-shaping guidelines. With respect to the outer areas, the categories of land use are only poorly applied (Laár 1973). The experimental planning project of the resort landscape of the Pilis mountain has been a successful, pioneer work (Korbonits 1973) on the basis of which the potentialities of landscape protection have been studied.

The project area is approx. 66,000 ha and includes the administrative territory of 2 towns and 27 communities (settlements). Owing to the proximity of Budapest, the area of the Pilis mountain with its landscape, natural and important cultural-historical treasures attracts many visitors. In order to protect the above-mentioned treasures and to make proper provision for tourists, in view of the expected increase in tourism, it has become necessary to study the peak capacity of the region. This is made up of the most favourable resort developments consisting of socio-economic forests, the afforestable marginal land recovered from agricultural production and the inner areas of settlements.

The launching of the project had been preceded by investigations into the relevant aspects of city planning, such as green space and traffic, which lasted one year. The investigations consisted partly of the survey of the present situation and partly of its analysis. On the basis of the preceding investigations, the programme summarized its proposals as follows:

— the role of the region,
— the expected population figures at the time of saturation,
— suggested functional structure and peak capacity of the region,
— suggested traffic system of the region,
— landscape planning and protection,
— proposed land use in the region (residential, resort, institutional, industrial area, the protection of monuments),
— proposed time-schedule and measures to be taken in the region,
— proposals for the development of public utilities in the region.

The main sphere of activity of the resort region which is within a maximum of one hour and a half travel time from the capital is to receive and cater for week-end tourism. Keeping in mind the viewpoints of environment control, the programme aims at securing week-end relaxation in a varied form and extent, in a natural environment, and further, it is to centralize the complex of catering facilities and servicing in the best possible way, at a rate which follows the increase in tourism.

In order to build up a satisfactory road network, that provides the requirements of tourist holiday-makers, it has become necessary to study the principle of the functional structure of welfare forests. The programme suggests a method for determining the peak capacity of these forests. Estimating the free-time and speed of walking of tourist-holiday makers, the programme distinguishes the different types of tourists. It also considers the need of tourists who arrive by and return to their cars, to have a walk along a circular loop route.

Reception areas (or service stations) sited on a by-pass to the roads constitute partly a place of relaxation for those wishing to stay at one place, on the other hand they are the starting points of the shorter or longer walks. Due to this, tourists are crowded mainly into those zones which are situated along roads (the noise belt), while the areas lying further off from the road (the quiet and calm belt) are not so packed. Areas along the roads form the starting points of walks, while the inner part of the area surrounded by roads contains the destinations. The catering system and facilities for maintenance should be designed on this basis (Fig. 73).

On the basis of the afore-mentioned structural principles following the planning principles of towns and residential areas motorcar and pedestrian traffic can also be separated in such forests. By constructing the suggested road-network, with respect to the relief gradients of the Pilis mountains, as well as to the requirements of tourism, the programme guarantees a network of tracks which is devoid of motorized traffic.

According to the proposals based on the conclusions of the studies made in 1970 and of the structural principles surveyed, the maximum capacity of the region is the following:

	1973	2000	
Permanent population	108,000 capita	175,000 capita	
Permanent resort population	33,000 capita	110,000 capita	the maximum number of those being present
Tourist population	40,000 capita	90,000 capita	
Total including the tourist population	73,000 capita	200,000 capita	

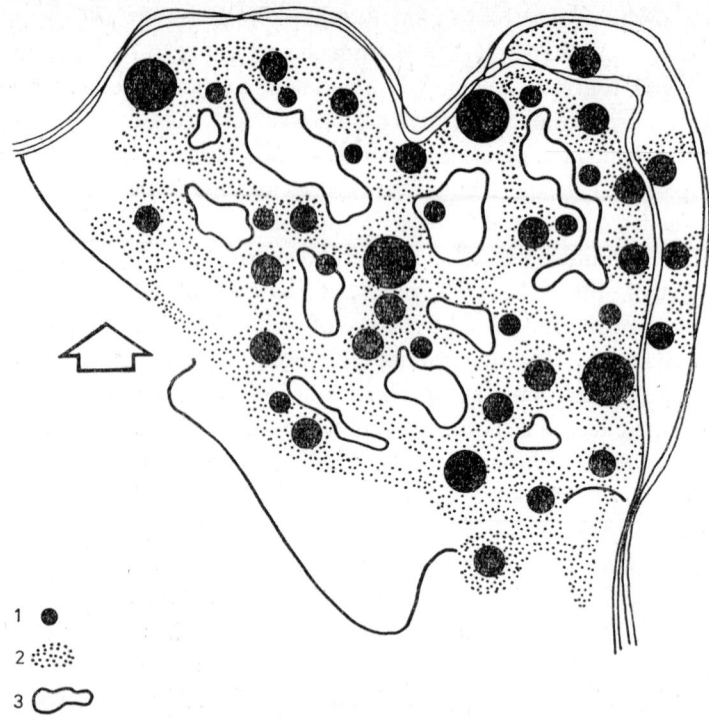

Fig. 73. Demand for recreation sites in the area of the Pilis Park-forest in the vicinity of Budapest. (*1*) settlements of interest to foreign tourism; (*2*) heavily loaded (noisy) resort belt, the starting and assembly point for hikers; (*3*) less loaded zone, quiet resort zone, destination for hikers

The saturation values indicate the three-fold increase over the present capacity. This might mean a 25–30 years' long perspective for the development.

The permanent and tourist holiday making function of the landscape region is developing around the settlement groups. For the future the project retains the settlement group of Szentendre, Esztergom and Pilisvörösvár as a permanent resort. In contrast to this, it suggests that the development of the settlement group of Visegrád and Dobogókő should serve primarily for week-end tourism. In order to secure the link between the green areas of the neighbouring region and the connection between forests and the Danube, it is essential to protect the green belt areas that divide the settlement groups.

The project emphasizes the importance of the designation of land areas unsuitable for large-scale agricultural production in landscape planning. Although, within the present resort, degraded and private areas or those harmed by game are very important, at present they are recreational areas which have a detrimental effect on the landscape. The programme proposes expropriation and following this, the afforestation of the greater part of these areas. This makes it possible to hinder the unhealthy development of resort areas, furthermore the park forest can be enlarged with forest areas that can be used to meet social needs. When implementing new afforestations, the demand of tourists for larger clearings and meadows can already be included. The present state of the forest cannot provide this.

The present area of the Park-forest farm amounts to 28,661 ha, of which 13,480 ha are park-forest. The project foresees the afforestation of 6,920 ha. Through this the area of park forests can be raised to 20,400 ha. When reckoning with 5 capita/ha in a park forest and 2 capita/ha in a productive forest the tourist capacity of the forest areas will be 132,500 capita. Consequently, the expected tourist population of 100,000 capita, as indicated by the project, will not lead to the overloading of the forests. The operative (productive) area of the Park-forest farm amounts to 15,261 ha. Questions of landscape aesthetics have an influence on the entire region, therefore it is reasonable to modify the normal dates of the gradual renewing by cuttings and the definition of the stage of the ripeness for harvesting and the manner of the final utilization of crops.

In the interests of landscape and nature protection, the project proposes that the landscape of the entire region should be protected. Based on geological, botanical and zoological expert opinions, it recommends a two-stage establishment of coherent nature reserves. Visitors to areas of stage I should be limited, if necessary, whilst areas belonging to stage II would be open to unlimited visitors, nevertheless, no buildings should be allowed in their vicinity. The leisure areas of the permanent resort and the tourist population are partly within the inner areas and partly at the tourist reception centres. Based on their capacity and standard of service facilities they can be rated into 3 categories: (a) riverside beaches and settlement centres providing entertainment, (b) assembly areas, which, by providing transport loading points, are restricted to the margins of forests, (c) riversides and roads. Those forest areas will be reserved for those wishing to do hiking which are devoid of traffic and are capable of providing the opportunity for circular walks of 15–30 min or 1–3–6 h. Numerous other possibilities of relaxation and green areas, or reception stations will provide rest for those not wishing to walk. Owing to the expected large number of visitors, the region will be capable of meeting its obligations only in an organized form. In addition to the councils and tourist offices, it will be the task of the Pilis State Forestry, to run the Park-forest maintaining approx. 50% of the region.

References

Babos, I. (1954): *Principles of regional sylviculture in Hungary* (in Hungarian). Budapest.

Bencze, L. (1964): Relations between the composition of the forests and the objectives of forest and game management (in Hungarian). *Az Erdészeti és Faipari Egyetem Tud. Közlem.* 185–202.

Danszky, I. (1963): *Forest generation and planting directives for the sylvicultural regions of Hungary* (in Hungarian). Budapest.

Francé, R. (1913): *Das Edaphon*. Stuttgart.

Gáspár, L. and Hantos, G. (1974): The plan for the development of our forest plantations. *Az Erdő* 2: 49–53.

Héder, S. and Mészöly, Gy. (1971): *Forests of the green area — landscape afforestation* (in Hungarian). Budapest.

Kárpáti, Z. and Terpó, A. (1971): *Applied phytogeography* (in Hungarian). Budapest.

Keresztesi, B. (1971): *Hungarian forests* (in Hungarian). Budapest.

Keszler, H. (1950): Utilizable precipitation in wooded regions (in Hungarian). *Az Erdő* 5: 3–6.

Korbonits, D. (1973): Proposed programme for an experimental development plan of the Pilis recreation area (in Hungarian). *Városépítés* 6: 25–27.

Krebs, E. (1970): Wald und Luft *Allgemeine Forstzeitung* 5: 132.

Laár, A. (1973): Regional planning — landscape planning (in Hungarian). *Városépítés* 6: 6–7.

Majer, A. (1968): *Forest associations of Hungary* (in Hungarian). Budapest.

Meister, F. Y. (1959): White hollow watershed management. *Journ. of Forest*

Pántos, Gy. (1966): Soil microbiology in sylviculture. Personal communications.

Roditchkin, I. D. (1973): *The building of park forests in the Soviet Union.* Moscow.

Tóth, S. (1973): Welfare forest. The tasks of sylviculture in the programme of the protection of man and environment (in Hungarian). Personal communication.

Chapter 11

Nature conservation

THE CONCEPT, SUBJECT AND AIM OF NATURE CONSERVATION

The *concept* of nature conservation comprises the protection and preservation of natural resources of scientific or cultural significance. Their development and preservation are the primary task of nature conservation, in a limited sense, as opposed to the so-called general nature conservation which refers to the entire natural world and is considered to be a task of secondary importance in this context. Its realization is not merely the duty of the organisations concerned with nature conservation. General nature conservation, i.e. the reasonable management of nature falls within the scope of the responsibility of other administrative bodies, certain branches of the economy, education, etc.

The *subjects* of nature conservation are natural sites of special interest, such as (*a*) geological formations (mountains, rock formations, caves, ravines, etc.) and waters (source, brook, river, waterfalls, lake, marsh-land, etc.); (*b*) plants and plantations living in a wild state (plant species, tree avenues, forests, other plant societies, parks, arboreta, etc.); (*c*) wild animal species which owing to their rarity or peculiarity are of interest or species facing extinction; (*d*) territories and landscape segments which, owing to their characteristic or favourable natural features, are of special significance.

Besides the above-mentioned classical subjects of the scarcely more than one-century-old nature conservation also the steppe, wild and domestic animals, several plants and microorganisms—representing genetic resources—can be enumerated into this category. Sites of archaeological, historical and cultural-historical interest and their surroundings can also be included.

The primary *aim* of nature conservation is to preserve and maintain the most important natural resources—in a certain state or rather in a definite process of change—for scientific research and for education and popular science. In order to do this, harmful human and natural impacts are to be eliminated or reduced to a minimum. The priority of this definite objective is underlined by the experts in natural sciences who call attention to the danger of decay and make proposals for the protection of the important natural sites.

The second—none the less important—goal of nature conservation is the maintenance of the cultural-social functions of the protected natural sites: to delight, to find relaxation and rest in nature. By performing this mission, nature conservation has to meet expectations of the society towards nature in such a way that natural resources should be preserved for generations to come.

Recently, the third aim—mainly of economic character—is the preservation of natural conditions, ensuring the survival of the plant and animal species which constitute our genetic resources.

Within the above-mentioned groups of nature conservation objectives the goals in connection with certain protected sites are most varied and manifold and occasionally contradicting demands may emerge simultaneously which should be met by taking into consideration nature protection and preservation.

THE EVOLUTION AND STRUCTURE OF NATURE CONSERVATION

Nature conservation in foreign countries

Nature conservation in the official sense can be considered hardly more than 100 years old. Its existence can be traced back to the establishment of the first national park of the world, the Yellowstone National Park, U.S.A., as the first definite measure for nature conservation in 1872. Of course, the scientific and social demands for nature conservation had everywhere preceded the organization of official nature conservation. In most countries it was the club activity, in others public donations, that had created the basis of the first nature conservation measures. By the turn of the century official nature conservation had already come into being in the European states. Nevertheless, owing to the varied nature of its objectives, government authorities continued to rely on the help of society, in the form of advisory bodies, for a guarding and monitoring service or occasionally, to help purchase and maintain certain areas under protection.

State responsibilities for nature conservation are generally performed by the branches of the ministry of agriculture, less frequently by those of the ministry for education or by the ministry of the interior. In certain cases they are carried out by committees, attached to the government, or by academies of sciences. In Europe, the first independent national authority working directly under government control, was established in Hungary in 1961. It was not until the end of the 1960s that some other countries (France and England) began to set up such authorities, even ministries. It is generally the former (e.g. agricultural, sylvicultural, or academic) organisations that also direct nature conservation, in addition to the newly set-up highest authorities or central organisations of environmental control.

Recently, nature conservation has become a major international topic of discussion and even UNO has been paying attention to it more frequently. In 1959, the resolution of the Economic and Social Council of UNO provided for the uniform registering of the most significant territories of the world under nature conservation—national parks and protected areas of equal importance. According to the register of 1977, the number of national parks had reached approx. 1,500, while that of the protected territories also grew proportionally.

Historical survey of nature conservation in Hungary

The first records on nature, condemning its destruction and calling attention to its protection, can be traced back to the end of the 1700s, in Hungary. These were records—in addition to the general praising of nature, that had dominated literature since its beginnings—the first public voices for the need of nature conservation, but they had found little responsed that time. The revelation of literary memoirs on nature conservation is, unfortunately, far from complete. Nevertheless, Károly Kaán's book entitled *Nature Conservation and Natural Monuments* (1931), which is considered to be the most comprehensive work even up to the present, mentions the animal dialogue by Mihály Csokonai Vitéz published in 1790 under the title *The Owl and the Heron* as the beginning of the literature on nature conservation. Csokonai's commentary, in 1804, on the origins of the town Debrecen, that can be considered a work of environmental control—even in the present sense of the word—is less well known. During the following decades, Count István Széchenyi wrote essays on the subject of nature conservation, thus well in advance of his time, though without any lasting effect.

The first public social action in Hungary, aimed at protecting natural monuments, took place on the occasion of the 20th Itinerary Congress of Hungarian Practitioners and Nature Explorers in 1879. The first legal measure—the Forestry Act of 1879—having a direct, significant effect on nature conservation, was enacted in the very same year. The introduction of the concept of protective forests and the prohibition on their felling ensured the survival of several natural sites. The Hunting Act of 1883 ordained the general protection of songbirds and other rare bird species during the time of hatching.

Far more outstanding was Ottó Herman's activity especially in the field of bird protection. Due to his efforts, the Ornithological Congress, in 1891, was a success and the Hungarian Ornithological Centre was established (1893) in order to organize and lead bird protection. On his initiative and subsidized by the Geological Society of Hungary, speleology and cave-protection evolved. In 1900—preceding a number of more developed countries—the Minister for Agriculture ordained the maintenance and pre-servation of trees and tree avenues of cultural-historical interest. In 1901 a departmental order ordained the protection of several useful bird and mammal species.

In 1908—initiated by Károly Kaán—the National Sylvicultural Society submitted a proposal to the Minister for Agriculture on the protection of certain natural resources of sylvicultural importance. As the Hungarian societies of natural sciences already strongly opposed the destruction of nature, foresters applied for the cooperation of the Royal Hungarian Society for Natural Sciences. The president of the Society soon put forward a proposal to the Minister for Agriculture, who in 1909 jointly with the Min-isters of the Interior, and religion and public education called on all mu-nicipal authorities to make a register of natural resources worthy of pro-tection and called on the different societies to give public support to this work. A copy of Károly Kaán's *The Conservation of Natural Resources* had been distributed to all interested. As a consequence of this enthusiastic action, a great number of natural sites became known to the public. At the same time it had also been demonstrated that these could not be saved without legal measures.

The enacting of legal rules had proved to be a very slow process, though the International Conference on Nature Conservation in Switzerland in 1913—where Hungary was represented by Károly Kaán—a draft-order had been prepared. According to this a committee would have been formed in each county and also a national committee, the representatives of state and natural scientific organisations, institutions and different societies involved. Official duties would have been performed under the auspices of a ministerial commissioner, whose sphere of activity had been regulated in a departmental order in 1914. However, the outbreak of World War I prevented the setting-up of an organization similar to those in the most developed European countries.

During the short period of existence of the Councils' Republic, in spite of the numerous difficulties, the question of protection of natural resources had been raised at higher administrative levels. For a long time, however, in the wake of World War I no noticeable progress took place in this respect. Although act No. XVIII of 1923 placed the responsibility for natural resources with the management and economic duties of the Hungarian Royal Sylvicultural directorates, practical activity did not have the support of legal protection or of any subsidy. An attempt by the Minister for Agriculture, to create these, had remained unsuccessful in 1923.

In 1926 Károly Kaán was commissioned by the Hungarian Academy of Sciences through a competition to write a comprehensive book on nature conservation. It was during this period that, and until then yet unseen public activity started in which natural scientific and sylvicultural societies and tourists' clubs played a leading role. Nature conservation had become a permanent topic in the daily papers and periodicals. It was in this atmosphere that, after a series of interventions, an interpellation was delivered in parliament on the protection of the surrounding area of Lake Balaton and of the Badacsony-hill. In the end—based on the preparatory work by Károly Kaán—the first Hungarian nature conservation act, the Forest and Nature Conservation Law of 1935 was enacted.

This law ordained the establishment of the National Council for Nature Conservation, on the proposal of which the Minister for Agriculture—leading nature conservation in the whole country—by agreement with the Minister for Religion and Education, was in the position to designate nature reserves and landscape reserves. The enacting clause of the law was adopted only in 1938. The statutes of the National Council for Nature Conservation were passed in 1944. The setting-up of the compulsory establishment of county councils for nature conservation and the legal basis for the establishment of national parks were neglected. The registering of natural resources worthy of protection was ordered in 1938, however, it was carried out only at some places. In spite of this, a very active protection movement had begun when, in 1939, a section of the Great-Forest (Nagyerdő) at Debrecen was declared the first national nature reserve. As the private owners of the territories to be protected had put obstacles in the way of protection, this proved to be a difficult task.

Until 1945 no landscape reserves had been established in Hungary. The territory of nature reserves declared amounted to 2,844 ha. From among them only 123 exist at present with an overall area of 1,084 ha; 96 reserves have either become part of neighbouring countries, or—mainly because of the war—have been destroyed and some of them have contracted. It is characteristic of the remaining reserves under protection that they are generally of small extent (in the mean 8.8 ha, with only 4 areas larger than 100 ha) and the majority is situated in forest areas. The most precious nature reserves remaining from this epoch are: Fehér-lake at Szeged, the juniper-covered area in the vicinity of Csévharaszt, the habitat of *Ferula sadleriana* at Pilisszentkereszt, the arboretum of Szarvas, Szársomlyó-hill, Baláta-lake. After 1945 nature conservation gathered momentum. The National Council for Nature Conservation was granted authority to take territories under its protection though in all the other relations (finance, structure) it belonged to the Ministry for Agriculture. After the Word War II the first nature reserve Bátorliget was established in 1950. From a scientific viewpoint it is one of our most precious protected territories even today. Its protection had been preceded and also followed by such a thorough scientific investigation which is, unfortunately, unparalleled in the history of Hungarian natural reserves. Bátorliget nature reserve is also a milestone in another context. In order to implement protection, the state expropriated this area from private owners. This was followed by the establishment of a number of nature reserves. The overwhelming majority of protected areas was situated in forests although later on a proportion of geological, botanical, zoological and landscape sites were also taken under protection. In the 1950s some 30 parks and arboreta were also declared protected, although protection could not be extended to all of the endangered parks. Consequently, it was only partially possible to prevent the improper use and, in several cases, the destruction of parks.

Although the increasing economic activity impeded nature conservation, the new social and political conditions, as well as the more extended state property helped to make this possible. The Secretariat of the National Council for Nature Conservation, with a very small number of members (5–6 persons) could only have designated the protection of 135 natural sites of special interest in 1950–1961, by making great efforts and with the effective support of the highest state administration. The land of this area was about 10,000 ha. Among the protected sites were: Little-Balaton (1951); the Tihany-peninsula, the first landscape reserve of the country (1952)—a site which had already been put forward for protection for several decades; the caves in the neighbourhood of Aggtelek (1951–1956); a section of Lake

Velence (1958); several botanical and geological resources. Because of the lack of defined spheres of authority and difficulties encountered by the practical and official executive organisations, it was not possible to protect several endangered natural objects and the management of already protected ones could not be looked upon as satisfactory.

The fact that nature conservation had no social basis and backing made more striking the lack of network of nature conservation organisations. At the same time, there was already an urgent need to modify the Forest and Nature Conservation Act of 1935. In 1961 our government—appraising the scientific and cultural significance of nature conservation—ordained the establishment of an independent authority, the National Office for Nature Conservation, which functions independently of all ministries, and is directly responsible to the Council of Ministers. In its own category, this authority of nature conservation had been the first and for some ten years, the only one in Europe. This government decree has been highly appreciated in the international spheres of science and nature conservation. As a sign of the international appreciation of its activities the National Office for Nature Conservation became a member of the International Union for the Conservation of Nature and Natural Resources (IUCN). In order to facilitate the more effective coordination and control of environment and nature conservation activity, both the law decree and the government edict on its execution have been modified in 1977. The Presidential Council has established the Office for Environment and Nature Protection which is the legal successor of the National Office for Nature Conservation.

MAIN REGULATIONS DIRECTLY PERTAINING TO NATURE CONSERVATION AND THEIR MAIN PROVISIONS

The law No. 18 of 1961 on nature conservation. This basic law of nature conservation took effect on 1. July 1962. Its main provisions are:

— Natural objects, the preservation and maintenance of which is of either scientific or cultural interest shall be taken under protection and be guarded against all impacts endangering them or colliding with their survival or characteristic natural properties.
— Caves—without any special decree—stand under protection.
— The definition of the concept of nature and landscape reserves.
— The destruction, damaging, disturbing of natural resources under protection, the alteration of their characteristics are prohibited.

— The National Office for Nature Conservation subordinate to the Council of Ministers is the supervising organ of nature conservation. Its sphere of authority comprises the whole country.

— Local duties connected with nature conservation are performed by the Department for Agriculture and Nourishment of the county councils at the first degree.

— The Council for Nature Conservation, as an advisory and expertise-giving organ, is co-ordinated by the National Office for Nature Conservation. Its members are delegated by the ministers, heads of the highest national authorities and other organisations designated in the enacting decree of the law.

— The National Office for Nature Conservation directly or through other organisations maintains the areas under protection and expropriation can also be implemented for the purpose of nature conservation.

As seen, this law has created the basis for the solution of the two fundamental questions—the establishment of authoritative organisations at the first and second levels of government and the nature conservation management of natural resources under protection.

Regulations made under the Nature Conservation Act (1961)

The first regulation made by governmental decree (the period between 1962–1971), due to the fact that there was an exaggerated centralization of duties, had given almost no authority to the nature conservation officials at the first tier (county). Consequently, the new structural form and the link with the highest authority, could not be properly exploited. On the other hand, the organisational structure had been brought into conflict with the principle to extend the sphere of authority of the county councils. Therefore, in 1971, further governmental regulations were issued:

— Natural resources of national importance have been selected. Their protection and management have been remitted to the authority of the National Office for Nature Conservation, (at present: National Office for Environmental and Nature Conservation) while the protection, preservation and management of other objects of local importance have been given to the councils of the county as authorities of nature conservation.

— In order to promote the realization of tasks connected with nature conservation, county committees for nature conservation should be organized. These committees are responsible for preparing and giving expert advice, as well as being the advisory bodies of the county organizations of nature conservation.

— The establishment of landscape reserves is submitted to the National Office for Nature Conservation.

— Resolutions on the establishment of national parks are adopted by the president of the National Office for Nature Conservation in agreement with ministers (heads of organizations of the national authority) concerned. It is this provision that primarily regulates the order for the establishment of a national park in Hungary.

— Each state or social organization and also citizens can make suggestions as to the protection of natural resources.

— The general protection of bird species living in the wild state and migrating through Hungary is provided for, with the exception of 19 commonly occurring species, which can be freely hunted.

— In order to implement projects connected with natural resources under protection the approval of the National Office for Nature Conservation is to be obtained. When preparing projects of landscape architecture, development, water regulation and those changing the character of the landscape, the National Office for Nature Conservation is to be consulted.

— In nature and landscape reserves or in a national park, no building or plant is allowed to be established which would have a harmful effect on the natural state under protection (the beauty of the landscape, the structure or view, the life of the plant and animal kingdom).

— Activities affecting raw materials of the natural resources of national importance under protection, especially in the case of the application of new tillage methods, the development of land, construction, works of water management, the sanctioning of mining, are subject to the approval of the National Office for Nature Conservation. In the case of local natural resources, the particular approval of the county organization for nature conservation should be obtained. This applies also for tree-cutting and for research.

— The authority for nature conservation can, in case of emergency, commission any organization (in exceptional cases also private persons) with the nature conservation management of natural resources under protection, providing for the extra costs that exceed normal management costs. The organization performing the natural conservation management is liable for the protection, maintenance and development of the natural object thus executing the protection-decree in accordance with the regulations.

— For protection of natural resources, nature conservation officers should be employed. They as well as the foresters, rangers, professional hunters, river inspectors and field rangers are obliged and authorized to see that regulations are observed and they should prevent contraventions and take legal action if necessary.

— Obligatory protection of animals and plants should be performed by the proprietor (maintainer, user) of the land where they occur.

— In order to increase the efficiency of nature conservation, authorities for nature conservation are allowed to organize a service for nature protection.

— Nature conservation is to be a permanent subject in the educational institutions and within the framework of this, it should be popularized on the occasion of a special day devoted to birds and trees and organized annually.

These provisions of the government decree—together with the law mentioned previously—create the preconditions for the modern activity in the field of nature conservation. Duties of nature conservation (management, watching and supervision) to be performed by forestry units, state-forest management and state farms have been regulated in detail by a joint directive issued by the Minister for Agriculture and the president of the National Office for Nature Conservation.

Regulations indirectly relating to nature conservation

There are approximately one hundred legal rules, at different levels, containing indirect or partial regulations on the observance of regulations in administrative processes and measures, as well as in the course of most varied economic, building and other activities in connection with the natural environment. The main fields of these legal rules are: administrative procedures, building affairs, land protection, plant protection, agriculture, forestry, hunting, fishery, mining, health affairs, education, the infringement of regulations. The observance of these regulations, indirectly affecting nature conservation can, in itself, secure the preservation of numerous natural sites of special interest to such an extent that, in the course of practical nature protection, it suffices to keep only these regulations. It is, however, necessary to systematize and harmonize this great quantity of ramifying regulations more completely.

THE SYSTEM OF HUNGARIAN NATURE CONSERVATION

Authority structure

The National Office for Nature Conservation—is the central leading, supervisory and controlling authority for nature conservation at the second level. The declaration and removal of protection falls within its competence. Besides general guidance, it conducts the protection of natural resources of national importance directly, provides for their preservation, management and in cases relating to them, it takes measures also at the first tier. Its duties are performed through its central and local organizations (inspectorates for nature conservation, national park directorates, etc.). The evaluation and publication of the results as well as the popularization of nature conservation also come under its duties. The declaration and cancellation of the protection of objects belong to the sphere of authority of the executive committee of the county councils. They are, consequently, the county organizations of nature conservation. They provide for the preservation of natural resources of local importance under protection and perform the authoritative duties connected with these, at the first tier.

Social organizations

County committees for the environment and for nature protection. In the governmental decree of 1977 cited previously the Council of Ministers ordered the reorganization of the county committees for nature conservation. They ordered further that these should be given duties also in the field of environmental control. The committees are advisory and controlling organizations of the executive committees of the county councils and that of the metropolitan councils. Their members are representatives of the state authorities and leaders of the state and co-operative organisations. In order to carry out their responsibilities the county councils have to employ a clerk for the environment and nature protection.

The Federation of Nature Lovers. Since the foundation of the first Hungarian League of Tourists in 1872, tourists' clubs have been permanent supporters of nature conservation. They are directly interested in the preservation of the harmony and beauty of the natural environment. The Federation of Nature Lovers, which comprises affiliated clubs throughout the country with 70,000 members, forms one of the most significant bodies providing a social basis for official nature conservation today. Nature conservation is one of the subjects at the courses for tour-leaders. The Social Forest Service has been functioning within the framework of the Federation since 1962. Its approx. 2,000 members, finishing the course on nature conservation, regularly walk on group patrol in the countryside. During their voluntary service they enjoy legal protection. The Service aims at guarding the forests, their installations, natural resources and open air sites. The National Office for Nature Conservation has entered into a contract of co-operation with the Federation of Nature Lovers for the social guarding of natural resources and, in some cases, for their maintenance.

The Hungarian Federation for Ornithology, following the traditions of bird protection launched by Otto Herman, was established in 1974. Its goal is to make known birds for the public and to advance practical ornithological nature conservation. It is an important social organization and all the more so as the endangering of avifauna has made it necessary to secure protection by governmental decrees, which is only possible with the support of the public.

The League of Hungarian Karst and Speleologists. They exert their activities in the protection and maintenance of caves. The National Sylviculture Federation plays an important part primarily in the control of forests. Members of the *National Association of Hungarian Hunters* and those of the *Hungarian National Association of Anglers* (25,000 and over 100,000 members respectively) actively support nature conservation. Apart from this, there are several special organizations which promote nature conservation. *The Young Communist League and Pioneer Association* should be mentioned first of all. Among their objectives nature conservation occupies a position of increasing importance. The Patriotic Popular Front has launched a campaign for nature protection which now extends to almost the entire country.

The multiple duties of environment control, in spite of the most perfect legal rules and most sophisticated authority structure, can be performed only with the support of the masses. Therefore, the co-ordination of nature conservation activity of public organisations is of vital importance.

Scientific structure

In Hungary—in contrast to many countries in Europe—there is no separate scientific research institute for nature conservation. Investigations in this field are going on jointly with other research in the scientific and educational institutions. In order to co-ordinate the more important investigations, the National Office for Nature Conservation has concluded an agreement of co-operation with the Hungarian Academy of Sciences, for studies necessary to lay the scientific foundations of nature conservation management and to secure undisturbed conditions for investigations in the protected areas.

It is the duty of the National Council for Environment and Nature Protection to determine the new directions of scientific research and to promote these investigations, while the Office participates in the organization of research projects and ensures proper conditions for these to be carried out.

The study of two partial areas, of particular importance in the field of nature conservation, is however the task of two institutions which work under the auspices of the National Office for Nature Conservation. These are: the Ornithological Institute (founded in 1893) and the Speleological Institute (founded in 1974).

The structure of nature conservation management

The management of protected natural resources of national importance is carried out by the regional authorities of the National Office for Nature Conservation. National parks in all instances are maintained by the national park directorates (established for this purpose), while certain landscape reserves and nature conservation areas, as demonstration areas, belong to the nature conservation inspectorates.

In 1979, 88% of the territory of the total natural resources was managed by the National Office for the Environment and Nature Protection. From this approx. 1,942 ha are self-managed and entered in the land register. The remainder of the objects of national importance is managed by the organizations responsible for the general maintenance of the area, such as state-owned forest estates, state estates, agricultural co-operative farms; however, the National Office for the Environment and Nature Protection provides for the upkeep costs. Protected natural resources of local significance are managed by various organizations of the county authority.

The organisations of nature conservation management employ nature protection watchmen, while the national park directorates national park employ watchmen and national park supervisors. By taking the oath the above-mentioned persons become persons of authority; they are entitled to carry a service rifle and to wear a uniform. During their service they enjoy the protection of the lawful authorities.

International relations of Hungarian nature conservation authorities

Within the framework of the joint executive agreement of COMECON member states on the protection of environment, the National Office for Environment and Nature Protection contributes to the elaboration of certain questions on nature conservation. As a member of the International Union for Protection of Nature and Natural Resources, it has played an active and internationally important part especially in the Commission for Education and Landscape Protection.

Hungary has been a member of the International Council for Bird Preservation since the time of its foundation in 1922. The international conference of the European Section was held in Hungary in 1968, with great success. In the activities of the International Wildfowl Research Bureau, Hungary has been playing an important part by observing wildfowl migration and stocks, as well as by the water protection measures. Hungary took part also in its conference in Leningrad, Iran and in the Crimean peninsula.

Within the framework of the International Biological Programme marking the beginning of general international research in the field of nature conservation, extensive research activity has started at several sites in Hungary, including the Man and the Biosphere Programme.

In view of the protection of rarely occurring natural resources, especially those of the migrating bird kingdom (avi-fauna) international co-operation, i.e. mutual information and utilization of experiences, is indispensable.

NATURE CONSERVATION CONCEPTS USED
IN HUNGARY

Protected natural formations and objects

Mainly caves, stone niches, and cliff cavities come under this definition
(their collective name is cave) and they are protected by the nature conservation law in every case from the time of its discovery.

Certain natural objects (e.g. trees) declared protected by the president
of the National Office for Environment and Nature Protection or the executive committee of the county councils are also included. Owing to their
place of occurrence or the conditions (private court, area built upon) these
cannot be declared areas under the nature conservation law.

Plant and animal species (protected species) under
nature conservation

This category includes those wild-living plant and animal species, which
are protected either by a legal rule of the highest degree or by the decree of
the president of the National Office for Environment and Nature Protection,
or the executive committee of the county council. As a rule, this kind of
protection is extended to each individual and all forms of development
(e.g. seed, shoot, cutting, egg, roe, cub, etc.) of a defined species generally
independently of their place of occurrence, in the entire territory or only
in certain areas of the country.

Owing to their usefulness or cultural-historical value, some plant and
animal species can also be taken under protection e.g. certain living organisms useful from the point of view of plant protection.

Nature conservation area

Herein belong territories which are declared protected by the president of
the National Office for Environment and Nature Protection, or the executive
committee of the county council with the aim to protect, preserve and maintain certain natural resources. As a rule, commercially oriented productive
activity is not allowed in nature reserves, though a nominated nature conservation management is compulsory. In order to ensure undisturbed research activity or the preservation of genetic resources, these reserves can

be strictly closed to the public. However for particular educational or popular scientific reasons and for tourists they may be opened to the public, though with certain limitations. The extent of the nature reserves is not defined by the regulations: there are very small (0.1 ha) and very large (several thousand hectares) nature reserves. The allocation of small areas is, generally, disadvantageous as they are hard to protect from external impacts.

Landscape conservation region

A landscape reserve is a landscape or a part of it which, in order to preserve its special landscape character and natural resources as well as to serve holiday resort purposes and tourism is declared protected by the president of the National Office for Environment and Nature Protection. Within a landscape reserve, the natural and artificial components should be maintained in a definite equilibrium which is in harmony with the goals of protection. Therefore, establishments disturbing the protected character of the landscape and their activities are prohibited. Activities, which do not affect the character of the landscape are permitted, while others, especially agriculture and forest management, are desirable. Landscape reserves serve either tourism, recreation, popular-science or scientific research and education. In order to achieve these latter objectives, at places where the most significant resources occur, more strictly protected areas are to be designated within the landscape reserve. Characteristics of these more strictly protected areas are identical to those of nature reserves. The extent of landscape reserves is not defined by regulations, though—as they generally comprise geographical units—they are, as a rule, larger than nature reserves: the smallest ones have an area of approx. 1,000, while the largest ones cover up to even several ten thousand hectares. Apart from the objectives of nature protection, the establishment of landscape reserves is of importance from the point of view of general culture and environment regulation as in Hungary there is no centrally organized landscape management that would include all landscape components. In spite of the landscape regulation projects, the authorities and firms involved have not carried out their recommendations in their entirety, but only separately and insufficiently. Landscape reserves mean the organized and comprehensive regulation and management of landscapes of outstanding natural richness.

National parks

National parks are the most complete units of nature conservation. They are generally of large extent and have the most varied locations. It is because of this that the way in which this concept is interpreted and national parks are protected—depending on national characteristics and population density—vary according to the continents and frequently with countries. In connection with the protection of the natural environment the significance of national parks has greatly increased. Therefore, in 1969, the General Assembly of the International Association for Nature Protection, in New Delhi, submitted a proposal for the national park concept. According to this national parks are those relatively large territories where:

— farming or settlements have not or only partly affected the natural ecological system and further, where geological and geographical rarities, vegetation and fauna are of great scientific, educational and recreational importance and the landscape is very interesting from the point of view of aesthetics;
— the highest responsible state authority takes measures in order to prevent possible development and the establishment of settlements and to provide suitable management for the ecological, geomorphological and aesthetic values;
— visiting is permitted—under regulated conditions—for educational, cultural and recreational purposes.

At the same time the assembly demanded that governments do not establish national parks (a) on territories protected by private persons or by lower tier authorities; (b) territories protected according to the definition of the international agreement of 1968 (its Hungarian interpretation means nature reserve); (c) economically utilized territories with settlements on which landscape planning, resort-development and industrial investment as well as settlement development are favoured in contrast to the maintenance of the natural ecological system (these can be landscape natural parks).

In Hungary, territories with unaffected ecological systems disappeared already a long time ago. Under our geographical distribution of population the concept of the national park corresponds to that territory on which our most precious natural and cultural sites occur more frequently and in a less affected state than generally and in which it is possible to harmonize economic interests with nature conservation objectives over a larger area. Owing to the great population density, the cultural-historical sites—especially the ancient ways of farming that adapt themselves to natural conditions and the form of life, folk-art, folk-architecture—necessarily become components of the national park, where it is possible to preserve their natural environmental harmony or at least, their character, this having evolved in the course of centuries.

In Hungary, the establishment of national parks falls within the competence of the president of the National Office for Environment and Nature Protection, in agreement with the ministers concerned. The main goal of national parks is to disseminate knowledge by the help of walking and recreation in the countryside. To serve this, both beautiful parts to visit (buffer-zone, front-park) and the more valuable parts where visits are controlled by certain regulations, most frequently in a guided form, should be marked out in the national parks. In order to encourage visitors whilst maintaining a high standard of protection, establishments should be created which harmonise with the landscape. The marking out of strictly closed areas may help to preserve the most important scientific sites and allow them to be studied. The efficiency of protection can be increased by an outer protective belt—with no strict regulations—around the national parks.

Although, among the protected areas, national parks are the most extensive nature conservation units, the most significant ones show the greatest variations in size. The largest national parks are of the order of millions of hectares. According to UNO records, the territory of the largest area protected—with the character of national parks—amounts to 5,280,000 ha (Botswana, Central Kalahari Game Reserve), which is followed by the Wood Buffalo National Park in Canada of 4,480,700 ha. The smallest national park of the world can be found also in Canada, it is called St. Lawrence Islands and has a basic area of 104 ha. The area of most national parks, however, ranges from some 10,000 ha to some 100,000 ha. Thus, the basic land area of the Hungarian national parks (30–50,000 ha) is normal by international standards. Not rarely, national parks are composed of several parts, so-called mosaics (Kiskunság National Park Hungary).

PROTECTED NATURAL SITES IN HUNGARY* (1977)

Caves

The number of registered, and therefore legally protected, caves (and formations belonging to this category) amounts to approx. 1,300. Owing to organized speleology and exploratory activity connected with mining, this number is gradually increasing. The majority of caves can be found in the area of Bükk mountain and the karstic region of Aggtelek. The rest of the caves—with the exception of a few—have formed in the other limestone mountains.

Geological and archaeological work is going on in some 100 caves. Two caves (the Lake-cave at Tapolca and the Béke-cave at Jósvafő) are used for medical purposes, while 8 others (at Abaliget, Baradla at Aggtelek, Lóczy at Balatonfüred, Pálvölgyi at Budapest, Petőfi and István at Lillafüred, lake-caves at Miskolc-Tapolca and Tapolca) are open for visitors. Nature conservation authorities have the right to protect caves from damage, in case of emergency, by blocking their entry. Speleological studies are to be carried out only in organized projects, under expert leadership and with the permission of the nature conservation authorities.

Protected plant species

Up to the present, nature conservation, unfortunately, has not been extended to the protection of certain plant species (in contrast to the protection of several animal species), but has been aimed at protecting those growing in a wild state by establishing nature reserves at their habitat. There is only one exception, the *Adonis volgenisis Stev.* Each individual plant of this species, occurring in the wild state, is subject to protection. By the end of 1977, the county councils had taken 13 plant species under protection, irrespective of their habitats. It is a disadvantage of the so-called land protection method that it does not cover rarely occurring species deserving protection which live outside nature reserves. There is no legal basis to prevent them from extinction. (One of the main tasks of botanical–nature protection is to put an end to this inadequacy as soon as possible. Preparatory work has already been completed in this field.)

* In the U.K. designated as sites of special scientific importance (S.S.S.I.).

Protected animal species

On the basis of the Nature Conservation Act bird species living in the wild state, or migrating via Hungary (there are 339 known species)—because of their usefulness or natural and scientific value—are protected, even in the absence of a specific declaration. Protection comprises nesting places and all developmental stages of the species mentioned, including also eggs and nestlings. There are 19 common species, which are excluded from protection. These species which do not cause significant damage and can be hunted, are the following: *Corvus corone cornix, Pica pica pica, Garrulus glandarius glandarius, Passer montanus montanus, Passer domesticus domesticus, Perdix perdix perdix, Phasianus colchicus, Streptopelia decaocto decaocto, Columbia palumbus palumbus, Scolopax rusticola rusticola, Lymnocriptes minimus, Anas platyrhyncha platyrhyncha, A. crecca crecca, A. querquedula, A. penelope, Nyroca ferina ferina, Anser fabalis fabalis, Anser albifrons albifrons, A. erythropus.*

The well-known economic usefulness of songbirds, unanimously warrants their protection. The stocks of other bird species under protection have significantly diminished which is the result of the unfavourable impact of man on nature (disturbing of nesting places, application of chemicals, hunting of certain species). Certain species face imminent extinction like *Egretta alba alba, E. garzetta garzetta, Ardeola ralloides, Platalea leucorodia leucorodia, Anser anser, Ciconia nigra, Recurvirostra avosetta avosetta, Hieraetus pennatus pennatus, Aquila heliaca heliaca, A. pomarina pomarina* (lesser spotted eagle), *Haliaeetus albicilla, Falco peregrinus peregrinus* (peregrine falcon) *F. cherrug cherrug* (saker falcon), *Circaetus gallicus gallicus* (short-toed eagle), *Milvus milvus milvus* (kite), *Bubo bubo bubo.*

Pisces: *Aspro zingel, A. Streber, Cottus poecillopus, Cobitis aurata balcanica, C. taenia, Nemachilus barba, Misgurnus fossilis, Hucho hucho, Lampetra Danfordi, Acipenser ruthenus, Gobio uranoscopus, G. albipinnatus, Umbra Krameri, Barbus meridionalis Petényii, Acerina Schraetzer, Alburnoides bipunctatus, Proterorhinus marmoratus, Leuciscus souffia,*

Amphibia: all species of frogs, *Salamandra salamandra,* all species of water-salamanders, lizards and snakes, *Emys orbicularis,* (common field vole) Mammalia: *Meles meles* (Eurasian badger), all species of shrews, *Microtus agrestis, Sicista loriger,* all species of bats, *Spalax leucodon* (mole sp.), *Mustela erminea* (stoat), *M. nivalis* (weasel), *M. eversmanni* (Russian polecat), *Sciurus vulgaris* (red squirrel), *Martes foina* (beech-marten), *M. martes* (pine marten), *Microtus oeconomus* (vole sp.), all species of dormice,

Erinaceus europaeus roumanicus (hedgehog sp.), *Felis sylvestris* (European wild cat), *Talpa europaea* (European mole), *Lutra lutra* (Eurasian otter).

Scientific institutions had been urging the protection of these animals. This can be ascribed to their increasing scarcity, partly the result of the intensification of agricultural production. The economic usefulness of certain species is outstanding (e.g. bats and other species feeding on rodents), and their decrease in number would accelerate the upsetting of the biological equilibrium. The collection of animals for commercial purposes and the excessive hunting of predatory species which are limited in number, have all necessitated the protection of these species. They are protected in almost all European countries. *Spalax typhlus,* the striped mouse and the *Vipera ursinii rakosiensis* are zoogeographical rarities.

It is prohibited to stalk, disturb and kill protected animal species.

Nature reserves

In Hungary, the number of nature reserves is 607. Their overall area amounts to around 40,000 ha. From among them 102 with a total area of 26,000 ha are of national importance whilst the area of 505 protected objects of local importance is approx. 14,000 ha (by 1st Jan. 1979; Table 29).

It is beyond the scope of this chapter to give a detailed survey of the numerous small nature reserves of local importance, generally smaller parks, groups or avenues of trees, geological formations, botanical and zoological species which are not rare or important, but scarce in a particular area.

In nature reserves, there are frequently several natural sites to be protected: cliff formations are generally nesting places for rare birds, reeds provide

Table 29

Land areas under nature conservation in 1978

Category	Number of areas	Area ha	Average area ha
National parks	3	121,403	40,468
Landscape reserves	27	259,279	9,600
Nature conservation areas of national importance	102	26,425	259
Nature conservation areas of local importance	505	14,012	28
Protected areas, total:	637	421,119	661

a home for waterfowl and for insects; natron (soda) lakes and pastures are habitats for rare plant species, as well as their plant communities; protected forests and their rare plant associations can be hiding places for a precious fauna. Nature reserves are established in areas which are least affected and therefore, at these places, nature is most varied and complex. In order to clarify and assist the organization of management, it is necessary to group nature reserves on the basis of the character of the objects under protection. Accordingly, geological, botanical, zoological, landscape and cultural-historical primary characters as well as their combinations can be distinguished.

Nature reserves primarily of geological character

These are surface areas listed in order to help the preservation of protected caves (the most important ones can be found in the proximity of Aggtelek); the exposure of geological layers and of primary formations (Kálvária-hill of Tata and the fossils of Ipolytarnóc); cliff formations.

Nature reserves primarily hydrological in character are few, which is due to the fact that areas with water surfaces have not been taken under protection as hydrogeological sites, but only because of the botanical and zoological rarities to be found at the habitat formed by water (the river bed of Ancient-Dráva at Szaporca; the backwater of Tisza at Tiszaug; Little-Balaton, Lake Velence, Lake Szelidi, the natron lakes in the Great Hungarian Plain, etc.). The main sources and waterfalls as complex treasures, are generally protected (Melegmányi valley), springs are mostly considered to be sites of local significance.

Nature reserves primarily of botanical character

These are the most varied protected areas. Artificially established botanical gardens, arboreta and certain parks, as collections of botanical rarities and generally aesthetical—in several instance landscape, cultural-historical —sites belong to this group (University Botanical Gardens, Budapest; the arboreta at Vácrátót, Szarvas, Kámon, Jeli; the parks at Zirc, Szeleste, Alsócsútdoboz, etc.). As a rule, native plant habitats under protection well represent the chain of habitats in Hungary (rivers and stagnant waters, marshes, swamps, meadows, various forest communities, sandy and salt-affected puszta, cliff-grass, etc.). Nevertheless, the network of protected areas is far from being complete and there are many precious and endangered plants awaiting protection.

Nature reserves primarily of zoological character

Their diversity is nearly as great as that of nature reserves of botanical character (artificial garden establishments are exceptions). As the plant kingdom frequently forms the basis of the animal kingdom, especially in the case of lower animals, there is a territorial coincidence with the occurrence of rare plant species (Sashegy in Budapest, Lake Baláta, Bátorliget). Where there are natural conditions favourable for plants as a direct consequence, animals also can survive more easily.

Nature reserves primarily of landscape importance

The most significant ones are: Melegmány valley in the Mecsek mountains, a picturesquely situated central mountain valley with interesting geological formations. Koloska valley at Balatonfüred, a clearing freshened by a spring; the surrounding hillsides are covered by *Quercus pubescens* (downy oak) and *Fraxinus ornus* (flowering ash) bushes.

Nature reserves primarily of cultural-historical or other importance

The preservation and maintenance of the undisturbed and natural environment of open air archeological sites (excavations), historical monuments (ruins of the fortresses at Füzér, Sümeg) as well as sites of special institutions (seismologic, magnetic field analysers, etc.)—in addition to special measures —also require nature conservation management. Furthermore the historical, cultural-historical and other sites (e.g. the Historic Memorial Site at Mohács) should be included.

Landscape reserves

Tihany-peninsula

The first landscape reserve in Hungary, with an area of 1,100 ha, was established in 1952. The protection of its special geological structure has been extended to the entire area of the peninsula. The outer parts of the peninsula could, partially, be protected against excess demand for building which centres on the resort area. The availability of building sites is, unfortunately, not in proper balance with the interests of landscape protection. In a particular section of the outer areas, there is sylviculture going on while elsewhere agricultural and viticultural activity characteristic of the region can promote the preservation of the typical landscape (small plots, the maintenance of lavender and almond cultivation).

Badacsony-hill

The conditions—especially the financial ones—for the protection of the characteristic basalt cone, known all over Europe, became propitious only in 1965. The landscape reserve of 1,330 ha was established in the same year. The removal of quarries to an area, where they would not exert such a great impact on the landscape cost large amounts of money. Simultaneously considerable efforts were made to conceal the destruction by the quarry, mainly by afforestation. As a result, viticulture both under the "basaltorgans" and on the hill top revives. The maintenance of a balance between the demands of the ever increasing holiday resort and the interests of landscape protection has been giving cause for much concern.

Flood-plain of the river Tisza at Mártély

It was drawn under protection in 1971 with a territory of 2,223 ha. On the Mártély-Hódmezővásárhely section of the river Tisza, between the left bank and the dam, the flood-plain meadows, willow and ancient poplar forests, a reminder of the natural conditions at the time of the regulation of the river, still survive. Today, such forests are scarcely to be found along the river Tisza. Commercial forest management and river regulation have greatly diminished these ancient landscape elements. This area is partly a favoured tourist attraction in the Great Hungarian Plain and partly the habitat of rare plant and animal species.

Ancient juniper coppice at Barcs

Protection of this site was declared in 1974. The landscape reserve is situated in the south-western corner of Somogy county; it has an area of 3,416 ha. Its north-south length is 15 km extending to the river Dráva. The main sites of special interest within this landscape reserve are: the backwaters of the river Dráva, extensive water surfaces, deep-lying marshes with Alnus (alders), swamps with special vegetation and forests comprising birch and juniper.

The alder forests of the boggy-areas, the marshes, the *Alnus glutinosa* (common alder) marsh-forests with water lily and peat-moss; the birch forests with *Nardus stricta* (mat grass) and rare species *Radiola linoides* (all-seed), *Ludwigia palustris* (a perennial aquatic herb), *Apium repens* (fool's watercress), *Hypericum humifusum* (Trailing St John's wort), *Centunculus minimus* (chaffweed) are unique in Hungary.

Ság-hill

One of the characteristic picturesque landscape sections of Vas county, looking over to Kemeneshát, a hill, the surviving evidence of a chain of volcanic hills and the last of the chain, is situated along Lake Balaton. Its 235 ha area was drawn under protection in 1975. For nearly 50 years a basalt quarry had been operating there, nevertheless, even with its jagged top Ság-hill dominates its surroundings. The steep cliff-walls of the deep open mine excavation offer an unforgettable sight and visitors can acquire a good understanding of the interesting layers formed by volcanic activity. Even today certain areas of the hill are covered with the ancient vegetation —today already very rare—and offer a favourable biotope for several protected animal species. Viticulture which has evolved on the less steep hillside, is renowned. It is a great event in the history of science in Hungary, that József Eötvös carried out one of his experiments, with the torsion-pendulum named after him, on the plateau of Ság-hill.

Ócsa

It is the most precious representative of the formerly extensive Molinia-Juncus marsh-meadows, which have been greatly reduced in size owing to human activity. Its vegetation and fauna—both most sensitive to anthropogenic impacts—had already been facing extinction when in 1975, a 3,576 ha section of its area was drawn under protection. The landscape is rich in low-lying marshes and fenwoods. The mosaic-like changing of its coenoses within small areas is the result of micro-environmental factors. The main cultural-historical sites of the landscape worthy of mention; are to be found at Ócsa: the church dating back to the 13th century in Roman style, is of national importance; old peasant houses preserving the village traditions; a line of cellars on the Oldhill and an old cemetery with carved wooden grave-posts.

Lázbérc

It is a landscape reserve with an area of 8,510 ha in Borsod–Abaúj–Zemplén county. By protecting the water quality of its reservoir, it serves the requirements of public health but the main aim of the conservation measures is to protect the landscape sites of the Uppony-hills, enriched with the storage reservoir, to preserve its geological sites and botanical rarities and maintain the undisturbed nestling of the protected avifauna—with special respect to the decreasing numbers of the birds of prey (raptors). The most precious sites of special interest and of outstanding importance are the remnants of the Sarmatian-flora preserved in the fossils of geological excavations, the Gothic church with its steeple surrounded by a wooden gallery, from the 14th century in the village of Bánhorváti.

Dévaványa

An area of 3,433 ha comprising salt affected pastures and arable lands as well as forests were designated as landscape reserves in the neighbourhood of Dévaványa and Egecsfalva in Békés county in 1975. The need for protection was urgent because of the bustard (Otis), a species diminishing all over the world. The largest bustard (Otis) population of the world, which is exceptional for its sexual-rate and age-distribution of individuals, lives in this area. The approx. 1,000 bustard individuals living here, might form the genetic resources of this diminishing bird species, consequently, it is the duty of this landscape reserve to maintain and protect their nesting place and to bring up and re-acclimatize the endangered individuals.

Pusztaszer

This vast landscape reserve of special beauty (22,226 ha) established between Pusztaszer and the river Tisza in 1976, forms part of the varied landscape of the land between the Danube–Tisza rivers. Surrounded by cultivated fields there are natron lakes, seasonal marshy tracks, pastures on salt-affected soils and patches of forest.

Its precious avifauna includes also species that rarely nest in Hungary. The water surfaces and varied habitats of this area provide suitable resting and feeding places for great number of birds that migrate through the Carpathian-basin. The flood area of the river Tisza, which is covered by alluvial forests, meadows and waters, is practically an open air museum of the river regulation works. The landscape reserve is also important as the scene of significant historic events.

Zselicség

In 1976, the landscape reserve was designated on a 9,046 ha South Trans-Danubian area of land, which is typical and rich in forests. The gently sloping hillsides covered by forests and the meadows sheltered by them, show a lovely scenery. Owing to its boundary situation, from the point of view of geobotany, it belongs to the Inner-Somogy floristic district of the South-Transdanubian province; with its transitional character tending towards the Mecsek-floristic district, it is a habitat for rare plant species and coenoses. Its forests are rich both in tree and bird species and the fish-ponds are important resting places for migrating waterfowl. The parish church of the village of Szenna, with its painted cofferwork ceiling and the belfry at Márcadó-puszta are important objects of folk-art. An open air museum surrounds the church.

Szentgyörgyhegy

This is a landscape reserve in Veszprém county established in 1976, on an area of 932 ha. The basaltic area of the Balaton highlands is an outstanding geological, landscape and cultural-historical site in Hungary. Among the basalt cones, Szentgyörgyhegy is one of the best examples of volcanic activity having taken place in this area. The vegetation which thrives here perpetuates the ancient vegetation in a relatively unharmed state. The beginnings of the famous viticulture on the hill can be traced back to the Roman age. There are numerous buildings of architectural and historical interest.

Szentgyörgyvölgy

It is a characteristic scenery in Vas and Zala counties, in Western Transdanubia. Its area (1,915 ha) is largely covered by forest. It was taken under
protection in 1976. Apart from the lovely valleys, stretching in between the
forests and the agriculturally used land, this is also an important landscape
section from the point of view of sylvicultural history. This is the only
place in the whole country where the so-called "select cutting" system of
forest management is applied. The former crop-rotation farming methods
of small farmers and the natural succession of arboreous vegetation are
easily available objects of study. Its forests and meadows are preservers
of ancient plant species and plant associations.

Orgovány

This landscape reserve in Bács–Kiskun county with a total area of 2,952 ha
was established in 1976. In this typical part of the Danube–Tisza area
there are reeds, marshy meadows and sceneries with sandhills. These form
not merely a landscape pleasant to look at, but also an unchanged world.
The characteristic way of life in the detached farms of Kiskunság, where
man and nature live together in interdependence, is a special feature of this
small area, guarding ancient conditions of living. The small thatch-roofed
farmhouses, built along the edges of reed-beds, display the harmony of
natural and landscape treasures.

Hanság

The ancient marshland with reeds, open water surfaces and marshy meadows
has been preserved in a relatively intact state in two larger patches in
Győr–Sopron county, north of Kapuvár and Csorna. The landscape reserve
was established in 1976, on 6,243 ha with four units (South-Hanság, North-
Hanság, Fehér-lake, Barbacs-lake). Within this area the different stages
of plant colonization area well illustrated from the first stage (aquatic
weed), through the reeds to marshy meadow, *Salix cinerea* (common sallow),
Alnus glutinosa (alder), *Quercus-Ulmus* (oak-elm), plantations of *Alnus* and
Populus (poplars). Along the former watercourses of areas covered by the
ancient vegetation, there occurs a rare plant, *Urtica kioviensis*. The marsh-

land with striped alder and King-lake alder, in the latter with the rare *Ribes nigrum* (black currant), offer a nice view. Peculiarities of the rich fauna are the long-nosed viper, black stork, hen harrier and the musquash.

Vértes

The landscape reserve was established in 1976, on 13,723 ha. The Vértes-mountains are surrounded by a rapidly developing industrial region. Both in the mountains and in its neighbourhood there is significant mining activity going on. Consequently, this landscape serves as a leisure and re-creation site of this mining district. The most important areas from the point of view of science are under strict protection. These are: Fáni-valley, Haraszt-hill at Csákvár as well as the surrounding land, the beech-wood of Pátrácos and the forest with its growths of cyclamen at Mindszentpuszta. There are relatively many caves in the mountain. Among them the most significant one is the cave at Báracháza, in which evidence had been found for the 10 million-year history of the animal kingdom of this region. The open dolomitic cliff grasses, karstland forests and the unique eastern horn-beam stand of trees in Southern Vértes are really picturesque. The beech forests of Pátráca, in the North-Western Vértes, are ecological rarities. The Fáni-valley preserves relict species of subalpine origin. Many large birds of prey facing extinction, nest in the Vértes-mountains such as the bald eagle, lanneret (*Falco falco biarmicus*) and honey-buzzard.

Hollókő

The inner area of this protected ancient village, its closed gardens and the fortress-hill were taken under control in 1977. The goal of the establish-ment of this landscape reserve was to protect one of the most beautiful forest-covered valleys of the Cserhát-hilly region, including the ancient village of Hollókő. The present appearance of the village has evolved since the great fire in 1909. The ruins of the fortress, which dominate the village, are the remains of the smallest but most perfectly preserved medieval fortress in Nógrád county.

Sopron

The Sopron-hills are situated in the north-western part of Transdanubia. It is a characteristic chain of hills in a relatively small area. It is a typical feature of Sopron, a town rich in historic monuments, that the town does not intrude but blends with its natural environment. Almost half of the territory (4,905 ha) of the landscape reserve is covered by coniferous forest, thus lending an alpine character to the environment. In the mountains approx. 70 sources are known to exist. Several rare subalpine-montane species are native to this area like *Alchemilla glabra, Arnica montana, Matteucia struthiopteris* and the characteristic plant of the region, *Cyclamen purpurascens,* can be found in great quantities. The acidophilous plant communities (acidophilous oak forests, heathery-heath, sweet chestnuts) with *Vaccinium myrtillus* (bilberry-huckleberry) make this range of mountains unique in the whole country. Common trout lives in the clean water of brooks and the rare *Regulus regulus* and *Parus ater* nest in the forests. At Várhely, peoples of Illiric–Celtic origin raised an imposing earthwork, enclosing within its tumuli.

Eastern Mecsek

The landscape reserve of approx. 9,248 ha basic area was established in 1977. As to its relief and hydrographic conditions Eastern Mecsek is a well-defined landscape of the Mecsek-mountains. Besides intensive agricultural and industrial development and mining, it is also an area containing important natural resources. Among its geological sites of special interest the feature of unbroken volcanic massive formations are of outstanding importance, this being their unique occurrence in Hungary. The circular valley displays volcanic formations dating back to the Jura-age. Their protection is therefore, of paleontological, paleo-geographical and stratigraphical importance. The large number of Mediterranean floristic elements like *Asperula taurina* (pink woodruff), *Orchis simia* (monkey orchid), and that of southern elements such as *Paeonia officinalis* ssp. *banatica, Doronium orientale* are also characteristic of this region. Its monuments of cultural-historical importance are: a church from the Arpadian age at Mecseknádasd, the ruins of the monastery from the age of St. Stephen at Pécsvárad, the fortress of Máré, the ruins on the top of Zengő-hill and the Crab-fortress (Rákvár).

Szabadkígyós

The salt-affected pastures, arable lands and forests around Szabadkígyós and the park situated in the village (3,785 ha) were taken under protection in 1977. The saline grass pastures composed of *Artemisia* and *Festuca* species, the remnants of the forest-covered puszta (saline oak forests), once characteristic of the Hungarian Plain, are still to be seen on vast areas. The already protected park at Szabadkígyós is a masterpiece of Hungarian garden-architecture. The castle and barn near to it were built by Miklós Ybl between 1875–1879. The saline-puszta is an important meeting and gathering place for migrating birds. Its bird of prey rarities are: *Accipiter brevipes* (levant sparrowhawk), *Gyps fulvus*, *Aquila heliaca* (imperial eagle) *Falco vespertinus* frequently nest in the forest-covered patches of the puszta. A protected characteristic mammal species is *Mustela eversmanni*, while among the insect species, the songarian spider can be considered as a rarity.

Gemenc

A 17,779 ha section of the Danube, between Tolna and Báta, including its flood area between Fajsz and Szeremle, was taken under protection in 1977. The high vaulted forests along the flood area of the Lower Danube belong to the most beautiful landscape of Hungary. The most famous part of this area is Gemenc. On the alluvial soils of the region the largest high vaulted forests of Hungary are to be found: *Salix triandra* (almond willow), *Salix alba* (white willow), etc. The *Querceto-Ulmeta* with much *Urtica*, *Clematis* and coppices resemble the luxuriant vegetation of the tropics. *Tulipa silvestris* and *Leucojum aestivum* are rarities in stands of *Convallario-Quercetum*. There are numerous oak, ash, silver, grey and black poplar trees of extraordinary form and size living in the flood plain. As regards the animal kingdom, the red deer stock forming genetic resources, is very valuable. *Lutra lutra* and *Felis sylvestris* are rare predatory mammals in this nature reserve. *Falco cherrug* (saker falcon), *Aquila pomarina* (lesser spotted eagle), *Haliaetus albicilla* (sea eagle) and *Alcedo atthis* (kingfisher) are some of the most precious birds. The reserve is also of great importance from the point of view of international wildfowl protection.

Gerecse

The part of the Gerecse-mountains, belonging to Komárom county, an area of 8,617 ha was declared protected in 1977. The many-sided mountains protrude like an island from the surrounding industrial and mining region. The limestone block of Great-Pisznice is suitable for the development of karst formations, consequently, a huge multi-levelled cave has evolved there, which is rich in archeological finds. The red limestone of Pisznice ("marble of Piszke") was quarried already in the Middle Ages but at present the quarries have been abandoned. The flora of Gerecse is similar to that of the Vértes-mountain (open and closed rocky grassland coenoses, slopes covered by steppe (puszta) grass, etc.). Karstic scrub with *Cotynus coggygria* and *Prunus mahaleb, Sorbus gerecsensis* and *Orobanche teucris* are characteristic and valuable species of its flora. The arboretum at Aggostyán is a habitat for numerous native tree species and exotic species of conifer. Birds worthy of protection are: *Falco cherrug* (saker falcon), *Hieraaëtus pennatus, Milvus migrans* (black kite), *Corvus corax,* and the six bat species living in the cave of Great-Pisznice. The model and training area for national environmental control is sited in the neighbourhood of Tatabánya. Gerecse, with its varied natural wealth also belongs to the model areas.

Lake Fertő

The most valuable areas (12,543 ha) of the territory of the third largest lake in Central Europe was taken under protection in 1977. About two-thirds of the area of Lake Fertő, which lies in Austria, has been under protection since 1965. The approx. 20 million year-old liassic limestone of the quarry at Fertőrákos is a storehouse of well-preserved signs of its marine origin. The quarry, regularly used from the Roman times until 1945, is also an important site from the viewpoint of industrial history. The flatland and shallow lake, with its salty water and mud with medicinal properties are the most significant natural endowment of the area. The medicinal spa and mineral water springs of the village of Balf are also of considerable value. The unrivalled botanical importance of the Fertő-district is represented by the abundance of species (1,513 vascular cryptogamic and phanerogamic species, several hundreds of cryptogams) and by such characteristic plant communities of the saline soils which starting from the region of Lake Aral-Caspian sea extend through the Great Hungarian Plain and reach their westernmost boundary here. At a certain section of the steppe-lake there are

17 saline communities which form a mosaic complex. The hills surrounding Lake Fertő are extremely rich in rare liassic limestone floristic elements. The extraordinary fauna of the area includes *Misgurnus fossilis, Cobitis taenia, Lacerta vivipara, Vipera ursinii* and *Lutra lutra.* The number of bird species which nest here or migrate via this area is extremely large and amounts to nearly 260 species. The Fertő area is the treasure-store of ancient settlements, archeological, artistic, cultural-historical and folkloristic ancient monuments and sites. Some outstanding objects are: the Romanesque church of Hidegség, the Baroque church at Fertőrákos and the church at Balf with elements of Gothic style. Since May 1979 a further 6 landscape reserves have been established on a total area of 116,000 ha in the Pilis-mountains, Middle-Tisza region, Őrség, Börzsöny-mountains, Aggtelek and Buda. The landscape reserves at Badacsony and Szentgyörgyhegy have been united to form an expanded landscape reserve.

National parks

Hortobágy National Park (HNP)

This was the first nature conservation unit in Hungary. As the increased economic exploitation had greatly destroyed or reduced the characteristic landscape of the Hortobágy-puszta, its saline-marsh plant and animal king-dom, folkloristic and other cultural-historical treasures, the establishment of the National Park in 1973 meant the realization of an old scientific expectation. At present, the precious natural state can be found only in one-third—still a large territory—of the former puszta. With proper mea-sures of protection it can still be preserved. Hortobágy a former flood plain, prior to its regulation was often flooded by the river Tisza. Comprising the back-waters, swamps and forest patches with oak as the dominant species, it was a grassland with several smaller villages in its higher-lying areas. During and after the Turkish occupation these villages became uninhabited. Regular cutting greatly reduced the tree stands. Following the regulation of the Tisza, in the second half of the 19th century, floods have ceased. The territory became a dry saline steppe (puszta), with its lower lying areas— depending on precipitation and soil-water—remaining more or less swampy. Consequently, it is not the climatic conditions but human impact that has turned Hortobágy into a "puszta" (steppe) and the characteristic saline vegetation, which had formerly grown only on its higher lying, drier and more saline areas, has spread widely.

The main characteristics of this area is the unbroken horizon, the silence of the puszta-landscape and its stillness where "Fata-morgana" (mirage) is a unique phenomenon. Hortobágy is a treasure-store of geomorphological, geological, botanical and zoological sights even today. It is known all over Europe as a meeting place of migrating birds in autumn and spring and is a protected area registered as a bird sanctuary, where hunting of waterfowl is prohibited. Shepherding is a characteristic economic activity. The ancient strains of domestic animals (grey cattle, "racka" sheep with spiny horns, buffalo, "mangalic" pig, "komondor", "kuvasz", "puli" and "pumi" dogs) are irreplaceable values. There are typical objects of folk-art and shepherd shelters. Because of their outstanding national and international importance the task of the HNP is to protect and develop the characteristic treasures of the puszta, to preserve, vegetation and fauna of Hortobágy to secure the unharmed nesting and migration of the extraordinary avifauna of this area to demonstrate the traditional lifeform of the puszta, to preserve the diminishing ancient Hungarian animals, the characteristic cultural-historical treasures and to preserve the historic monuments of Hortobágy in their natural and original form.

The territory of the HNP is 52,000 ha of which 73% is pasture. The national park was established on a relatively less affected area of the puszta. Outside the national park, surrounded by arable land, there have survived a few patches of puszta and swamp. These have been declared as nature reserves and are managed by the National Park Directorate. There are seven such areas, with a total area of 11,000 ha, which form an organic part of the national park. In addition to them, there are further 5 areas (their total territory is 2,500 ha), which also come under the same management. The most difficult task of the HNP Directorate is to harmonize the economic activity going on in the puszta, with landscape conservation. In 1973, some 100 co-workers of the Hungarian Academy of Sciences began to take an inventory of the natural treasures of Hortobágy. Similar work has begun in the field of ethnography. In 1977 a round-shed was built beside the shepherd-museum, which now displays specimens from the National Park.

Kiskunság National Park (KNP)

The second Hungarian national park was established on 30,000 ha in 1975. In contrast to Hortobágy, it is a so-called "mosaic" national park. Its territory consists, namely, of six different blocks. In addition to this, it comprises also eight smaller or larger nature reserves and two landscape reserves. Their total area amounts to 82,000 ha. Owing to its mosaic-like character, it is most varied and rich in natural sites of special interest. The areas under protection have survived in an almost unaltered state; there are almost no landscape spoilt by man. It is a great advantage for the management of the national park that the largest proportion of its area is unsuitable for agricultural cultivation. Tőserdő is situated east of Kecskemét bordering Lakitelek, along a 4-km long section of the Dead-Tisza. In the high vaulted forests of the flood area *Quercus robur* (oak), *Fraxinus excelsior* (ash) and *Ulmus laevis* (European white elm) grow. *Convallario-Quercetum roboris* associations are also frequently to be seen. The Kiskunság-saline puszta (Apaj) lies south of Kiskunlacháza, near to Kunszentmiklós. It is a famous area also from the geological point of view as the only coherent puszta in Hungary with limerich-sodified soil. On the salt-affected soil characteristic salt-favouring vegetation has evolved, and it is here, where the richest *Otis tarda* stock of the Danube–Tisza region can be found. The ancient "puszta-way" of animal keeping is also famous.

At the meeting point of Fülöpszállás and Szabadszállás, there has formed a chain of natron lakes. Shallow water surfaces with alkaline reaction, having numerous tiny islands and clumps are typical of the area. As the natron lakes are nesting or living places for 70–80 bird species, they are of great importance from the point of view of bird protection. As the nature reserve is situated on the route of migrating birds it is a resting place for them. The only drift-sand area in Europe preserved in an unaffected state can be found west of Kecskemét, near Fülöpháza. The sand was blown off from the bed of the ancient Danube and deposited at irregular distances, in three great groups of hill, from west to east. The last coherent areas of reeds, marshy meadows, hayfields formerly characteristic of the Great Hungarian Plain, can be found in their original state around Lake Kolon. Swamps in the fields of Csengőd and Dáhi, with *Fraxinus* sp. and *Alnus* sp. as well as plant rarities of the "Karagala" swamp at Orgovány are also of importance.

The nature conservation unit at Bócsa–Bugac is the largest coherent territory of the national park. The so-called "ancient junipery area" with a completely unharmed vegetation and fauna offer an imposing sight. 120–130-year-old juniper trees are mixed with white, grey and trembling, as well as black poplars. In contrast to all other puszta in Hungary, the puszta at Bugac has sandy soil. On the west it is bordered by the Great Forest of Bugac, which offers a magnificent scenery. The former shepherd life is illustrated in the Shepherd Museum, opened a few years ago. Bács–Kiskun is the largest county in Hungary with respect to the number of farmsteads. It is the most important task of KNP to preserve and protect the most beautiful and characteristic farmsteads.

Bükk National Park (BNP)

The third national park in Hungary was established in 1976 on 38,775 ha in the Bükk-mountains, situated in Borsod–Abaúj–Zemplén and Heves counties. In order to increase the efficiency of protection, a 5,664 ha area of the national park is subject to strict protection, which means that only experts with special permission are allowed to carry out investigations there. The richness of geological formations in the Bükk-mountains, which is similar to the Dinaric Alps, is unparalleled in Hungary. As to their formation, they are unique geological sites not only in Hungary, but also in the Carpathian basin. The plateaus, separated by couloir-like deep valleys, offer insight into the structure of the mountains and lend an alpine character to the Bükk-mountains. Within the territory of the limestone mountains, all kinds of karstic formations can be found. Among the caves, that number is more than four hundred, there are several larger ones, and all of them are richly decorated by dripstones. As to its formations the Petőfi-cave at Lillafüred, in non-saline water limestone, is the richest of the four tufa-caves in the world. The veil-like waterfall in the Szalajka-valley and the tufa-deposits of Sebesvölgy are of charming beauty.

The Bükk-mountains abound in rare plants, endemic, relict and montane species. Prior to the extension of agriculture, the characteristic vegetation of the surrounding hill region had been wooded steppe with *Acer tataricum* (tartar maple), *Quercus petraea* (durmast oak), *Q. robur* (English oak), *Q. cerris* (Turkey oak), while the lower lying slopes belong already to the belt of closed oak forests. In Southern-Bükk, there are oak forests with *Quercus cerris* as well as calciferous oak forests, while on dry, warm slopes and the southern edge of the highland, various steppe and scrub-forest communities can be found. At the bottom of the valley arid oak forests are replaced by horn beam oak forests, then gradually by the sub-montane beech forests. In southern aspects and on acid rock-beds, acidiphilous beech and oak forests have found favourable conditions. On the limestone and on boulder strewn rocky slopes various rock-forest communities have evolved. On the steep dolomitic slopes, there is a rare plant community: the rock-forest with *Sorbus* (rowan) and *Tilia* (limes) species. The Bükk-plateau and the northern valleys are covered by montane beech forests. Stands of *Larix decidua* (European larch) and *Picea abies* (Norway spruce) are extraordinary both in size and in age. Similarly to the vegetation, the fauna of the Bükk-mountains is also rich in species. Several of the rare species are recorded treasures equally in native and international nature conservation. Some of the rarities of the rich fauna characteristic of the Bükk-mountains are: alpine Cerambycidae, green spring-snail, *Barbus meridionalis* (southern barbel) Petényii, *Ablepharus Kitaibelii, Coluber jugularis caspicus, Corvus corax, Falco cherrug* (saker falcon), *Aquila heliaca* (imperial eagle), *Tetrastes bonasia, Meles meles, Felis sylvestris.*

Numerous findings of paleontological and paleoarchaeological importance have come to light from the great number of caves, proving that man had lived in the Bükk-mountains already in the Pleistocenic (glacial) epoch.

FUTURE DEVELOPMENT OF NATURE CONSERVATION

In January 1979, approx. 4.8% of the total territory of Hungary stood under protection. Nevertheless, there is still a large number of natural objects of outstanding importance awaiting protection. Scientific spheres and society itself urge the most complete realization of environmental protection possible. Man's impact on nature is also increasing in Hungary. It can be estimated that within 5–10 years one has to reckon with the destruction of the largest part of the natural sites that cannot be taken under protection. On the basis of the most useful suggestions put forward by scientific and administrative organizations, as well as on the basis of the records made by the organizations responsible for nature conservation, for a long time it has been stated that natural objects worthy of protection occupy a total area of over 600,000 ha in Hungary. However, the economic burden of limitations caused by protection must not be neglected, either.

Cultural interests connected with nature conservation are to be harmonized with the economic capacity of the geographical conditions and population density of the country on a realistic basis. By the sensible selection of objects most worthy of protection and by protecting the individual monuments on sites at their most characteristic and possibly well-distributed places of occurrence, one has to find the means by which the requirements of the scientific spheres and the society can be satisfied.

The National Office for Nature Conservation, which has elaborated the prospective programme of development, recommended that by 1990 all of the territories worthy of protection should be protected (Table 30). In contrast to the 600,000 ha suggested originally, this programme amounts to only 500,000 ha. By the time the environment programme has been completed, approx. 5.5% of the total area of Hungary will be protected. This rate of protection would secure that our characteristic natural monuments and sites of special interest: geological, hydrological, botanical, zoological, landscape and cultural-historical treasures of importance can survive in the long run. (Only a certain proportion of this would be taken under strict protection, while the greater part would be under a looser form of landscape protection.)

Table 30

The prospective state of the protected land areas in 1990

Category	No. of areas	Average area ha	Total of areas ha
National park	5	40,000	200,000
Landscape reserve	45	4–5,000	200,000
Nature conservation areas of national importance	150	300	50,000
Total of national value	200	2,250	450,000
Nature conservation areas of local importance	1,800	25–30	50,000
Total	2,000	250	500,000

It is obvious that—because of external anthropogenic effects—proper nature conservation can be realised only in protected units of large extent (some thousands of hectares). Therefore, forces have to be concentrated in those—generally extensively utilized—regions and areas, where natural sites have survived in the greatest number and in a more extended, coherent system than elsewhere: such are the less explored parts of woodlands, the flood basin of rivers, natron lakes and pastures, sand deserts, swamps, marshes, naked rocks, etc. By the earliest possible protection of such areas, in accordance with the requirements of economic life, the further deterioration of the relatively less disturbed natural conditions should be prevented.

Farming, which blends with the landscape and does no harm to it, is not only permissible in landscape reserves but, for reasons of landscape management, it is essential. Therefore, the regulations of landscape protection do not involve such a burden, as do the restrictive regulations pertaining to the strictly protected areas. Such strictly protected areas will be established in certain, most valuable parts of landscape reserves and additional reserve areas of national importance are mostly of similar character. With regard to all this, strict protection applies to only 2.5% of the total territory of cca. 5.5% planned to be protected.

According to plans, protection activity will not be completed by 1990. To save endangered sites, together with the already existing ones, a total of 470,000 ha will have been taken under protection. Accelerated nature conservation activity is motivated partly by the ever increasing public need or else because the valuable territories are rapidly deteriorating. On the other hand, since 1980, the intensive development of already protected areas has meant an even greater task. According to the plans in the period between 1980 and 1990 30,000 ha of natural monuments and sites of national and local importance should be taken under protection.

The establishment of further landscape reserves can be expected in the different regions of the country. These landscapes form a more or less homogeneous network and comprise many of the Hungarian sites: the most important geological exposures, caves, archaeological finds, springs, natural forest communities, many places with cultural-historical associations and the largest part of the areas suitable for natural genetic reserves.

As those territories of the "classical" nature conservation which deserve protection are rapidly decreasing or are being destroyed, more and more attention is paid to the areas with a disturbed ecological equilibrium, most suitable for recreation and tourism. The goal is to secure the protection of these areas. This enormous task can, however, be realised only by the rational work of the different branches of the economy in harmony with their prospective plans and by the gradual development of the environment and nature protection network.

References

Kaán, K. (1931): *Nature conservation and natural monuments.* (in Hungarian) Budapest.

Kenyeres, L. and Tildy, Z. (1960): *Our protected natural rarities* (in Hungarian). Budapest.

Kopasz, M. (1978): *Our protected natural endowments* (in Hungarian). 2. ed. Budapest.

Kovács, G. (Mrs.) and Salamon, F. (1976): *Hortobágy—from the nomadic puszta to the national park* (in Hungarian). Budapest.

Országos Természetvédelmi Hivatal (1977): Prospective development project (in Hungarian) 3/1977. sz. Presidential decree. Budapest.

Rakonczay, Z. (1976): Nature conservation and environment protection (in Hungarian). *Valóság* **19:** 8–21.

Seléndy, Sz. (1977): The protection of our old trees, and tree avenues (in Hungarian). *Kertgazdaság* **9:** 63–73.

Seléndy, Sz. (1977): The councils and nature conservation. *Búvár* **32:** 152–157.

Tanácsok Közlönye (Bulletin of Councils) (1975–1977): Regulations of the president of the National Office for Nature Conservation (in Hungarian).

Tóth, K. (1978): *National Park in Kiskunság* (in Hungarian). Budapest.

Varga, I. (1973): The structure of nature conservation. *Búvár* **28:** 323–327.

Chapter 12

The legal basis of environmental protection

Law deals with the protection of the human environment from pollution, harm, damage and detriments in three dimensions—legislation, law observance and the application of the law—and it also classifies them. In each dimension and in each legal solution action must be based on actual social conditions with circumspection to modern scientific-technical data. As we live in a society law plays a necessary role in environmental protection, though an indirect one especially in the elimination of detrimental factors in the environment or it can be a link of a chain in reaching a particular result. The system of legal norms—including the coercive power of the state—is the entity of permissive, limiting and prohibitive measures. It aims at the prevention of environmental harm, the control of environmental factors and the application of sanctions (norms of responsibility) against those who violate the permissive, limiting or prohibitive measures. It is namely, the starting point of law that the different degrees of pollution are not independent of the human mind and will, but there are circumstances which are recognisable and surmountable. Therefore, for the lawyer, it is never a particular factory, machine, energy, active substance that means the final source of the pollution, but always the human activity hidden behind it. Similarly, the final target of the pollution is also man itself. Law as a means of environmental control, combines a definite social requirement with scientific recognition together with a respect for the economic capacity of society, and on the basis of these it forms a system of legal norms in environmental control.

For a long time the concept of an environmental protection measure has been a disputed subject. This is not merely a theoretical question, since it has rather serious practical consequences. The primary measures may provide for the total, interdisciplinary and complex protection of the entire human environment or only for one of its components. The secondary measures give a relatively independent expression of a particular aspect of the environment and of environmental necessity. Concerning this classification, it is worth mentioning that at the beginning of the 1960s there was a more intensive legal regulation on the protection of certain parts of the environment without having a complex guide-line in environmental control.

This partial regulation can be ascribed to the fact that decay manifests itself in certain groups of objects in the initial stages and it becomes a rapidly extending process only later on. The year 1961 was especially important in Hungary in this respect. That year marked the passing of measures of vital importance regarding the protection of agricultural land, forest and game management, and the protection of the purity of waters. Although at that time, these measures constituted the foundations of the environmental law to come, there was no mention of environmental law at all. Systematically, these measures belonged to the systems of land-law and of administrative law.

Since the end of the 1960s and the beginning of the 1970s the viewpoint of environmental protection has been mentioned more frequently. This can partly be ascribed to the increasing legislative activity in Europe in the field of environmental law. These partial measures can be characterized by the strengthening of the quantitative-technical attitude with the requirements expressed in qualitative norms, emission values determined in terms similar to quantums being increasingly emphasized. Nevertheless, jurisprudence had not come to recognise environmental protection law, as an independent complex domain of jurisdiction. None the less, it deserves attention that, in both the Hungarian and the international literature on law the relationship of legal and technical standards became a subject of intense discussions. Codification could be characterized by the establishment of closer links between these two norms. The notion of qualitative standard values, expressing the degree of pollution or damage, was introduced into legal measures. It had become clear that the determination of limit values, described in legal measures, is of vital importance and this is the precondition for the effective applicability of legal measures. Because of this, the dispute on the clarification of the relationship between legal and technical standards forms one of the codificational-technical preconditions for the legal regulation of environmental protection.

HUNGARIAN CODE OF ENVIRONMENTAL PROTECTION

Since the beginning of the 1970s, a growing number of environmental protection acts have been put into force.

These comprehensive laws which were accompanied by the consolidation of earlier measures, in certain partial domains, aimed at totality. It was characteristic of the preparatory work and also of the content of the Hungarian Act II of 1976 on the Protection of the Human Environment, that the entire environment, as a whole, was taken under protection, while it also attempted to regulate certain domains as coherent units in a state of interdependence. As a first step the object of human environment was to be determined from the point of view of legal protection. These were atmosphere (air), water, land, the living world, landscape and residential (settlement) environment. In the second phase, those features connected with the environment giving cause for concern were to be clarified. These were the notions of pollution, damage and harmful effect which were to be controlled by relevant legal means. Finally, the sequence, the implementation, the listing of those responsible and also the possible forms of natural and artificial protection were to be regulated. These two main directions of protection implied also the determination of the compulsory standards of operation. The latter postulates the general and special activity of the operator in the field of organization and technology alike.

This codification effort marks a qualitative change in contrast to the former situation. Nevertheless, the most significant results in regulation have been achieved in the already traditional domains (those which have been regulated relatively fully) thus, in the field of water conservation, forest protection, soil protection. However, the first steps have been taken by the act on environment protection, also in the field of protection from radiation and noise. Administrative and judicial practice still have to face many questions of interpretation in this context.

THE PLACE OF ENVIRONMENTAL PROTECTION IN THE LEGAL SYSTEM

The developing codification in the field of environmental protection all over Europe also stimulates jurisprudence. Jurisprudence has to cope with many problems simultaneously. It has to determine the place of environmental protection law within the legal system. This is, however, not merely a question of formal systematics, as the arsenal of legal means and the way of their application is also closely connected with the place of environmental protection law in the legal system. The phase delay, by which it can be characterized in comparison with the natural and technical sciences, has to be eliminated. (As the adaptation of already recognised ecological, biological and technical principles and practice forms the precondition of the codification of legal standards, this phase delay was justifiable to a certain extent.) Finally, an answer was to be given to the question, whether the traditional armoury of legal powers had been enough to enforce the regulations of environmental protection law or whether an attempt should be made to work out completely new measures.

The research activity in the field of the environmental protection law started in 1971 with some confusion at the beginning in the legal literature as the proper place of environmental protection is concerned in the legal system. Not only was environmental protection to be blamed for this, but also the situation. In the modern society, with the complexity of intensifying socio-economic relationships there is a growing tension between the structure of circumstances to be regulated and the structure of the legal system. This has an influence on the structure of the legal system, on the formation of the interdisciplinary institutions, in other words, the quasi-branches of law. Keeping in mind its own structural regularities, jurisprudence is looking for their proper place in the legal-system. Following the initial exploratory work, specialists in environmental protection law are of the opinion that it does not form part of any kind of an already existing branch of law, but it is such a complex, interdisciplinary law province, in which administrative law, land-law, civil law, international law and criminal law are equally involved. This interdisciplinary attitude has also been adopted by the Hungarian Act on environmental protection of 1976. This interdisciplinary attitude has several consequences:

1. First of all the fact that environmental protection law and other measures more or less connected with environmental protection (such as land protection law, nature protection law), form such a unit, in which the unity-diversity predominates in such a way that the unusual—that possesses, naturally, an independent form of motion—cannot be opposed to the general measures of environmental protection. The principle of unity and diversity is effective in all dimensions of legal existence.

2. Since the juridical system of measures in environmental protection comprises prevention, defence, reparation and repression equally, the interdisciplinary attitude forms only a starting point in a process in which

the individual branches and domains of law adapt the system of their means to the requirements of environmental protection, in cases where none existed and they elaborate new ones. This process has been started by codification, first of all. This was the case when, the law recognised the right to clear (pure) environment as human rights and in comparison with this, considered it an institution of state-constitutional law; on the other hand, the act on environmental protection completed the Criminal Code with a new penalty statement—the statement of criminal offence violating environmental protection.

3. Environmental control, in general, and within it the formation of environmental protection law had led to a certain confusion of ideas, which made it more or less difficult to determine the place of environmental protection law. The idea of environmental protection law and nature protection law are often used as synonyms. Similarly, the right connection between land protection and nature protection is also frequently misunderstood. The broadest legal-idea is the environmental protection law, which is directed at the macro-environment and the settlements in it. Consequently, it takes the complexity of the human environment under protection. The resolution of the environmental protection law is to define the protected legal objects. These are land, water, air, living world, landscape and settlement environment. It also denominates the entity of phenomena with a negative effect on the protected legal objects. These are pollution, harm, exposure to harmful damages and the releasing of the forces of nature. Nature conservation is a smaller sphere than this. It aims at preserving natural areas worthy of protection for posterity, culture, scientific research and tourism in their original, intact state, devoid of external, mainly human impacts. Land protection is another idea, its main objective is the proper use of agricultural land. Though being an independent idea, it also forms part of environmental protection. In this context, land protection and nature protection are parts not only of environmental protection law, but that of land-law, which is also a branch of the Hungarian legal system. Moreover, environmental protection law (within this the act on nature protection) has utilized, in more than one respect, and developed the former measures pertaining to land protection and nature protection.

THE RIGHT TO A CLEAN ENVIRONMENT AS A BASIC HUMAN RIGHT

Hungary, similarly to several countries in Europe, recognizes the right to a clean, "man-worthy" environment as a basic human right. "Every citizen has the right to live in an environment worthy of man"—states the Act. This is natural, as the concept of human rights is also a historical legal category. Its 200-year-old history proves that its individual components have been enriched in the course of social development. The sporadic industrial development and the environmental protection coupled with it, have also upset the rights to life and health in other aspects. In the absence of legal measures the declaration of the right to a clean environment, as a human right would remain merely a phrase, though true enough the importance of legal measures can greatly depend on whether they are codified as basic human rights or not. As the right to work is also not merely an empty declaration in our legal system—its reality is secured by a broad spectrum of legal and social norms—it is to be hoped that the effective system of norms will evolve also in the right to a clean environment. Nevertheless, it might be useful to emphasize that, in the present instance, the other side of the civil right also denominates an obligation.

LAND TENURE, LAND USE AND ENVIRONMENTAL PROTECTION

The regulation of land tenure and land utilization—since the category of proprietary rights has existed—is one of the central questions of each ruling class. The effect of the Roman legal concept, according to which water and air are free "spoils" could be felt for a long time. In connection with the history of the civil revolution, in the 17th and 19th century it was obvious that the regulation of the proprietary right of land, as well as its liberation from the feudal-bonds were in the focus of jurisprudence and codification.

The classical codification of the 19th century, such as the French Civil Code, the German "Bürgerliches Gesetzbuch" considered land, as the other objects to be of proprietary rights. In principle, the owner had an unlimited command of the ownership of land and was allowed to utilize it according to his own wishes. At that time, it was the right of disposal, which from among the three partial rights of ownership (right to possess, utilization and disposal) was most closely related to circulation. It stood, therefore, in the foreground of legal regulation. In the socialist countries of Central Europe, this process has been carried out over a longer period in several stages, reaching its perfection in the course of the great land-reforms of 1945 and the codification activity connected with it.

The second phase of regulation evolved in the first half of the 20th century. Due to the interaction of several components the priority of public interest was gaining emphasis in contrast to the unlimited private ownership of land. There have evolved the most varied legal solutions of this basic idea aiming primarily at tillage obligation. According to the democratic civic constitution in Weimar, the tillage and utilization of land is an obligation of the owner to society. The French theoretician Duguit elaborated a concept on "fonction sociale", according to which the aim of proprietary right is to satisfy the social requirements for goods by the goods of private persons. In general, the number of examples on production regulation is endless. At that time, nature protection law had already evolved the legal system.

Requirements directed by the technical development of agriculture could not be satisfied by measures guaranteeing land utilization but, by organization and legal measures an attempt was made to wipe out the contradiction between the parcelization of agricultural land and the need to raise the technical level. Agricultural cooperatives have come into existence both in the socialist and many Western European countries (France and Italy, etc.). These agricultural cooperatives which, though by the most varied regulation of proprietary and user rights have created large-scale land utilization, have seen a rapid development since then. In other countries as in Switzerland and Austria by limiting the rules of inheritance an attempt has been made to solve the contradiction between the technical level and the farm size by sustaining an optimal farm size under the given conditions). Superficially, it would mean the modernization of the right of land disposal though, in essence it is the conversion of utilization right—the other partial domain of proprietary right—into large-scale development, that has come to the fore.

The third phase of legal regulation is evolving at present. It is characteristic of this phase that the protection of the natural environment, land and water plays a double role; on the one hand it is a factor playing a significant role in the maintenance of the equilibrium in the biosphere, on the other hand, it is a fundamental base of food production. Industrialization and urbanization exert a double effect on land. It endangers the equilibrium of the biosphere and it brings some factors into being that are independent of the landowner's or land user's will and his concepts concerning production both in a quantitative and qualitative respect. The formation of the land surface and that of the impacts on it include two spheres of interest: a common social interest and that of agriculture. These spheres are convergent, as detrimental impacts exerted on agricultural production also hurt the interests of mankind but rarely, they can also become antagonistic (the excessive application of chemicals in plant protection). Two concordant spheres of interest—land and agricultural production—require a new type of regulation in which the trend of external factors influencing the way of land utilization, soil protection and soil reclamation, are not merely the problem of the owner and land user, or that of the agricultural sector, but a public affair, incorporating the public interest. Compared with this, the third stage of legal regulation is the most complicated.

The effect of the above-mentioned three phases of development manifest themselves in each country differently, both in time and in space. In reality, however, the situation is not so simple either in the developing countries or in Europe. In the industrially developed European and North-American states it is either the third phase, or the complex effect of the second and third phases of regulation that dominate. In the developing countries the requirements of all the three phases dominate equally. In countries with sophisticated economic development and a complex industrial structure, during a relatively short period of history, the consequences of all the three phases of development will culminate, will make their highest impact.

THE LEGAL PROTECTION OF AGRICULTURAL LAND

The legal protection of agricultural land forms a separate question within the huge complex problem of environmental protection. The extent of agricultural land has been rapidly decreasing. Nevertheless, the trend of decrease is a problem in those countries where there is no possibility of adding to the absolute area of agricultural land. Developing countries having a relatively large territory today, will be faced with similar problems tomorrow. Undoubtedly, developing productivity, plant protection and plant protection technology can to a certain extent compensate for the lack of land, though beyond a certain level, no technique or technology can compensate for the deficiency in land.

Although the decrease of land is an objectively inevitable process, its pace and rate do not always harmonize with the requirements of necessity. In Hungary we have come to the conclusion, too, that, with respect to the interests of the people's economy and within this, to that of agricultural production, the unreasonable misuse of agricultural land must be stopped by administrative measures. The institution of land protection has been developed by legal regulations aimed at this.

Land protection is meant to guarantee that all agriculturally utilized or utilizable territory of the country remain in the sphere of agricultural production and the entire arable land area be utilized according to its proper suitability. According to this, in view of higher interests, the land protection law limits the right of disposal of both land owner and land utilizer. This limitation is to serve the quantitative and qualitative protection of land. These limitations and legal measures can be summarized as follows:

It ordains the obligation of the proper use of land for the owner and land user alike, the violation of which leads to sanctions. We believe that the world-wide nutrition problems will inevitably decide the dispute concerning the obligation of land cultivation, which has existed since the time of Diderot. Diderot was still of the opinion that the administration had no right to interfere with the will of the land owner whether to cultivate his land or not. In contrast to this, Mercier declared that those leaving their land lying fallow could be obliged to leave the land for all. This requirement was realised in the French law relatively soon. However, in the legal system of socialist countries the right to land utilization and its obligation form unity with each other.

— Any utilization different from the given designation of land for other purposes thus, the changing of the branch of cultivation and its withdrawal from cultivation, is made a precondition of the previous permission, determining the conditions of issue. Thus only such land can be expropriated, the withdrawal of which from production has been authorized.
— All kinds of changes in the ownership and utilization of land are to be declared. The supervision of registered or licensed changes should be carried out to secure the identity of data in the state land-register and the actual situation as a basis for the national and farm-size planning.
— In the case, where industrial and other establishments are closed, the formerly occupied territories, those withdrawn from cultivation are to be recovered and passed over to agricultural utilization.
— Finally, the Act ordains the protection of soil. Soil protection is a primary duty of both the land owner and leaseholder, who are obliged to maintain and increase the productivity of the soil by all means and to protect soils exposed to devastation by natural forces. State organizations also outline, in detail, the implementation of soil protection and its means to be carried out by farms on their own, within the framework of their own economy. Besides this, owing to the general interest attached to the tillage of less fertile areas, the State makes great financial efforts in order to increase soil fertility.

In Hungary, the act on land protection was passed in 1961 and had a leading role at that time. Its implications, with the complexity of environmental protection, has made it necessary to re-evaluate some of its aspects and to draw appropriate conclusions. Today the cultivation obligation, the preservation of vegetation of territories is not only a question of food-production but, one of general human interest. Finally, mention should be made of the varied system of sanctions imposed on the contraveners of the land protection act. This comprises sanctions varying from paying a penalty to the deprivation of the ownership of land.

WATER AND AIR PROTECTION

The proprietary rights to waters and their use had already been regulated in the earlier stages of legal development. Qualitative changes in the regulations are taking place, however, only at present. The act on water-rights of 1885 also legislated on water pollution and imposed a fine on persons who polluted waters. Those who deliberately spoil wells, sources or water systems with the aim to make water undrinkable, may be punished. There was, however, no mention as yet of the prevention of industrial pollution. This could be ascribed to the initial stage of industrial development on the one hand, and to the fact that it was the owner of the land who disposed of water, on the other. The development of law has the same three phases as described in connection with land: the right of free disposal, the age of interference and at present, the age of protection.

Water and air are two basic elements of human life. Concerning their legal aspects, there are many differences between them, although their protection from pollution also entails several similarities.

When considering the prevention and the protection from water and air pollution, as main tasks in the present phase of development, the following regulations hold true for both the notion and kinds of pollution. The general prohibition of pollution, the determination of the limit values of pollution licensed norms (emission effluent and emission standards) and the obligation imposed upon the owner and user of purification plant, are backed by the possibility of imposing fines and in the worst case, by the limitation and prohibition of the polluting activity.

In Hungary legal rules were issued in 1966 and 1969 on water and in 1971 on air pollution even providing substantial state powers to prevent pollution and the Environmental Protection Act has completed this regulatory process.

COMPREHENSIVE NATURE PROTECTION

According to the Environmental Protection Act, comprehensive nature conservation comprises two main spheres of environmental protection: the protection of the living world and of the landscape. By determining prohibitions and obligations, the protection of the living world covers the flora and fauna. Thus, it is prohibited to collect or damage plants to an extent and in a manner, which may lead to a harmful alteration of a species or a variety, or to their extinction. In order to protect the living world the total area of forests shall not be reduced. Afforestation is made obligatory in certain areas. In order to secure the survival of animal species and varieties, a methodical animal protection policy is to be carried out.

The protection of the landscape extends to natural landscapes and to areas and objects, the preservation and maintenance of which is necessary for scientific, cultural or for other public interests. They must be protected from any effect that may endanger or harm their survival and for this very reason, they must be declared protected. Areas and parts of landscapes declared protected must be maintained as nature conservation areas, protected landscape zones or national parks.

THE PROTECTION OF THE ENVIRONMENT OF SETTLEMENTS

Before the coming into force of the Environmental Protection Act, a multiplicity of national and local measures regulated the protection of the environment of settlements. In spite of the great number of measures regulation was not complete. According to the general phrasing of the Environmental Protection Act, the protection of the environment of settlements shall extend to residential, resort and institution areas and also to other lands serving as human abodes. For this purpose the Act sets limits or prohibitions on the building and the erection of workshops obliging local organizations to plant trees and build parks and also limiting the sphere of activity of factories. Thus, in the environment of settlements, it is prohibited to cause dangerous and harmful noises, other vibrations (lights, and shaking) and radiation (radioactivity and heat). Finally, it provides the maintenance of public hygiene in settlements. Moreover, it is the protection of the environment of settlements by which the obligatory side of civil rights can be illustrated in the most flexible way. The Act's provision is not without any reasoning. Everybody must cooperate efficiently in the maintenance of public hygiene (public health) of settlements.

THE SYSTEM OF SANCTIONS AGAINST
ENVIRONMENTAL POLLUTION

This section deals with the sphere of responsibility in the environmental protection law. Responsibility law is one of the classical spheres of legal system. It has four basic types: criminal, administrative and labour-right penalty liability and liability for damages. Environmental protection as an idea has affected also the law of liability. In administrative law there appeared the penalty for discharges of sewage, later on the penalty for polluting the sewers, finally, in 1975, the air-pollution penalty. In the law of liability for damages, it was primarily judicial practice, later on, the Environmental Protection Act that qualified dusting, spraying, water pollution with poisonous chemicals as a dangerous activity attracting consequently increased liability as this has been extended to the sphere of objective liability. Persons causing damage through their environment-endangering activities must compensate for the damage, pursuant to the rules of the Civil Code relating to activities involving increased danger. The Hungarian Penal Code has also formed the concept of violating environmental protection as a crime and those shall be punished, who pollute objects under environmental protection or who expose them to harm or damage in such a way that human life and health are affected unfavourably to a considerable extent.

The Environmental Protection Act has united all possible legal sanctions: (*i*) the limiting and prohibiting of activity, (*ii*) prohibition on the utilization of a product, (*iii*) paying a fine or imposing other penalties, (*iv*) special compensation for damages and (*v*) sanction according to the Penal Code. The sanctions are complex, variable and jointly applicable. The Act has, consequently, completed the traditional armoury of liability types, without forming a coherent liability system of environmental protection, based also on the foundations of traditional forms. Concerning the legal regulation of legal responsibility for the environment, the first steps have already been made.

The theoretical questions of the environmental protection can be realized by the establishment of legal basis not by extending aims and principles. Within the liability law of environmental protection there are questions to be solved such as the correlation between necessity and unlawfulness, the complex problem of causation connection and the synchronization of personal rights and duties. In view of all this, in the course of the execution of the objectives of the act on environmental protection, jurisprudence must not be satisfied by the loosening or tightening of liability standards but, it is necessary to review the entire system of legal responsibility in its own complexity, as well as to elaborate the coherent synthesized system of environmental responsibility.

THE ROLE OF ENVIRONMENTAL PROTECTION IN INTERNATIONAL CO-OPERATION AND LEGAL SYSTEMS

Air and water are not discriminated with respect to social systems of societies and countries. Consequently, international co-operation, the activity of international organizations, their recommendations, the regulations in the form of mutual international agreements play an ever increasing role in the regulation of environmental protection. (European socialist countries have concluded, both among themselves and with countries with a capitalist social system, some 200 bilateral agreements, which directly or indirectly are related to environmental protection.) Solutions applied by other countries are inspiring for the regulation of individual countries, where a particular approach can also be followed. It is one of the basic problems, in this context, as to how and to what extent legal systems and certain national solutions hinder international integration, the all-European solution. Legal science has, basically, two attitudes as to whether they take national or international law as a basis. These solutions are easy either to defend or to attack, though the basic problem is, that it is not only national and international, but universal human relations that really matter. Anyhow, it is an accepted rule in the international system of environmental protection—as a minimal right or obligation of countries—that *sic utere tuo ut alienum non laedas,* in applying its sovereignty, a state should act in a way so as not to cause any harm to other countries. This principle has been accepted both in Stockholm and in Helsinki. There is a promising international activity going on in the International Commission of Jurists of the UNO, which aims at the determination of the responsibility of states violating the principle of *sic utere tuo.*

Glossary

A description and definition of the most frequently occurring and most important terms used in environmental control

Owing to its special character, environmental control comprises several scientific disciplines. Scientists involved in relevant studies, such as biologists, chemists, engineers and hydrologists, specialists in agriculture and viticulture, as well as representatives of the technical, medical and legal professions play an active part both in the studies on environmental control and in the publication of the results achieved. Due to its interdisciplinary character, environmental control is very rich in new technical terms and several ideas have acquired new meanings resulting in a specialized vocabulary.

This glossary, based on the data of the *New Hungarian Lexicon,* the *Lexicon of Natural Sciences* and the *Lexicon of Water Conservation* as well as that of several relevant scientific papers, contains the most frequently occurring technical terms used in the international literature on nature conservation, without attempting to achieve completeness. Since our book aims to deal with the biological basis of environmental control, the items are mainly the technical terms used in biological and related sciences.

Naturally, a book, e.g. a similar glossary appended to a book on the technical problem of environment control would contain other items. Besides the main technical terms, the glossary contains, for those wishing to study the Hungarian and international specialized literature, the generally accepted abbreviations of international organizations and institutions (e.g. MAB-programme, FAO, WHO, ICSU, etc.) which are involved, in some way, with international or Hungarian environmental control.

In addition to the authors this glossary has been compiled by the following contributors: B. Jankó, G. A. Manninger, M. Mőcsényi and T. Várkonyi, with some revisions and additions by the Translation Editor who has consulted, *inter alia,* the Concise Oxford Dictionary (COD), 6th edition, Oxford, 1976; the Pan Dictionaries, 1976; the Dictionary of the Environment, Allaby, 1979; Henderson's Dictionary of Biological Terms, 9th edition, 1979 and other sources included in the list of references. Definitions and expressions used in genetics have been checked by Dr. J. Heydecker.

AAS American Association for the Advancement of Science. A scientific society, aiming to popularise science in the United States of America, which also deals with environmental control. The corresponding 'British Association' was founded in 1831.

abiotic factors Components of the inanimate environment (climate, edaphic (soil characteristics) and orographic factors), which affect man.

abundance Frequency of species and number of individuals in plant and animal ecology.

acaricide See pesticide.

acidity Sourness, the hydrogen ion concentration of aqueous solutions. (*See* pH value.)

activated sludge Biological purification method in which sewage is purified by a sludge consisting of colloidal matter and living organisms maintained in suspension under aerobic conditions.

accumulation The gradual accumulation of certain compounds which are incorporated in the food-chain (DDT, etc.).

adaptation The emergence of structural and external morphological and physiological properties in the living organism or group of organisms which, under given environmental conditions, increase in vitality and fertility: it results in e.g. better development, more vigorous or more rapid growth, a longer life-span and the better exploitation of matter and energy resources, etc.

adaptive value The degree of adaptability of an organism or a group of organisms to an environment, in relation to that of other organisms or populations.

AEC Atomic Energy Commission (U.S.A.); Atomic Energy Authority: U.K.

aerobic A process taking place in the presence of air (O_2).

aerial plankton Airborne living organisms: viruses, bacteria, spores, pollens.

aerosol Dispersed solid (smoke) or liquid (mist) particles of colloidal size in the air.

agglomeration The concentration of a population within a small area. Generally, the concentration and rapid increase of population in large towns and their suburbs.

agricultural ecosystem A man-made cultivated ecosystem, generally, monoculture, one cultivated species used for human or domestic animal food.

agronomy Science of soil management and crop production including arable farming. *See* agricultural ecosystem.

air Gaseous mixture forming the atmosphere surrounding the Earth. Its composition, as a percentage by volume, is the following: nitrogen 78.09, oxygen 20.95, argon 0.93, carbon dioxide 0.03, other gases less than 0.0025.

air (clean) In which the concentration of pollutants does not exceed the physiological or other specified limits.

air (polluted) Which does not correspond to the definition of clean air.

air pollution Detrimental changes in the natural composition of air as affected by air pollutants, e.g. dust, aerosols of different composition, sulphur dioxide, carbon monoxide, nitrogen oxides, etc. Air pollutants originate from industrial and domestic heating, factories, vehicles, etc.

air pollution (local) Pollution in the immediate neighbourhood of the source of pollutants (factory, town).

air pollution index Mathematical coefficient (formula) for the calculation of pollutants (U.S.). Now replaced by 'Air Quality Criteria' and NAAQS (*see* NAPCA).

air plankton See aerial plankton.

Aldrin (HHDN, 1,2,3,4,10,10 hexachloro-1,4,4a,5,8,8a-hexahydro-1,4-exoendo-5,8-dimethanonaphthalene.) A non-systemic insecticide with a high activity and long persistence which was in widespread use in the 1950s. Because of its toxicity to man and useful animals, its use has been prohibited in several countries including Hungary. It has been substituted by insecticides containing Lindane (Gamma-HCH).

alga Collective name for autotrophic uni- or multicellular plants (marine and aquatic weeds). Owing to their wide ecological distribution, they are widespread ranging from snow fields to thermal springs. Some of them are known as biological indicators. Due to increasing eutrophication, some blue-green algae, particularly in filamentous forms, propagate in masses and cause algal blooms.

algal bloom See lake bloom.

algicide See pesticide.

allele Allelomorph, one of the structurally and functionally different alternative modifications of a particular gene. At the identical loci of homologous chromosomes, the gene is represented by one of its alleles.

allergy Inherited or acquired hypersensitivity of organisms to certain substances (pollen, chemical compounds, etc.).

allergenic agent Substances causing the allergic reaction of organisms.

alteralogy Science dealing with the deterioration of the environment.

ammonifying bacteria Collective name for bacteria converting nitrogen-containing organic compounds into ammonia in the course of their metabolism (ammoniacal fermentation). The most well-known ones are: *Bacillus subtilis, Pseudomonas fluorescens, Escherichia coli, Proteus vulgaris, Clostridium putrificus.*

ammonification Decomposition of plant and animal protein (nitrogen-containing organic compounds) affected by bacteria. The final product is ammonia.

anaerobic A process taking place in the absence of air (O_2).

anthrophilous Plant or animal species living in human environment. Their existence and distribution are affected by man.

aphicide See pesticide.

API See Air Pollution Index. Also refers to the American Petroleum Institute oil gravity scale and to type of separators used for oily mixtures (effluents).

apomixis Asexual reproduction as shown in *Phanerogamae,* in which the more or less reduced sexual organs, tissues or cells take part without a normal fertilization, i.e. the fusion of haploid gametes.

arsenic Chemical element, its compounds—owing to their toxicity—were used as insecticides. In Hungary it was used until the mid-1950s.

assimilation Living organisms build up their body out of simple substances present in their environment: water, carbon dioxide and different ions, e.g. nitrate. Autotrophic organisms require light or chemical energy only derived from photosynthetic or simple inorganic chemical processes. Heterotrophic organisms produce the energy required by the decomposition of their own organic matter.

association A plant community characterized by particular types of species. It is composed of specific species which remain relatively constant and of populations that regularly reproduce themselves.

assortative mating See preferential mating.

atmosphere Gaseous cover around the Earth. For composition *see* air.

atomic wastes Solid or liquid wastes containing radioactive material or materials polluted by radioactive matters that are produced in the course of the use of radioactive substances and which are no longer usable. As these wastes remain active over a long period, they have to be stored for a long time. The so-called isotope cemeteries and abandoned salt mines are used for this purpose.

avicide See pesticide.

autogamy Self-fertilization that can be facultative, preferential or obligatory.

automobile exhausts See exhaust gas.

autotrophs Organisms of independent nutrition, building up their body from the organic matters present in the environment using energy supplied by an external energy source. *See also* assimilation.

background pollution Degree of air pollution of areas not directly affected by point sources of pollution. According to their extent global, continental, regional and local background pollutions can be distinguished.

bacterial count Bacteriological and public hygiene coefficient based on the number of bacteria in a given volume of water. According to the purpose of utilization the permissible number varies. According to the Hungarian Standard in chlorinated drinking water it cannot exceed 50/ml, in untreated artesian and piped water supplies 100/ml, in other drinking waters 1,000/ml.

bactericide See pesticide.

bacterium Unicellular or multicellular, mostly heterotrophic organisms. They play an important role in biological decomposition. Certain species (pathogens) cause serious diseases.

Bacterium coli See Escherichia coli.

Basudin granulates Heterocyclic nitrogen compound based insecticide, used in the form of granulated particles. *See* Diazinon.

benthos Community of plant and animal organisms living on the bottom of the sea, lakes or rivers.

Biochemical Oxygen Demand (BOD) The amount of oxygen required by microorganisms for the decomposition of organic material in water at 20°C in a five-day laboratory incubation test.

biocide Collective name for matters selectively damaging certain groups of living organisms. This term includes insecticides (against insects), bactericides (against bacteria), fungicide (against micro-fungi), etc. *See also* pesticides.

biocoenosis A well-established associated group of organisms (plant and animal species) that is composed of defined characteristic species and forms a natural community at a particular site. The specific interrelationships of the group are determined by the local environment. It is characterized by a definite nutrient and energy regime and by its ability for self-regulation.

biodegradation (Mineralisation decomposition). Transformation of organic compounds by microorganisms, consisting of large molecules (proteins, long-chain hydrocarbons, carbohydrates, fats) into smaller sized molecular compounds and eventually into simple inorganic substances such as CO_2, H_2O and NH_3. The decomposition can be either aerobic or anaerobic and plays an important role in the biogeochemical cycle and in the self-purification of waters.

biogeosphere The place of emergence of the biosphere from the Earth's crust. A concept introduced by Zabelin.

biogeochemical cycles Circulation of matter between the living and dead (animate and inanimate) components of the biosphere (water, carbon, nitrogen, phosphorus, etc.). The recycling of chemical elements leads from the inanimate environment to the animate, living organisms and back again. The localised cycle of elements takes place in the ecosystem, while a similar large circulation occurs in the biosphere.

biogeochemistry Science relating to the cycling and dispersion of elements consumed by plants and animals. It studies the role of living organisms in the mobilization (release) and migration (transport) of elements.

biogeocoenose The complex unit of plant (phytocoenosis) and animal (zoocoenosis) associations, as well as the land area and its underlying geological base, the soil and (micro-)climate. A concept introduced by Sukatsov.

biological accumulation Accumulation of elements and compounds in living organisms: It is either a specific characteristic of certain species or it can be determined by the geochemical environment. Biological accumulation is a frequent phenomenon in alga and aquatic weed species in waters. These are capable of accumulating certain elements by a factor of 10^4 or 10^5. Biological accumulation can take place also in the food chain of producers and consumers. Harmful bioaccumulations are: DDT, Aldrin, Dieldrin, cadmium, mercury, lead, etc.

biological elements Vital chemical elements taking part in the building up of the body of living organisms or participating in the metabolic processes. Such elements are: C, H, O, N, S, P, further Cl, Na, Ca, Mg, K, Fe, Si, Mn, etc.

biological indicator Biotest, living organisms, the occurrence or absence of which indicates the characteristics of the environment and any detrimental effects that may be present. The reaction can be negative; the species becomes latent, or their number decreases or they perish. Such negative indicators are the lichens (*see* lichen-test), showing the intensity of air pollution in towns and in industrial regions. In the case of a positive reaction, species may propagate in an explosive manner, e.g. the intensive proliferation of certain blue-green algae indicates the eutrophication of waters.

Biological Oxygen Demand (BOD) see Biochemical Oxygen Demand.

biological protection Prevention of the excessive propagation of parasites or pests and killing of parasites with biological methods. The application of bacteria, fungi, insects, birds and mammals against different groups of parasites. Self-destruction of species is achieved by chemical or radioactive sterilization.

biological sewage purification Sewage treatment by living organisms and microorganisms as well as by the use of higher plants, e.g. club-rush (*Scirpus Sylvaticus* L) or bulrush (*Schoenoplectus Lacustris* (L) Palla).

biological water purification Determining the qualitative values of matters on the basis of the presence (*see* saprobity), absence or reaction of living organisms.

biome Vegetation belt, a particular region of the Earth's surface, determined by climatic conditions like tundra, deciduous forest, savannah, desert, tropical forest, etc. and their plant and animal communities.

biomass The amount of living things present in a given site or unit area at a specific time. It can be expressed by the number, living or dry weight and by the energy content of individuals.

BIR Bureau International de la Recuperation, an international organization founded in 1948 for the study of waste utilization. It plays an important role in the international cooperation in the field of recovery or salvage of materials. Its seat is in Brussels.

biosphere That part of the Earth's surface which is inhabited by living organisms. It comprises the surface of the Earth (lithosphere), that part of the waters (hydrosphere) and the air with a normal oxygen content (atmosphere), which are inhabited by living things, i.e. all the ecosystems. The biosphere is estimated to be 15–16 km thick.

biota Living things (plants and animals) within a given territory at a specific time.

biotic factors Environmental influences arising from the activities of living organisms, e.g. the interrelationships of plants and the impact of animals and man on the environment.

biotope A territory inhabited by a definite group of living things. Owing to its specific characteristics, it can be identified as a special environment (e.g. sea, lake, forest, etc.) and is typified by definite ecological factors (climatic, edaphic (soil), orographic and biotic). It is a specific environment in which the life communities have established themselves.

blue-green algae See Cyanophyceae.

BOD See Biochemical Oxygen Demand.

cadmium A white, crystalline metal, its water-soluble compounds are poisonous. Introduced into the human organism it reduces the Ca-content of bones (Itai-itai disease).

California test A test series carried out in California, in which the concentrations of pollutants in the exhaust gases (carbon monoxide, unburnt hydrocarbons and nitrogen oxide) can be determined under conditions typical of urban traffic.

calorie The amount of heat required to raise 1 g water from 14.5°C to 15.5°C. One calorie or Kilocalorie kcal equals one thousand calories. Expressed in SI unit one calorie equals 4.2 J.

carbon dioxide (CO_2) A gaseous component of air (0.03%), which is important in maintaining organic life. Living things and organic matter produce carbon dioxide when burnt. Industrial combustion processes increase the CO_2 content of air.

carbon monoxide (CO) Colourless, toxic gas produced in the incomplete combustion of hydrocarbons. Diesel engines are the main source of CO pollutants of the atmosphere. Its 0.05% concentration, severely damaging the haemoglobin of blood, is lethal.

carcinogens Tumour-inducing aromatic hydrocarbons (e.g. coal-tar).

carnivore Feeding on animal organisms or animal-derived matter (flesh) secondary, tertiary, etc. consumers in the food-chain.

CCMS Committee on the Challenges of Modern Society, a special organisation set up by NATO in 1969 to examine the tasks of creating a better environment. Studies on air pollution, oil pollution of the seas, traffic safety, sewage purification, etc., have been carried out on a concerted action basis, i.e. with each government paying its own costs.

CEE Communauté Economique Européenne, (EEC), an organization with nine member-states in 1980, founded in 1958. The Directorate responsible for environmental control was established in 1972. Its seat is in Brussels.

CEAM Commission on Environmental Assessment and Monitoring.

CEIF Council of European Industrial Federations.

cement A binding agent, its main components are limestone and clay. The composition of Portland cement—according to data provided by the Danubian Cement and Lime Works—is the following: SiO_2: 23.28%, Al_2O_3: 7.34%, Fe_2O_3: 2.56%, CaO: 59.66, MgO: 2.87, SO_3: 2.66, Na_2O: 0.12, K_2O: 0.42%, loss on ignition 0.95%.

cement pollution Pollution caused by dusts containing CaO, Al_2O_3, SiO_2, in the vicinity of cement works due to the lack of solids-separation equipment or due to its inefficiency.

CENECA Centre National des Expositions et Concours Agricoles. An agricultural society dealing with questions of environmental control in France.

CEP Commission on Environmental Planning, an organization within the framework of IUCN. Its seat is in Morges (Switzerland).

CEQ Council on Environmental Quality, a federal organization in the Executive Office of the President of the United States of America, established under the 1970 National Environmental Policy Act. The Council assists the President in preparing an annual report and improving environmental quality. It appraises the effect of federal programmes and activities on environmental quality. The Council's concern is with the whole spectrum of environmental matters, including parks and wilderness preservation, wildlife, natural resources and land use.

CERBOM Centre d'Etudes et de Recherches de Biologie et d'Oceanographie Médicale. An oceanographical institute in Nice, studying marine pollution and the pollution of beaches and coastline.

cesium 137 A radioactive isotope which is introduced into the atmosphere by atomic explosions. It is accumulated in the human body.

"chandelier" Aq. weed (Charophyceae, Chara Spp. part of *Charophyta*), large-bodied green algae (Stonewort), the thallus of which is regularly divided into "stem" and "leaf". Indicator plants of oligotrophic stagnant or slowly flowing waters. As a result of increasing eutrophication it disappears from these waters.

Chemical Oxygen Demand (COD) Analytical test, similar to permanganate "oxygen absorbed" Q.V., using potassium dichromate, now used as a standard test.

chemicals (manufactured) Introduction of chemicals into the environment through the widespread application of chemicals in agriculture, use in different sections of national industries and domestic use, etc. In addition to the several advantages (e.g. protection against agricultural pests, the use of synthetic detergents) the main disadvantage of this spread of chemicals is the excessive pollution of soil and waters and the destruction of parts of the living world.

chemosynthesis A kind of nutrition (carbon source) of certain plant organisms, in which chemical energy freed (liberated), by oxidation of organic matters, is used to build up complex organic compounds.

chiasma The interchange of homologous chromosomes, visible in the form of an X in the initial phase of meiosis (reduction division), which follows the mutual exchange of chromosomes or chromosome segments. *See also* crossing-over.

chlorine (Cl) A pungent, cough-irritating gas. It rapidly destroys many compounds. It is a reactive element and readily replaces H in its various organic compounds. In the presence of water it is a strong oxidizing agent and is therefore used in disinfection.

chlorination A method used for disinfection (sterilization) of drinking water or swimming-bath waters. Gaseous chlorine or chlorine-containing oxidizing compounds are added to the water.

chromosome Genetic material of the cell nucleus which forms thread-like structures.

chlorophyll A pigment, present in green algae and higher plants, playing an active role in photosynthesis.

CIIE Centre International de l'Industrie pour l'Environnement, an organization founded in 1973. It resides in Nairobi.

CIFE Conseil des Federations Industrielles d'Europe, *see* CEIF.

CITEPA Centre Interprofessionel Technique d'Etudes de la Pollution Atmosphèrique. It resides in Paris.

Clear Lake A lake in California, in which incorporation of DDT in the food-chain as well as pesticide accumulation in living organisms were first studied in detail.

Club of Rome An independent organization, established in 1968, on the initiative of the economist A. Peccei. In 1977, in Geneva, it was entered on the list of officially registered organizations. On the initiative of the Club of Rome the Massachusetts Institute of Technology (MIT) studied the variables influencing the development of the world (population, natural resources, industrial production, food quality, environmental pollution, etc.), which are interdependent factors. The results achieved are meant to influence politicians and the public to adopt a new policy and to pursue new activities.

CNAT Commission Nationale de l'Aménagement du Territoire.

CO *See* carbon monoxide.

CO_2 *See* carbon dioxide.

COD *See* Chemical Oxygen Demand.

coli See Escherichia coli.

COMECON See Council for Mutual Economic Aid.

compost Organic manure produced by anaerobic organisms from organic waste.

composting Bacterial decomposition of putrescible organic wastes. The aim of composting is to reintroduce organic matters—following mineralization—into the food cycle.

CONCAWE Concentration of Clear Air and Water — Western Europe, an international organization founded in 1963.

consumers Heterotrophic organisms using easily biodegradable organic matter for their nutrition (source of carbon). From the point of view of bioenergetics they are energy-storing or -accumulating organisms.

copper Red-coloured metal, which may be harmful to human health in concentrations in water higher than 1 mg/l. Though poisonous, it is far from being as toxic as lead or mercury. Living organisms belonging to the lower orders (bacteria, mould fungi, algae) are most sensitive to copper. Even traces of diluted copper compounds will kill them.

coprophagous Waste (faecal) matter-consuming organisms. *See also* recuperation.

corrosion Chemical or electrochemical change (oxidation) taking place on the surface of industrial materials and solid bodies (metals). Its most frequent form is rust formation. The pollution of air by sulphur dioxide is one of the causes of corrosion.

Council for Mutual Economic Aid (CMEA) Within this organization the socialist countries are concerned with several research themes on environmental control. In harmony with the complex programmes of the economic integration of socialist countries, a treaty on environmental control measures was signed on the 28th April 1971. Yugoslavia has also joined the treaty. In the socialist countries approx. 400 institutes study the problems of environmental control. These are co-ordinated by the co-ordinating centres. In 1973, a Council for Environmental control was established.

Council of Europe (COE) Founded in 1949 with headquarters in Strasbourg, it consists of 21 European countries. Since 1968 its scientific programme has included work on environmental control. It was the first organization to prepare an agreement on the use of "hard" and "soft" detergents in 1968.

crossing-over During the pairing of chromosomes at meiosis (reductional nuclear division) the mutual exchange of certain parts of linked homologous chromosomes or chromatids. *See also* chiasma.

Cyanophyceae Blue-green algae, unicellular autotrophic organisms, reproducing by cell division, that form cell families or colonies. Widely distributed all over the world. They occur and thrive equally well on moist soil, cliffs or bare rock faces, on the bark of trees and on the surface of water, etc. Several species (*Anabaena, Anabaenopsis,*

Coelosphaerium, Microcystis, etc.) cause the algal blooms of eutrophic waters. They are biological indicators of water pollution. Several species of blue-green algae are toxic.

DDD See DDT

DDE See DDT

DDT [1,1,1-trichloro-2,2-di4(chlorophenyl)ethane($C_{14}H_9Cl_{15}$).] Contact poison first synthesised in 1874 by O. Zeidler with its insecticidal properties discovered by Müller, at Geigy, in 1936–37. Full-scale production began in 1943, using Zeidler's original method of synthesis. After the World War II it was widely used and distributed all over the world. By accumulating in the fatty tissues of animals, DDT and its derivatives (DDD, DDE) enter into the food-chain and thus also into the human organism. Its use (application) is prohibited in several countries, including Hungary. Effective regulatory action on pesticide residue was first taken in the U.S.A. in 1954 by the pesticide ("Miller") amendments, 1954 which amended the food, drug and cosmetic act of 1938, and gave the FDA the authority to set and enforce safe tolerances for pesticide residues.

decomposers Organisms (bacteria, fungi) participating in the decomposition of organic matter.

decomposition Biodegradation of organic compounds of large molecules (proteins, hydrocarbons, lipoids) into stable organic matter of smaller molecules and (finally) into organic compounds by microorganisms. The final product is, generally, CO_2, H_2O and NH_3. Decomposition takes place under either aerobic or anaerobic conditions and plays an important role in the biogeochemical cycle and in the self-purification of waters.

de-icing salts NaCl or MgCl mixed with sand or other material. In winter it is used against the formation of ice on roads. The freezing point of the mixed salt solutions is lower than that of water therefore the ice-cover of roads will melt, unless temperature drops to a value corresponding to the freezing point of the salt solution. Salting, and Cl accumulation in leaves following its use, is harmful to certain tree species alongside roads (conifers, lime, etc.).

denitrification Anaerobic process, the opposite of nitrification, which takes place, generally, in the absence of oxygen when nitrates are reduced to nitrites and nitrogen.

density, population The number of individuals on an area of a definite size. Variations in the density of populations are an important factor characterising environmental changes.

denudation Erosion, devastation by storm, weathering and erosive effect of wind, water and ice.

deoxyribonucleic acid (DNA) The carrier of inherited material, a polymerized nucleotide chain which, together with RNA, is to be found in all living organisms.

deposition Deposited on a given area (dustfall).

desert formation The creation of desert conditions, in a certain arid area due to climatic factors or human activity.

detergent Surface-active organic compounds, used as washing ingredients or as a cleansing agent. These are known as synthetic detergents as opposed to soap products. In water they may cause substantial foam building. In contrast to the so-called hard detergents, soft detergents can be decomposed biologically: they are biodegradable.

By regulations made in F.R.G. in 1964 and in the U.S.A. in 1965, and by voluntary agreement in the U.K. made in 1964, only such detergents can be circulated 80% of which can be decomposed within a definite period of time.

detritus Organic debris, the product of decaying organic matter and arising from the disintegration of solid particles.

detritus feeders Living organisms that, in waters, consume settled or suspended wastes, generally originated from plants.

Diazinon (00-diethyl 0-2-isopropyl-6 methylpyrimidin-4-y1 phosporothioate, a heterocyclic nitrogen derivative.) It is the active substance present in granulated Basudin, a nonsystemic broad-range insecticide with a moderate persistence.

Dichlorodifluoromethane (Freon-12) Colourless, almost odourless gas, soluble in alcohol, ether and chloroform. The carrier substance of aerosols. In the atmosphere it endangers the belt of ozone surrounding the Earth.

Dieldrin (HEOD, 1,2,3,4,10,10-hexachloro-6,7-epoxy-1,4,4a,5,6,7,8,8a-octahydro-exo-1,4- -endo-5,8-dimethanonaphthalene.) An insecticide that persists in soils for a long time. As it is capable of entering the food chain, its use is prohibited in Hungary.

diffuse emission Pollution getting into the atmosphere from a large-sized area, e.g. the dust of a slag heap. The opposite of a concentrated emission from a point source.

dissimilation Decomposition, in which compounds of complex structure are converted into simpler ones, energy being liberated the converse of assimilation.

dominance In phytosociology, the extent or percentage cover of a species or community or a coenosis (dominant coverage).

dominant In genetics, one of a pair of alleles, for an external or internal structure or function, which dominates the phenotype of a heterozygous individual.

drift See genetic drift.

dust Solid particles in the air (1 to 200 μm). They can be either organic dusts (pollen, spores) or dusts from an industrial source (dust from quarries, cement dust) and may occur in the form of aerosols.

dust loading The amount of dust deposited on a definite area during a certain unit of time. It is expressed in g/m^2 per month, or t/km^2 per annum.

dust pollution A form of particulate air pollution caused by organic or industrial dusts.

dystrophic Stagnant water, deficient in lime (calcium) and therefore with an acidic reaction. It is poor in plankton due to lack of nutrient salts in solution. Owing to the great amount of humus (peaty) colloids the water is generally brown. Typical examples are peat-bog lakes (*see* biological classification of lakes).

Earthwatch A monitoring programme organized for the observation of substances polluting the Earth and co-ordinated by UNEP. Its establishment was decided on at the Stockholm conference in 1972, within the framework of the environmental control programme.

EAWAG Eidgenossische Anstalt für Wasserversorgung, Abwasserreinigung und Gewässerschutz. (Swiss Federal Research Institute for Water, Sewage Treatment and Water Pollution Control).

ECDIN Environmental Chemical Data and Information Network. A data bank working within the framework of a programme elaborated by the EEC. It records physical, chemical and technical properties of industrial and commercial products. The availability of this data can help to reduce the environmental impact of accidental release of toxic substances.

ECE Economic Commission for Europe, part of the United Nations Economic and Social Council. This organisation sponsors environmental control and related health questions.

ecological factors Collective name for inanimate (abiotic: climatic, edaphic (soil), hydrographic, physiographic) and animate (biotic: plant and animal kingdom, man) environmental factors determining the processes of living organisms and their distribution.

ecological pyramids (Elton-pyramid) On a given area (in a specific ecosystem) smaller-sized animals occur more abundantly than those of large size. A diagrammatic representation of the participants of the food-chain, set out one above the other, shows that the width of the column of numbers rapidly decreases. This aspect of the food-chain is called an Elton-pyramid. Carnivores with the smallest number of individuals and with the largest size, are situated at the top of the pyramid. The principle of the ecological pyramid is as follows: *(a)* small animals are consumed by larger ones, *(b)* small animals are more prolific than the large ones.

ecology Science of the relations between living organisms (man, animal and plant) and environmental factors.

ECOSOC Economic and Social Council of the United Nations (*see* ECE).

ecosphere A synonym for the biosphere and all the ecological factors that affect it.

ecosystem A division of the biosphere, characterized by common environmental factors (biotope) and living world (vegetation, fauna, biocoenosis). A functional unit, producing the renewable organic reserves of the biosphere. Thermodynamically an open system: absorber (solar energy, mineral elements, etc.) and emitter (heat, oxygen, carbon dioxide). The functioning of ecosystems requires the following components: *producers:* energy absorber, biosynthesizing organisms (plants), *consumers:* energy storing, accumulating organisms (animals), *regenerator decomposers:* the latter two groups comprise plant and animal organisms, which decompose the organic matter of soils and water.

ecotope Ecological interpretation of biotope, a type of landscape with ecologically homogeneous areas.

ecotype Stabilized forms of one and the same species having adapted themselves to different environmental conditions. Systematically, they are equivalent to the category (taxon) of subspecies.

ECSM European Coal and Steel Market.

edaphic factors Physical, chemical and biological characteristics of a soil, which determine the distribution and metabolism of plants.

edaphon Collective name for the bacteria, fungi and lower animals living in the soil. They play a significant role in biological decomposition.

EEC European Economic Community (CEE: The Common Market). In 1972, it produced a joint programme for environmental control with ECSM and Euratom.

EFG Europäische Föderation fur Gewässerschutz (FEPE, Féderation pour la Protection des Eaux), with its seat in Zurich. A European organization, founded on the initiative of F.R.G., for the prevention of water pollution.

EFPW European Federation for the Protection of Waters (as EFG).

ELCA European Landscape Contractors Association.

Elton pyramid See ecological pyramid.

emission The emission of air pollutants, the introduction of pollutants into the air and the concentration of trace elements and transformation products of emitted substances in the upper layers of the soil.

emission limiting values Limit values for different air pollutants, generally guidelines regarding concentrations of these that can be tolerated in air.

emission damage Harmful effects of air pollution on living organisms works of art and historic monuments, etc.

emission resistance The ability of living organisms to resist the deleterious effects of emitted substances.

emission source The place of emission.

endemic Indigenous, where the particular distribution of a plant or animal species is limited to a relatively small area.

Endrin (1,2,3,4,10,10-hexachloro-6,7-epoxy-1,4,4a,5,6,7,8,8a-ocathydro-*EXO*-1,4-*EXO*-5, 8,0-dimethanonaphthalene, the isomer of Dieldrin.) A persistent chlorinated hydrocarbon, a most poisonous substance used against rodents. It is especially harmful to fish. In Hungary, its use is prohibited.

energy flow The flowing of a certain proportion of solar energy through the ecosystem. By passing through the food chain, the solar energy absorbed by green plants in the form of chemical energy, passes on its basic energy to all the life phenomena of each group of living things. At each link (consumer) a definite amount of energy is liberated, while another definite amount is transformed by consumption and transferred to the other organism. The energy flow becomes more and more deficient, especially in the case of large-bodied animals, at the end of the food chain.

entomophagous Insectivorous.

environment Collective term for the entity of abiotic and biotic factors among which organisms live and with which they are connected. The equilibrium of living organisms within their environment is the result of a long evolution. Certain species occur only under particular environmental conditions; these are the so-called species of little tolerance (stenoecius) and species belonging to them, are not able to tolerate environmental changes or only able to do so to a limited extent. Species with a wide ecological amplitude can exist under various ecological conditions and are capable of enduring greater changes in environmental conditions.

EPA Environmental Protection Agency, U.S.A., which originates standards for the protection of the environment and also, inter alia, conducts research to study the adverse health effects of air and water pollution. (*See* ORD.) Its overall responsibility is to administer and conduct federal pollution control programmes.

epilimnion The upper layer of deep lakes, rich in oxygen and nutrients, in which the primary production of producers takes place (trophic level).

erosion The surface destroying and devastating effect of wind (deflation) and water (ice).

ERTS Earth Resources Technology Satellites, the global environmental control observation programme of UNEP.

Escherichia coli A bacilliform (rod-shaped) bacterium living in the intestinal tracts of man and warm-blooded animals, which plays a part also in the decomposition of cellulose, but can become also pathogenic. Its occurrence in waters indicates faecal pollution. Standards based on the numbers of coliforms (coli number) are used to indicate the maximum levels at which water is suitable for drinking or bathing. The Hungarian standard limits for potable water are as follows: the filtered and chlorinated tap-water is not suitable for drinking, should the coli number exceed 0.88–0.97/100 ml; untreated water or mineral water, if the coli number exceeds 4.4–5.0/100 ml; artesian well and borehole water, if the coli number exceeds 10.0/100 ml. Should the coli number exceed 51 the water is not suitable as a source for drinking water.

exhaust gases Gases produced by the burning of petrol (gasoline) in combustion engines. Exhaust gases contain, mainly, carbon monoxide (CO), unburnt hydrocarbons (CH), nitrogen oxide (NO), sulphur and lead compounds, soot and water vapour. Exhaust gases are harmful to the human organism, as well as to plants and animals. Vegetation alongside motorways may accumulate significant amounts of lead. According to statistics from different countries, in some cities, a large part of air pollution is caused by motor vehicles.

ethology Science of animal behaviour under natural conditions.

EUCARPIA Society of European Plant Breeders, a social organization with its secretariat in Paris. Its special sections are: cereals, potato, fodder plants, horticultural crops, methodology and technology, mutation and polyploidy, wild species and maize.

EURATOM European Atomic Energy Community, international organization which also deals with questions of environmental control arising from the use of nuclear energy. It lays down basic radiation standards for the protection of the health of both workers in the industry and of the general population.

EUREL European Association of Free Nature Resources, its seat is in Brussels.

euryecious Species of wide ecological amplitude. They can exist under varied ecological conditions and are capable of enduring greater changes in the environmental factors.

European ECE Driving Cycle test System of measuring the carbon monoxide and hydrocarbon content of exhaust gases of vehicles under different operating conditions that are related (correspond) to various modes of driving.

eusaprobic A concept for the qualitative assessment of water. Waters containing such an amount of pollutants that can be decomposed microbiologically.

eutrophic A concept applied to the biological classification of lakes. It is characteristic of waters rich in nutrients and living organisms. (*See* biological classification of lakes.)

eutrophication The process of the changing nutrient regime of lakes and other water bodies, the increase in nutrients (phosphorus, nitrogen, potassium, etc. compounds). Owing to the enrichment of nutrients, aquatic plants (algae and macrophytic weed species, reed, bulrush, etc.) appear in the lakes. These produce more organic matter than that consumed by heterotrophic organisms, thus accelerating the ageing and silting-up process of the lake. The infiltration of fertilizers and other pollutants (e.g. domestic sewage) may accelerate the process of eutrophication of lakes.

faeces Human or animal excreta (excrement).

FAO Food and Agricultural Organization, the specialized agricultural organization of the UNO. It deals, among other things, with environmental control, e.g. the increase and development of forest, soil and water resources.

fauna The animal kingdom of a particular locality.

filter An equipment used for the elimination of solid, liquid or gaseous pollutants.

fish mortality The mass killing of fish, which indicates the rapid qualitative deterioration of waters. It can be caused by large amounts of poisonous substances getting into the water (ammonia, phenol, chlorine, cyanide, metal salts, etc.), chemicals leached out from agricultural areas and the thermal pollution of waters, which can result in the reduction of dissolved oxygen, etc.

flora The plant population (vegetation) in a specified area.

flotation An aeration method. A purification method used for the elimination of floating pollutants in industrial effluents and now in water treatment. Foam building chemicals and air are introduced into water under pressure. The generation of foam lifts the pollutants to the surface, from where they can be removed.

fluorine compounds Hydrogen fluoride (HF) is a poisonous gas, a by-product emitted from aluminium smelters. It affects (destroys) the chloroplasts of plants. Hydrogen fluoride can accumulate in grasses, thus becoming a major protoplasmic poison for animals grazing them.

food chains The transformation of energy derived from food, through multiple consumption, from green plants through animal organisms. Each species in the food-chain becomes food for some other organism and at the highest levels, the number of individuals decreases (*see* ecological pyramids).

food-pyramids See ecological pyramids.

forest, recreational Afforested areas in which, through up-to-date game and forest management, landscape protection and the provision of cultural and resort facilities become of prime importance.

formation Entity of plants of a similar life-form, e.g. forest, meadow, bog, etc.

FRC Federal Radiation Council, an organization for the control of radiation in the U.S.A.

fungicide See pesticide.

Freon See Dichlordifluormethane.

gamete A gamete, which contains a haploid chromosome complement deriving directly or indirectly from meiosis (reductional nuclear division).

GARP Global Atmospheric Research Project.

gasoline See petrol.

gene An organizational and functional unit of genetic information carried on the genetic material (DNA). It is located at a definite point of the chromosome (the gene locus) and either alone, or together with its pair or allele, or by the contribution of other genes, regulates the phenotypic appearance of one or more (functional or physical) characteristics within the limits of environmental factors.

gene bank A collection which aims to contain the complete genetic variability of cultivated and related species and the (gene) alleles which determine this variability.

genetic erosion The large scale impoverishment of the genetic pool of a population that can be ascribed either to the perishing of a large part of the population or to the disappearance and loss of many alleles, as a result of a very strong selection pressure.

gene flow The transfer of alleles, by way of exchange or migration, from one population to another in which they are absent or only occur at a frequency which is small.

gene introgression The incorporation of one or more genes of one species (or population) into the gene pool of other species by hybridization and subsequent back-crossing with the individuals of the recipient species or population.

gene locus That point of the chromosome, where one of the alleles of a certain gene is located. Homologous chromosomes contain identical or different alleles in identical gene loci.

gene pool The total genetic information of a population encoded in genes, which is characterized by the relative frequency of particular alleles.

genetics The science of heredity.

genetic capacity The total genetic information to be stored in the entire DNA complement of one cell, organism or of one population.

genetic coherence The close correlation of certain inheritable characteristics in the individual descendants, resulting from the crossing-over of different races and subspecies.

genetic drift The changing of genotype and allele-frequency, in a population consisting of relatively few individuals, brought about by random, non-systematic (e.g. non-selectional) effects (e.g. by natural disasters or destruction of the environment).

genetic load A decrease in the mean adaptive value of a given genotype or population, in comparison with other genotypes and populations, owing to the effect of damaging alleles reducing vitality and reproductive capacity.

genetic variance A statistical coefficient (square of the standard deviation) applied to denote that proportion of phenotypic variance which is caused by variation in the genetic constitution of individuals.

genome A complete set of chromosomes, e.g. the chromosome complement of a diploid species has only one genome.

genotype The complement of genes determining the inheritable properties of the individual, i.e. the complete genetic information stored in the inherited material: DNA. As DNA can contain various alleles of the genes, the genotype of individuals can also be most varied.

geochemistry Science, which studies the distribution of chemical elements and of their isotopes on Earth.

geohygiene Science of the harmful effects brought about by man in the biosphere.

geosphere The solid mineral of the surface of the Earth together with the three-dimensional space or concentric regions of the Earth and its atmosphere.

GESAMP Group of Experts on Scientific Aspects of Marine Pollution. A consultative international organization dealing with marine pollution.

GIFAP Groupement International des Associations Nationales de Fabricants des Pesticides comprises eleven countries, approx. 600 enterprises (which supply the major proportion of herbicide production in the world). Its headquarters is in Brussels.

global equilibrium According to a recommendation by MIT, in order to achieve a general world equilibrium, it would be necessary to slow down or stop the further growth of the Earth's population, to reduce the exploitation of raw materials and energy carriers, to limit economic expansion to a minimum and simultaneously to provide for the maximum protection of the environment. This recommendation has met with an intense dissatisfaction in the third world (developing) countries, though politicians of developed countries also accept the impossibility of realising a general world equilibrium on these lines.

greenhouse effect As a result of air pollution more than 360 billion t of carbon dioxide have been introduced into the air, in the course of the preceding one hundred years. The increased CO_2 content of the air absorbs heat emitted by the soil. Owing to this, the temperature of the surface should become substantially higher, so that a sufficient amount of infra-red radiation leaves the satellite, which, in turn, establishes the state of equilibrium with its environment. According to forecasts, should the present pace of CO_2 accumulation continue, it would mean that, by raising its mean temperature by 2°C, the Earth would become a huge glasshouse.

half-life A time-interval during which the radiation from a radioactive substance is halved. Each radioactive element has its own characteristic half-life.

haploid A nucleus, cell or organism, the genome of which contains only a single set of unpaired chromosomes in each nucleus.

HCH ($C_6H_6Cl_6$, hexachlorocyclohexane), an insecticide, which can be harmful to plants at low concentrations. Because of its unpleasant odour and taste it is not now widely used. The symmetric isomer: Hexachloro Benzene is known as Lindane Q.V.

heavy metals A collective name for metallic elements of high density, used particularly in water pollution and fish toxicity studies, e.g. iron, zinc, cadmium, copper, lead, mercury, etc. whose relative density ranges from 7 to over 13.

Helsinki rules A resolution adopted by the congress of jurists in Helsinki. It regulated the legal aspects of the thermal loadability of natural waters. In 1970, the draft resolution was submitted to the UNO by Finland.

heptachlor (Heptachlor-tetrahydro-endomethylen-indene), a highly poisonous cyclodiene insecticide which is accumulated easily. In Hungary it is not licensed and it is no longer on the U.K. approved list due to the fact that it breaks down in soil to give a stable more toxic substance.

herbicide See pesticide.

herbivores See primary consumers.

heterotrophic Consumers of organic matter produced by autotrophic organisms. They utilize the products of these latter organisms in their metabolic processes.

heterozygous An organism, the genotype of which has different alleles of one or more genes.

homozygous An organism the genotype of which contains identical alleles of a particular gene or genes.

Hungarian Academy of Sciences Hungarian scientific body of the highest level; it plays a leading role in the direction of the scientific life of the country, the co-ordination of different themes. Within the national research programme, entitled "The most favourable development of the macro- and micro-environment of man"; it is the co-ordinating body for work on the theme "Studies in connection with environmental control".

humid A territory with a high rate of precipitation, where the annual amount of rainfall exceeds that of evaporation.

humification The formation of the organic material content of soil (humus) in the course of chemical–microbiological decomposition.

humus Complex organic matter content of the soil, which results from the decomposition of plant and animal organic matter in the metabolic processes of organisms living in the soil.

hybrid An organism resulting from parents of different genotype, the composition of the homologous chromosomes in the parents differing in varying degrees (*see* heterozygous).

hydrology Science of the physical and chemical properties of waters, especially with regard to its flow in relation to land.

hydrosphere The waters of the Earth's surface, i.e. the entity of waters of different physical state throughout the world. This includes the water content of air, rivers and seas as well as ground water, etc.

hydrofluoric acid See fluoro-compounds.

hygiene Science of the maintenance of health and the prevention of harmful effects that may cause illnesses. It studies the impact of the environment and living and working conditions on the human organism.

IABG International Association of Botanical Gardens. An organization founded in 1954, for the promotion of scientific co-operation among botanic gardens. At its session in Moscow, in 1975, the new responsibility of botanic gardens for the protection of species was emphasized.

IAEA International Atomic Energy Agency, its seat is in Vienna. It was founded in 1956, with the aim of promoting the peaceful utilization of atomic energy.

IAM Internationale Arbeitsgemeinschaft für Müllforschung; an international organization, founded in 1956, for the co-ordination of investigations into solid wastes (refuse/trash). It has its seat in Zurich. Its publication "Müll und Abfall" appears in German.

IAP-index Index of Atmospheric Purity, which has been developed by Le Blanc and De Sloover (1970). It is used for biological indicators of air pollution (e.g. lichens). IAP$=\Sigma(Q \cdot f)$ where Q=degree of tolerance to toxic effects, f=frequency, coverage and vitality value of the species.

IASH International Association of Scientific Hydrology, an organization established in 1924, for international co-operation in the field of hydrological research.

IAWPR International Association on Water Pollution Research, an international organization, founded in 1965, in London, for the co-ordination of research into water pollution. It organizes biennial conferences and specialised workshops, held in different countries.

IBP-Programme International Biological Programme. In accordance with plans first proposed for its establishment, in 1961, and a proposal by ICSU, this international programme was launched in 1964, with the following objectives: the assessment of the biological potential of both productivity and the welfare of humanity. The studies were made in order to estimate organic matter production (primary and secondary production) of dry lands, seas and non-saline waters and further, to determine the factors which influenced this production. The IBP also included research related to nature conservation. At the same time the objectives of the IBP-programme were to prepare the background for the MAB-programme which was to follow.

ICBP International Council for Bird Preservation, its seat being in London. This international society was founded in 1922 and deals with bird preservation on an international scale. With IUCN, (Q.V.) is responsible for up-dating of red data book.

ICNP International Commission on Natural Parks.

ICRP International Commission for Radiation Protection.

ICSU International Council of Scientific Unions. A specialized organization of the UNO, that co-ordinates the activity of scientific societies in the field of exact and natural sciences.

IDOE International Decade of Ocean Exploration.

IFLA International Federation of Landscape Architects. An organization, founded in 1948, for the preservation of natural and artificial types of landscape. Its seat is in Lisbon.

IHD International Hydrological Decade, a decade-long research programme, launched in 1965, on the initiative of UNESCO. Its objective was the preservation and proper distribution of water resources for humanity.

ILO International Labour Organization, which works within the framework of the UNO. It deals with population, employment and labour problems.

imago Adult sexually mature insect.

indicator See biological indicator.

infant methaemoglobinaemia See methaemoglobinaemia.

infiltration Infiltration of gravitational water into the deeper layers, as opposed to capillary water which is held within the micropores in the soil.

infrastructure The complex industrial production system of a country together with the necessary public buildings and basic services that meet the needs of the population. Branches of infrastructure include the road and railway network, means of public transport, municipal supply undertakings (electricity, gas, water and sewerage), housing, public health, educational and cultural facilities and the commercial network.

inhibitor A substance that prevents certain chemical processes (e.g. corrosion).

initial growth period The initial phase of slow growth preceding the multiplication (e.g. of algae) in large numbers: the logarithmic growth phase.

insecticide See pesticide.

integrated plant protection A system involving the simultaneous application of physical, mechanical, agronomical, chemical and biological methods of plant protection.

interdependence Mutual dependence. When taking steps to control the environment, the side-effects of these should also be considered. In a given area, one and the same measure can prove either positive or negative. For example too intensive fertilization may both increase yields and contribute to water pollution.

INTECOL International Association for Ecology. Its seat is in London.

introgressive hybridisation See gene introgression.

inversion A meteorological phenomenon, in which—in contrast to normal conditions—air temperature does not decrease with altitude, but rises only to a certain level. Inversion contributes to smog formation.
In genetics: 180° rotation of a segment within a chromosome; consequently, the sequence of genes in the inverted phase will become opposite to that in the original state of the entire chromosome.

IOC Intergovernmental Oceanographic Commission, an organization for the purity and protection of the oceans.

ionosphere Atmospheric layer at the height of about 80 km, which is strongly ionized by the ultra-violet and particulate radiation from the sun and from space (*see* thermosphere).

IRCWM International Reference Center for Waste Management, functioning within the framework of WHO and UNO.

irreversible process Changes in the environment or living organism, which result in a stable state from which the original state cannot be re-established.

IRS International Referral System for Sources for Environmental Information, which works as part of the "Earthwatch" programme of UNEP.

isolation The genetic separation of species, populations, i.e. the limitation of unilateral or mutual gene flow among them, as brought about by geographical, ecological, physiological or genetic factors (e.g. sterility of hybrids).

ISWA International Solid Wastes and Public Cleansing Association, where representatives of European and overseas countries work together, with the aim of co-ordinating research on solid wastes.

Itai-itai disease A disease that developed along the river Jintsu in Japan. The disease, the symptom of which is bone atrophy, is caused by the cadmium sulphate content of the water of the river. The source of cadmium sulphate was an abandoned zinc mine.

IUBS International Union of Biological Sciences, an international organization, founded in 1919, for the co-ordination of research activity.

IUCN International Union for the Conservation of Nature and Natural Resources; an international organization, founded in 1948, for the protection of plant and animal species, as well as for the protection of the natural environment. Originally based in Morges, it is now in Gland (Switzerland). The IUCN is responsible for the publication of the Red Data Book, listing rare and threatened species, the latest deals with vascular plants.

IUFRO International Union of Forestry Research Organizations, an international organization, established in 1890, for the organization of scientific research programmes and conferences.

IWRB International Wildfowl Research Bureau, an international organization, founded in 1947, for the study of wildfowl.

IWSA International Water Supply Association, its secretariat is located in London. A federation of national associations, of members involved in the water supply industry, which deals with questions of water conservation and water supply and organizes technical international conferences, held in rotation in different world-wide centres.

IYF (IYFSCN), International Youth Federation for the Study and Conservation of Nature which was founded in Salzburg in 1956.

kcal Kilocalorie, amount of heat required to raise 1 l or 1 kg water from 15°C to 16°C at normal atmospheric pressure, its equivalent is 1000 calories. This is the unit used to measure the energy equivalent of food but see note under calorie.

key-process Process which determines and regulates the functioning of an organism and which is of vital importance and the main factor affecting the metabolism of biocoenoses, e.g. enzyme systems involved in protein or fat synthesis.

lake bloom The rapid propagation of certain floating or suspended organisms (algae) indicating qualitative changes in water quality.

lakes, classification of lakes The biological classification of lakes is based on the amount of available essential food and the trophic level. Accordingly the following lake-types can be distinguished: oligotrophic: poor in nutrients; eutrophic: rich in nutrients; dystrophic: lakes with a humus-type bottom deposit but with a poor mineralization, i.e. scarcity in solution of nutrient salts. On the basis of the origin of food the following classification is used: inorganotrophic: the lakes contain food of inorganic origin; autotrophic: the food (nutrients) is (are) produced in the lake; allochthonic: the food (nutrients) is (are) introduced into the lake from outside.

landscape A unit of the Earth's surface that is determined by relief, climate, geological and hydrological conditions, and by the activity of the living world and of man. Depending on the human activity, the following types are distinguished: natural landscape with no, or only partly, predominating anthropogenic activity; agricultural landscape: with different agricultural crops (ploughland, meadows, etc.); tourist resort, industrial, etc. landscapes.

landscape planning The proper utilization (arrangement) of landscape in order to secure optimal living conditions for man, e.g. this includes different plans for the establishment of a tourist resort environment and of industrial and resort buildings.

larvicide See pesticide.

LCP Landscape Planning Commission of the IUCN, its seat is in Morges (Switzerland).

LC$_{50}$ See lethal concentration.

LD$_{50}$ See lethal dose.

lead A metal of grey colour, its compounds are highly poisonous to protoplasm. The lead content of petrol, introduced into the environment through exhaust gases is harmful to health. In areas polluted by exhaust gases lead accumulates in plants.

lethal concentration for 50 per cent of the animals (LC_{50}) A concentration of toxic substances which, during a definite period of time (e.g. 96 h) and under defined conditions, kills 50% of a definite organism (e.g. the water flea).

lethal dose for 50 per cent of the animals (LD_{50}) The toxicity value being the concentration of a given poison (mg/body weight in kg), that kills 50% of the test animals (e.g. rats) exposed to it, within a specified time.

lichen Symbiosis of autotrophic algae and heterotrophic fungi. Different species occur alike on soil, tree-bark and on rocks. They are negative biological indicators of urban and industrial air pollution. The lack of lichens, or the extent of their occurrence, indicates the intensity of air pollution. Due to intense pollution, especially by sulphur-dioxide, the so-called lichen deserts, areas devoid of lichens, develop in towns and industrial centres.

limnology Science of the ecology of freshwaters; a branch of hydrobiology.

Lindane gamma HCH (formerly BHC) The biologically active isomer of technical hexachlorocyclohexane. A non-selective soil insecticide, toxic to bees and to other useful insects.

LIRM Laboratoire International de Pollution Marine.

lithosphere The solid crust of the Earth, i.e. the surface of dry land (*see* biosphere).

littoral The shallow region adjacent to the shoreline of lakes and rivers and the shallow coastal zone lying along the sea-shore.

loading The loading in respect of both environmental factors (air, water, soil) and living organisms, by pollutants of human origin, e.g. the loading of waters by different pollutants; the loading of air by dust, polluting gases, etc.

load capacity (pollution load capacity) The sensitivity of ecological factors and of the ecosystem and its components to anthropogenic effects (pollution). The existing degree of loading of ecological factors and of living organisms has not passed the limit of their capability for recovery or for regeneration.

London-smog This was a characteristic air pollution phenomenon with reducing matters (SO_2, smoke and soot) predominant. Before 1956, it occurred generally in the morning, under conditions of low inversion with no wind, mostly at a temperature around zero centigrade and with a high relative humidity. If it was accompanied by real fog then, in the worst cases, daylight was blacked out.

Since 1958–59, in central London, the smoke content has been reduced to about one-fifth of its previous level and the sulphur dioxide content to nearly a half.

Since then, by 1977–78, there has been a further 50% reduction in smoke and a 45% reduction in sulphur dioxide.

Los Angeles smog Photochemical smog, which develops under conditions where oxidizing matters predominate (ozone, nitrogen oxides). Intensive isolation (ultra-violet radiation) initiates photochemical reactions in the atmosphere; it develops under a clear sky, at noon, at relatively high temperatures and with a low relative humidity.

MAB See Programme on Man and the Biosphere.

MAC Maximum Allowable Concentration of air pollutants (gas, vapour, dust, etc.) which man is able to tolerate, when working daily 8 hours, in a closed space containing the given pollutant. (It is expressed as cm^3/m^3 air/day.)

macroelement Chemical elements occurring in relatively large quantities in living organisms, e.g. C, O, N, H, P, K, Ca, Mg, Na, S, Si, Cl and Fe.

magnesium chloride $MgCl_2$, colourless crystalline substance; as the freezing point of its solutions is lower than that of water, it is used for the deicing of roads.

Malathion S.1,2-di(ethoxycarbonyl)ethyl 00-dimethyl phosphorodithionate (dimethyl-S--(dicarb-ethoxi-ethyl)-dithiophosphate). A broad range insecticide and acaricide, toxic to warm-blooded animals and highly toxic to bees. WHO recommends it for use against mosquitoes in malaria control. Its lethal doses are: for man: 0.8 g/kg; for domestic animals: 50–200 mg/kg; for fishes: 5–10 mg/l.

MAR Marshes, Bogs and other Wetlands, an international programme for the protection of marshes, bogs and other wetland habitats in the temperate zone. It is co-ordinated by IUCN, ICBR and IWRB.

MCA Manufacturing Chemists' Association, founded in 1872. Its membership comprises mainly American and Canadian companies and it plays an important part in environmental control. In 1936 the Water Resources Committee, in 1949 the Air Quality Committee and in 1969 the Solid Wastes' Management Committee were established.

MEC Maximum Emission Concentration; the emission value from a chimney expressed in g/m^3 (p.p.m.) or mg/m^3. maximum emission concentration of pollutants in the air of the environment.

meiosis A form of nuclear division, with two stages, sometimes separated by one or more development stages, preceding the formation of gametes. In meiosis the chromosome number is reduced to half the number of the somatic cells, in such a way that homologous chromosomes separate and each one goes to the opposite division pole. Consequently, the chromosome number of gametes, thus formed, will be half that of the somatic cells.

Melipax (Camphecor U.K.; Toxaphene U.S.A.) polychlorinated-camphene containing insecticide which is harmless to bees, but toxic to fish.

mercury A fluid, silver-white metal, that is volatile at room temperature. Pharmaceutical, dye and other industrial factories can introduce it into bodies of water through their effluent discharges. The various mercury compounds are toxic to man, animal and plants alike. It can also enter into the food chain.

mesoecology The science of the connection between environment and populations.

metabolism The whole of the vital processes going on in the living organism. Plant, animal and human organisms take up substances essential for their existence and either store or transform the energy hidden in them. On the other hand, they decompose these substances in order to cover their energy requirements.

methaemoglobin The product of the reaction between NO_2 and haemoglobin. Methaemoglobin is incapable of absorbing atmospheric oxygen. NO_2 and NO_3 absorption in food and also in drinking water may lead to the formation of this compound. This disease, which mainly affects infants, is extremely rare in the U.K.

methaemoglobinaemia NO_2 and other poisonous compounds induce the reduction in the oxygen-transporting capability of blood.

microelement Trace element, elements occurring in the living organisms in small amounts, e.g. B, Fe, Mn, Cu, Mo and Zn.

microorganism The collective name for, generally, unicellular organisms (viruses, bacteria) which can be seen under the microscope.

migration In genetics, the transfer of genetic information, from one population to another, with the help of the migration of gametes (e.g. pollen), individuals or groups of individuals. Its consequence is that the allele frequency ratio may be modified in the recipient population.

milieu (ecological niche) The entity of factors which influences living organisms. Regarding man, milieu means not only the physical environment but also economic and cultural factors and social surroundings.

Minamata-disease Between 1956–60 a mysterious disease was observed among the inhabitants of Minamata (Japan). The majority of people were affected by paralysis, impaired hearing and eyesight, the loss of mental abilities and died rapidly. The disease was caused by mercury that had been accumulated in toxic quantities in the fish and shellfish taken from Minamata bay, which formed the main diet of the fishermen and inhabitants. Mercury was being discharged into the sea-water by a chemical factory sited near the bay, producing acetaldehyde by a mercury-catalysed process.

mineralization See decomposition.

mineral cycling See biochemical cycles.

MIT Massachusetts Institute of Technology (*see:* Club of Rome).

MLD Minimum Lethal Dose; the smallest concentration that can cause the death of the test animals.

molluscicide See pesticide.

monitoring A regular system of observing and controlling action. Often used for pollutant surveys based on automatic sampling and analytical systems.

Morges-manifesto Guidelines and duties proposed by WWF (in 1961, Manifesto I and in 1971, Manifesto II) for nature conservation.

MPN Most Probable Number. The most probable number of coliform organisms to be found in 100 ml water (based on methods used in the U.S.A. and the U.K. using probability tables first published by McCrady in Canada in 1918.

mutagen Collective name for all those factors (irradiation, the drug colchicine, mustard gas, etc.) by which mutation, the abrupt change of inherited properties, can be induced.

mutation Structural change in a gene that can be caused by changes in the base pairs of DNA, their loss or duplication. Generally, more drastic changes in the chromosome structure are related to these changes. Mutations can be either dominant or recessive. As a result of mutation, a given inheritable characteristic can change abruptly.

muskgrass 'Chandelier'-type aquatic weed *(see Characeae)*.

NAPCA National Air Pollution Control Administration. Its seat is in Washington. Under EPA, it is responsible for setting up national ambient air quality standards: NAAQS, in accordance with the Clean Air Act.

national park Defined areas of large extent, where the complete protection of nature can be achieved on the basis of enforceable regulations. National parks are established with the aim of protecting nature, of carrying out scientific work and of attracting visitors. In 1962, IUCN issued a recommendation that national parks should be established. The first national parks were established, in the U.S.A., in 1872. Today the area of the national parks amounts to 1% of the territory of the U.S.A. In the Soviet Union, the area of national parks amounts to 7 million ha. In Hungary, the first national park was established in 1973, on the Hortobágy, with full weight being given to the importance of its living world, its national and international scientific value and to its special geographical, as well as landscape character.

nature reserve A defined area of landscape, where either the complete area or its vegetation and fauna are protected and are to be preserved in their original state.

NATO North Atlantic Treaty Organization (*see* CCMS).

necrophagous Microorganisms, insects and other animals feeding upon dead organisms.

nekton Aquatic animals capable of active movement from place to place. These include, e.g. fishes, mollusca, etc.

nematocide See pesticide.

net primary productivity The amount of organic matter formed in excess of that used in metabolism.

neustron The complex of microorganisms living on the surface film of water.

niche The ecological place of living things in the environment and in the food chain. The special place of a population in the ecosystem, i.e. in the mass and energy flow taking place in it.

nitrate Salts and esters of nitric acid, all of them being water-soluble. It is leached from soil easily.

nitric oxide NO, a colourless gas, which is transformed to nitrogen dioxide in the air. It is an air pollutant present in exhaust gases and in emissions from industrial establishments, mainly from combustion processes.

nitrate bacteria Bacteria living under aerobic conditions in the soil. They transform nitrite into nitrate *(Nitrobacter* Spp., *Nitrocystis)*.

nitrification Conversion of ammonia into nitrite and nitrate by bacteria *(Nitrosomonas)*, under aerobic conditions. Thus, nitrogen becomes available for plants.

nitrite Salts and esters of nitrous acid. It is produced by the mineralization of nitrogen-containing proteins. Its presence in natural waters indicates pollution, particularly recent sewage contamination. In drinking water of good quality, only 0.1 mg/l of nitrous-nitrogen content is permissible. Nitrites should be absent in other drinking waters.

nitrite bacteria Aerobic bacteria in soil, which convert ammonia into nitrite *(Nitrosomonas, Nitrosospira, Nitrosocystis* and *Nitrosogloea)*.

nitrogen Colourless and odourless gas in an elementary state, one of the constituents of air (78%). In soil, it occurs in the form of soluble nitrites and nitrates and complex nitrogenous substances. It is a biogenic element, one of the most important components of protein.

nitrogen oxides A collective name for N_2O, N_2O_3, N_2O_4, N_2O_5, NO, NO_2 and NO_3 compounds, all gaseous at room temperature.

NNI Noise Number Index, used for the measuring of the noise level of airports and calculated by an empirical equation. The equation contains the following factors: noise intensity (in decibels), the number of aeroplanes and a constant.

NOAA National Oceanic and Atmospheric Administration, an organization for environmental control in the U.S.A. Its main objective is to control activities affecting oceans and the atmosphere. Amongst other activities, it controls environmental satellites which can transmit visibility data from remote locations in national parks.

noise An audible sound, such as noise from factories, aircraft and vehicle traffic and street and construction activities, that exerts an unpleasant, objectional and detrimental effect (impact) on the human organism. Noise intensity (its degree) is measured and expressed in decibels or phons. In the U.K., general nuisance from noise is now controlled by Part 3 of the Control of Pollution Act, 1974 which repealed the Noise Abatement Act, 1960. Occupational noise is the responsibility of the health and safety executive.

noosphere A concept introduced by Le Roy and Vernadski. That part of the biosphere which is dominated by anthropogenic activities.

NWF National Wildlife Federation, a federation of bodies promoting nature conservation in the U.S A.

oceanology The science of the physical, chemical and biological study of oceans and seas. In the U.K. the Institute of Oceanographic Sciences (IOS), part of the Natural Environment Research Council (NERC), was formed, in 1973, by amalgamating existing institutions.

OECD Organization for Economic Cooperation and Development; it was founded by eighteen European countries, Canada and the U.S.A. (At present the number of member states is 24.) The organization, based in Paris, studies economic, international trade, technical, natural scientific and environmental subjects. In 1970, the organization established a separate council for environmental control.

oil Dark-coloured, dense, odorous liquid burning with an intensively sooty flame (an air pollutant). One of the most damaging water pollutants.

oil spills Polluting and destructive effect of large amounts of oil on the vegetation and fauna of waters, as well as on their coasts. For example, in 1967, following the catastrophe of the tanker Torrey Canyon, approx. 117,000 t crude oil was spilled into the sea, causing the death of nearly 500,000 birds. According to estimates, 1 million t of oil is spilled into the oceans and seas annually. The Persian Gulf, the living world of which has disappeared, has also become a victim of oil pollution.

oligo-elements Trace elements which occur in soil or in plants in small quantities (e.g. Fe, Mn, Cu, B, Mo and Zn, etc. many of which play an essential part in enzyme systems).

OPP Oxygen Potential Production, which is a function expressing the dynamics of the metabolism of flowing water used in quantitative measurements of photosynthesis.

ORD U.S. Office of Research and Development, Washington; part of the EPA Administration.

orographic factors Relief factors, such as altitude, exposure and slope angle.

ovicide See pesticide.

ovolarvicide See pesticide.

ozone O_3, it is produced by irradiation in the presence of electric charges and by ultraviolet radiation. There is an approx. 15–20 km thick layer of the atmosphere, at heights of 15 and 30 km, that contains ozone.

oxygen Gas of somewhat greater density than that of air. The atmosphere contains 20.9% by volume of oxygen.

oxygen diagram Indicator of the self-purification of waters. The oxygen curve shows the amount of dissolved oxygen, i.e. the oxygen deficiency, compared with the state of 100% saturation, as a function of the distance from the source of pollution, allowance being made for the time required to cover that distance.

oxygen absorbed (O.A.) from permanganate A unit (P.V.), similar to biological oxygen demand, expressing the amount (in mg) of potassium permanganate, as oxygen equivalent, required to oxidize the organic matter content of one litre of water under acid conditions. According to Hungarian Standards, for drinking water, this may amount to 1.5–3.0 mg/l. In the U.K. this long-established method refers to O.A. at 27°C, in 4 h. Other countries estimate the O.A. after 30 min at 100°C.

oxysphere A concept introduced by Brycenko (1967) for that part of the biosphere which is rich in oxygen.

panmictic population A group of individuals of common origin, in which all have the chance of mating and reproduction. Within this group there is no obstacle to free genetic recombination.

parabiosphere Biosphere layer above 9,000 m, in which life exists in a certain "latent" (dormant) form. Spores, bacteria and fungi can be found in this zone.

parasites Organisms that live in or on another organism.

parc national See national park.

parthenogenesis Reproduction, without fertilization, by means of egg cells which are capable of direct development.

pathogen Pathogenic effect of microorganisms in another living organism.

PCB Polychlorinated Biphenyl, an organic liquid, the chemical structure of which is similar to that of DDT. It has been manufactured since 1930 and although now only used as an insulator, it was previously widely used in plastics, paints and as a heat transfer fluid. Its incorporation into human and animal organisms is slower than that of DDT, however it can persist in the living organism, practically, until its death. Its toxicity and wide distribution has been recognized relatively late. Since 1971, it has been manufactured only for restricted specific uses.

pelagic Open sea, an area lying far from the coast and marine life in the upper layers.

periphyte The community of living organisms which forms a living coating on stones, bridges and the substratum: algae and attached diatoms, mosses, liver- and stone worts.

permanent hybridity See hybridity.

persistence Long-term persistence of plant protection chemicals, and of other chemical compounds which remain in an unchanged state over a long period.

pesticides The collective name of all those chemicals that are used for plant protection and against the pathogens of human and animal diseases. Pesticides are known under the following collective names: insecticide (against insects), fungicide (against fungi) and herbicide (against weeds). According to their effectiveness on pests, the most common types of pesticides are classified as follows: acaricide (mites killer for mites which mainly infest fruit trees); algicide (algae); antibiotic or antiviral agent (virus); aphicide (plant lice-aphids); avicide (Corvidae — poisons used to kill predatory birds and other bird pests); bactericide (bacteria); biocide (killing all living organisms e.g. antimildew agent); fungicide (plants and seed dressing); herbicide (grasses); larvicide (larvae); miticide (for control of mites); molluscicide (Mollusca, Gastropoda); nematicide (nematoda); ovicide (egg and cyst killer); ovolarvicide (egg and larvae killer); rodenticide (rodents including rats); sylvanicide (arboreous vegetation); tickicide or ixodicide (for control of ticks).

pesticide resistance The ability of insects and weeds to resist the effect of chemicals used against them.

pesticide residue Chemical and pesticide residue in foods. Certain pesticides may be accumulated in different plant and animal products. FAO, jointly with WHO, has determined the limit values for permissible amounts of residues in foods. For U.S.A. see note under DDT.

pesticide rotation Successive application of plant-protecting chemicals containing different active substances, on a given area in order to eliminate resistant species and any reduction in the number of the individuals of useful species and also to prevent the killing of these useful species.

petrol A distilled product of crude oil. The octane number of the petrol of motorcars is improved by the addition of the tetraethyl compound of lead. 1 kg petrol contains 0.4 g of lead. When the engine is running, $^3/_4$ of this lead is introduced into the atmosphere through the exhaust, some of this being deposited on food and absorbed in the lungs.

pH value The negative logarithm of the hydrogen ion concentration of solutions. Its range is from 0 to 14. Values under 7 indicate acidity, 7 is neutral, values above 7 indicate an alkaline chemical reaction.

phagoinhibitor A substance that helps to reduce an insect or other animal's appetite.

phenol (C_6H_5OH), crystalline substance with a characteristic odour. Frequent starting raw material for the plastic, dye and pharmaceutical industry, as well as for the manufacture of plant protection materials. A dangerous water pollutant.

phenotype The sum of the external and inner structural or functional properties of the organism, the result of the interaction between the genotype and its controlling environmental factors.

pheromone A substance excreted by insects, or other animals, in minute amounts, which transmit information to members of the same species that may be near the excreter.

phosphorus In compounds such as phosphate, a wide-spread element in the form of its compounds both inorganic and organic. These are vital components of human, animal and plant organisms. Living organisms obtain their phosphorus requirements directly or indirectly through the mediation of plants. Phosphorus compounds are introduced into waters by soil erosion and the leaching of fertilizers. The phosphorus content of sewage is derived, mainly, from faeces and detergents. Phosphates play an important role in the eutrophication of lakes.

phosphate stripping A method for the elimination of phosphate compounds from water. Bacteria are introduced into the chemically purified sewage, vhich consume phosphorus compounds. The activated sludge is then separated, most of it being recycled. Phosphorus compounds can be extracted from their highly concentrated solutions by a relatively simple and expeditious method.

photosynthesis Synthesis of energy-rich organic compounds, in green plants, from inorganic matter (carbon dioxide and water) using solar energy.

physiographic factors See orographic factors

phytoncide, insecticide of vegetable origin Pyrethrum, derris etc. oils, organic acids, alkaloids and glycosides, with biocidal properties, extractable from or excreted by green plants.

phytocoenology Science of plant communities and their classification.

phytography A biological science, comprising several specializations, which studies the plant kingdom.

phytomass The amount of living organic matter of plants to be found on a given area at a specific time.

phytoplankton Floating aquatic plant organisms of microscopic size (*see* plankton).

phytophagous Consumers of plant organisms.

plankton The entity and community of very small, floating plants (bacteria, algae, and fungi) and minute animals (protozoa, crustaceans and larvae) that populate an aquatic environment. They play an important role in the biological self-purification of waters. They react sensitively to qualitative changes in water quality (pollution) and consequently, they are good biological indicators.

plant protection The science of the protection of plants of economic importance and the prevention of the harmful effect of plant pests.

plastic Substances containing organic macromolecule (polymers) produced from natural or artificial raw materials, which have good characteristics of durability and insulation. The majority of them cannot be decomposed biologically.

plume Characteristic distribution pattern of substances emitted by chimneys and stacks as a visible cloud.

PNDB Decibel of Perceived Noise Level, the unit of noise intensity.

pollution An anthropogenic ecological factor, that causes a changing, qualitative deterioration of natural environmental factors (air, water, soil). These ecological factors or physical conditions, that are vital for the living organism, can change to such an extent that harm is caused to living organisms and may result in their death.

pollution control An action taken to prevent, to reduce or eliminate sources or the amount of pollution.

polyelement See macro-element.

polymorphism The simultaneous occurrence of different varieties of a particular character at a frequency which cannot have been derived either from mutation or from gene flow.

polyploidy A state in which the cells of the organisms contain more than two genomes, i.e. sets of chromosomes. According to the genome number tri-, tetra-, penta- and hexaploidy, etc. can be distinguished.

polysaprobic Organisms living in intensively polluted waters (*see* saprobic system).

population A group of individuals, standing in a more or less close relationship, with a common origin, which, together with a long series of descendants, generally constitutes one reproductive community.

population dynamics Regular changes in the size (number of individuals), composition, interrelationships, external and internal factors of populations.

population ecology The study of the factors that affects individuals of one species in relation to their environment.

potassium Its compounds can be found only in nature. With N and P, it is one of the most important biogenic elements of plants. It can accumulate in plants (algae) up to a concentration of 1–3%.

potassium permanganate Dark-violet crystal, strong oxydizing agent and disinfectant. It destroys organic matter.

preferential mating Mating of individuals of a certain genotype or phenotype at a frequency higher than the mean.

primary consumers In the ecosystem, primary consumers are herbivores. The energy fixed in them is transmitted to the following members of the food chain, the secondary carnivores (consumers).

probiosphere According to Kovalsky's definition, it is that part of the Earth's crust from which the biosphere has emerged.

production The mass of a certain plant or animal species on a given area. The changing weight of living matter during a unit period of time.

production biology Science which studies matter and energy flow and the production of biocoenoses.

production, primary The total rate of assimilation of organic matter formed by the producers in the ecosystem. The total amount of fixed organic matter, including that consumed in metabolism.

production, secondary The amount of organic matter produced by consumers and decomposers in a definite period of time.

productivity The amount of biomass produced during a definite time-interval (day, year).

producer Autotrophic higher plants or plants at a lower level in the ecosystem, which transform the radiant energy of the sun, parallel with the uptake of carbon dioxide from the air, water and mineral nutrients, into organic matter and potential energy.

Programme on Man and the Biosphere An international research programme, launched in 1971–72 by UNESCO. Its main objective is a more intensive protection of the environment of man and natural resources against the detrimental effects of increasing population and industrial production.

protection of the environment The total range of regulations meant to preserve the environment for man, in a definite state, or to create such living conditions which are essential for the existence of mankind. It is the task of environmental control to protect the biosphere, the environmental factors (air, water, soil) and vegetation, as well as fauna, against harmful anthropogenic impacts. The necessity of environment control is underlined by the fact that the increasing world population pollutes the environment to an increasing extent. Environmental control also includes measures taken to eliminate the build-up of pollutants in the environment.

PVC Polyvinylchloride, a plastic consisting of carbon, hydrogen and chlorine. In sheet form it is used mainly in packaging. It is a common solid waste that decomposes slowly. When being burnt, chlorine and in the presence of water vapour, hydrochloric acid is produced.

putrefaction The anaerobic decomposition of protein compounds by microorganisms.

pyramids ecological See ecological pyramids.

radiation injury Injury of the living organism which is caused by radiation. Radiation is very harmful to bone marrow, lymphatic tissues and leucocytes (white blood cells).

radiation load (a) The loading of living organisms due to naturally occurring radioactive substances: 90 mrem /year and by cosmic radiation 30 mrem/ year *(b)* The artificial loading of living organisms by artificial radiation: 1 mrem/ year, e.g. by the fission products from atomic reactors /20 mrem/ year, etc. Maximum permissible body burdens are listed by ICRP.

radioactive pollution Isotopes, emitting radioactivity, which can be introduced into natural water courses by the effluent discharges from industrial sites and from public health institutions (hospitals, etc.).

radioactive wastes Unusable solid or liquid wastes, which are polluted by or contain radioactive matters: the products of the utilization of radioactive matters. As the harmful effect of radioactive wastes is persistent, their long-term storage is necessary. This purpose is served by the socalled "isotope-cemeteries" and abandoned quarries.

radioactivity Radioactive elements emit a large amount of radiation. The biological effect of radiation depends on the type (relative biological efficiency) and on the intensity of radiation. In large dosages, radioactivity destroys the cells of living organisms.

radioecology A new branch of ecology which studies the impact of radioactive pollutants and radioactive matter on the biosphere.

RBE Relative Biological Effectiveness, the effect of different types of radiation on the living organism. Its value denotes the biological efficiency of a particular radiation, in comparison with changes brought about by a specified dose of X-radiation.

recessive An inheritable external or internal structural or functional factor (allele) which, in contrast to its converse, (the dominant allele) is not evident in the phenotype of a heterozygous individual.

recombination Formation, in the offspring, of combinations of characters not present in the parents. It is based on the separation of the loci of chromosomes in meiosis, which is followed by a random assortment of different sorts of gametes at fertilization.

recuperation The return of dead organic matter into the nutrient cycle by way of the so-called recuperants, e.g. detritus-feeding organisms.

recreational forest See forest recreational

rem The unit of the biological efficiency of ionizing rays. 1 rem denotes a dose of the ionizing radiation, the biological efficiency of which equals 1 rad. (rad = the product of the dose equivalent to 0.01 joule of energy, absorbed by 1 kg of the test-medium, multiplied by an empirically determined value.).

repellent Insect repelling agent, the odour of the plant protection agent repels the pest.

reserve natural See nature reserve

residual Chemical residue, e.g. the amount of pesticides retained in food, plants, crops, atmosphere, in the soil and in waters.

residual oil A residue of crude oil distillation, which can be fractionated further or utilized for heating.

respiration The process whereby living organisms take in oxygen from the environment and give off carbon dioxide.

rodenticide See pesticide

salt (NaCl) Colourless, odourless crystal, in an unpurified form it is used for the de-icing of roads in winter (*see* de-icing salts).

salt-load (-burden) Salt accumulation in soil and in surface and ground waters. It is introduced into surface waters mainly by factories, while the increased chloride load of ground waters, above the background level, may result from the de-icing salt applied in winter or by infiltration from estuaries or from the sea.

Salmonella The species of pathogenic bacteria included in this genus produce internal toxins that cause serious infections /typhoid, food poisoning (gastro-enteritis), etc./ — *S. typhi, S. paratyphi.*

sanitation See hygiene

saprobic system Biological classification for the qualitative assessment of waters. Waters, depending on the degree of pollution, contain characteristic living organisms. On the basis of the organisms occurring in waters, they are ranked into the following categories of quality: 1. Oligosaprobic: clear water with no, or only very slight degree of pollution and a low content of nutrient salts. Such waters can be characterized by the high, dissolved O_2-content, the occurrence of diatoms, the number of bacteria in them is usually below 100/ml. 2. β-mesosaprobic: moderately polluted waters, the dissolved oxygen content being still high. The occurrence of green algae, snails, crabs, fishes and aquatic vegetation is characteristic of them. 3. α-mesosaprobic: polluted waters, with a not too high content of dissolved oxygen, generally below 50% of saturation. Flagellates and ciliates being typical organisms present. The bacterial count is normally greater than 100,000/ml. 4. Polysaprobic: the water is strongly polluted and the O_2-content low or absent. The concentration of ammonia is frequently high, the bacteria culture count can exceed 1 million/ml. 5. Antisaprobic: the waters are completely devoid of life and described as "dead". They are polluted to such an extent, that no organism is capable of living in them. The organisms belonging to each category of the saprobic system can be used as biological indicators. Their predominance or occurrence in significant quantities indicates a particular degree of pollution.

saprophagous Organisms that consume dead or decaying organic matter including midge larvae: blood-worms, etc.

saprophile Organisms, particularly bacteria and fungi, that live on decaying matter or inhabit putrid matter.

saprophyte A plant living on decaying matter.

saprozoic An animal living on decaying matter.

SCIBP Scientific Committee of International Biological Programme, a special committee established, within ICSU, in 1963.

SCOPE Scientific Committee on Problems of the Environment, a special committee established within ICSU in 1969 for the co-ordination of research connected with environmental control.

secondary consumers Animals (carnivores) feeding upon plant-eating organisms (herbivores, e.g. aphids).

secondary productivity The sum of organic matter production by consumers and reducers.

sedimentation The settling of particles suspended in a liquid (in a river, lake or sewage treatment plant) in the case of air pollution, the amount of particulate pollutants.

selection The emergence of such individuals and genotypes in the gene pool of successive generations, which have greater vitality and produce more viable offspring with a greater power of adaptation. Its three basic components are (*see* chapter 4): 1. Stabilizing or normalizing selection: this favours variants that are near the mean of the population the extreme variants, the rarest genotypes, being eliminated. As a consequence, in the next generation, the range of variation decreases, while the mean remains unchanged. 2. Directional selection: where progressive changes are taking place, the advantageous (positive) variants of the population are favoured, the weaker (negative) variants are eliminated or vice-versa. Consequently, the range of variance remains unchanged in the progeny, though the peak of the distribution curve is shifted in either a positive or negative direction. 3. Disruptive or diversifying selection: the extreme variants, with higher adaptive values, are favoured, while those variants close to the average are eliminated. As a consequence, the range of variation increases in the progeny although the mean of the whole population remains unchanged. There will then be two peaks in the frequency distribution curve.

selective increase in nutrients A process evident in the complex biological activity of aquatic living organisms, in the course of which the amount of certain polluting, primarily inorganic—though not toxic—matter reaches defined optimum limits. Consequently, water quality will improve, both for the community of living organisms functioning in it and also for human consumption.

seston The total amount of inanimate matter and living organisms suspended in water.

sewage See wastewater

sewage purification The elimination of pollutants from industrial and domestic sewage by different methods (mechanical, physicochemical and biological).

SIL Societas Internationalis Limnologiae, one of its main objectives is to study the biological conditions of rivers and lakes, as well as, water pollution effects.

smog Visible, gaseous and particulate pollution containing SO_2 and CO_2, that, owing to meteorological, orographical and other factors, occurs in the atmosphere of towns and industrial plants. The concentration of pollutants significantly exceeds normal limits over a large area and remains for a longer period. It is toxic for living organisms. (*See* London smog, Los Angeles smog.)

smog alarm At any time when smogs are recognised and the SO_2 content of atmosphere has reached a dangerous concentration, a smog alarm is declared. For example, in the case of a smog alarm, the production of industrial units is stopped. This is done for instance, in the Ruhr area. The smog alarm being announced by radio, press, etc.

smog disaster The occurrence of deaths and illnesses resulting from smog.

smoke The dispersed solid or liquid combustion products (ash, soot, tar, etc.) which can be found in the air.

smut Generally, small flake-like, finely divided, particle of soot, the combustion product of organic materials. One of the air contaminants.

SO$_2$ See sulphur dioxide

sociosphere Cultural landscape transformed by man.

sodium chloride See salt

stenoecius Species with a narrow tolerance limit that exists only under defined environmental conditions and is not capable of surviving even limited changes in the environment (e.g. stenohaline can tolerate only a narrow range of salinity).

Stockholm conference A conference held in Stockholm, in 1972, by member states of the UNO. Here they discussed the problems of environmental control from the point of view of the whole of humanity.

Strontium^{90} Radioactive isotope which, by entering into the food chain, is accumulated in living organisms. In man and animals the accumulation of Strontium^{90} can be observed in the bones.

structural heterozygosity Structural differences (inversion, translocation, or deficiency) between the homologous chromosomes of diploid organisms, which can comprise one or more or even all of the chromosome pairs of homologous genomes.

sulphur dioxide SO$_2$; a combustion product, colourless, pungent gas. One of the main components of polluted air. It is harmful to the human organism, vegetation, buildings, historic monuments.

supergene A group of—also functionally—linked genes which, owing to inversion, are excluded from chiasma formation.

sylvanicide See pesticide.

synecology The ecology of biocoenoses (natural communities, e.g. in a freshwater pond or other habitat).

synanthropic plants Synanthropisation, due to anthropogenic effects, native species disappear (their number decreases), in a given area and are substituted by ubiquitous (weed) species.

technosphere A landscape formed by the artificial environment created by towns, residential areas, industrial plants and agricultural enterprises.

tertiary consumers A collective name for carnivores feeding upon secondary carnivores.

thermal pollution Factories, normal and atomic power stations load the natural waters by heated discharges. In the case of atomic power stations approx. $^2/_3$ of the heat equivalent of the raw material used (in electric power stations half of it) is released in the cooling water, in the form of waste heat, resulting in a thermal load. The warming-up of waters accelerates decomposition processes and causes oxygen deficiency, while certain alga species proliferate excessively.

thermosphere Atmospheric region above the mesosphere, 50 to 85 km above the surface in which, owing to photodissociative processes brought about by solar radiation and high temperature, the dissociation of molecular oxygen takes place.

TLM Tolerance Limit Median, the mean tolerance limit in toxicology. The concentration of toxic matters in water, which causes a 50% death rate under experimental conditions. When defining the limit of tolerance, the time is also considered, so that 24, 48, 96, etc. hours' TLM values can be distinguished. *See* lethal concentration: LC_{50}.

TOC The total amount of organic matter in water, expressed as carbon (mg/l).

tolerance A property of living organisms and their communities (biocoenoses) by which they are capable of tolerating the detrimental effects of an environment within certain limits.

TOVALOP Tanker Owners' Voluntary Agreement Concerning Liability for Oil Pollution. An agreement made by oil carriers and by the oil industry for the prevention of marine oil pollution.

toxaphene (U.K.: camphecor) a chlorinated camphene, applied against the insect pests of *Papilionaceae* (vetches, garden and field peas, etc.) and other agricultural crops such as cotton. It is highly poisonous to warm-blooded animals. Certain vegetable (cucumber) and fruit species (stone fruits) are sensitive to toxaphene, and this insecticide can also be one of the causes of fish kills.

trophic levels In an ecosystem it means nutrition at identical levels, e.g. herbivora represent one (the second) trophic level of the food chain.

troposphere The lowest layer of the atmosphere, variable but approx. 15 km thick, in which the composition of air is almost constant and in which almost all weather phenomena take place.

UNEP United Nations Environment Programme. An organization that was established at the Environmental Control Conference of the UNO in Stockholm in 1972. The secretariat is in Nairobi (Kenya).

UNESCO United Nations Educational Scientific and Cultural Organization, an organization founded in 1946, within the framework of the UNO.

UNDP United Nations Development Programme.

UNIDO United Nations Industrial Development Organization.

UNO United Nations Organization, the world organization of independent states, which was founded in 1945, and has its headquarters in New York.

urban ecosystem An artificial ecosystem created completely by man. It has no regulating or self-sustaining system. Massive energy flow and an interrupted or distorted food chain distinguish it from the natural ecosystem or from those only slightly affected by man's activities. Among the biotic factors, the number of producers is extremely small, the consumer being man itself. The reducers are almost completely missing

urbanization The development of urban settlements and the consequent process of increasing population density, the concentration of population in large towns, agglomerations and the spreading of the urban way of life.

USPHS United States Public Health Service, part of the Department of Health, Education and Welfare, with an international reputation, one of its responsibilities being the fixing (determination) of drinking water standards.

Vavilov A Russian geneticist after which the Vavilovian gene bank centres are named.

variance A statistical coefficient expressing the distribution of variants around the mean deviation and providing a quantitative measure of the extent of variation (the square of the average of the deviation).

vegetation The flora of a given area or territory.

vinyl chloride $CH_2=CHCl_2$, a gas which is easily polymerized, an important starting material for the manufacture of plastics. In vapour form the monomer (VCM) is highly toxic and the emission from these processes is strictly controlled.

viral agent, anti- See pesticide.

virus Cell parasites, incapable of independent metabolism, assimilation or of reproduction outside of the host cell.

waste A collective name for substances which have already been used. Industrial and commercial solid wastes: the garbage/refuse from factories, offices, carwrecks, etc. Urban solid wastes: domestic, street and market garbage/refuse, bottles and tins, discarded items, PVC-wastes, etc.

wastewater (Sewage); unpurified liquid which is discharged from industrial units, households and the polluted rainfall (stormwater) from urban settlements. Industrial sewage may contain large amounts of toxic pollutants (e.g. from sugar and cellulose factories, abattoirs, etc.), including chemicals and metal salts. Domestic sewage can introduce faeces, detergents, etc. into waters. Atomic power stations introduce warm water into rivers (*see* thermal load). To avoid intensive pollution, it is necessary to purify effluents even before they are discharged from industrial sites. The large amount of organic matter introduced into surface waters accelerates the process of eutrophication.

water H_2O, 71% of the Earth's surface consists of water. Its forms of occurrence are: surface waters (river, lake and sea), spring or borehole (artesian) water and ground water. Its utilization in the form of drinking water is subject to strict regulations (*see* water, drinking).

water, bathing Lake, river or swimming-pool water used for bathing. According to the Hungarian Water Quality Standard, water is suitable for bathing, if the coli number is less than 100/ml, the number of bacteria cultured at 37°C is not more than 20,000/ml and oxygen consumption is not more than 6.0 mg/l.

water, drinking Water used for domestic and food industry purposes. Its parameters in the Hungarian Water Quality Standard are the following: temperature 7–14°C, total hardness 5–15 gdh (German degrees hardness equivalent to 89–267 mg/l, as $CaCO_3$.), pH above 7, biological oxygen demand 1.5 mg/l, the amount of ammonium, sulphide, iron max.: 0.5–0.1 mg/l. It should contain neither matters harmful to human health nor bacteria.

water pollution The deterioration of the physical, chemical and biological properties of surface and ground waters caused by foreign substances, pollutants, which reduce its value from the point of view of utilization.

water protection area Drinking water protection area, in the vicinity of water reservoirs, where the application of pesticides and other poisonous substances, grazing, fertilization, camping etc. are prohibited.

water quality The complex of physical, chemical and bacteriological properties of water. According to the purpose for which water is to be used (drinking water, bathing water, industrial water) different standards regulate the main parameters of water quality. Biological indicators can also be used for the classification of waters, *see* saprobic system.

water, rain Water in a fluid or solid physical state precipitating from atmospheric humidity. Owing to increasing air pollution, rain water contains more and more nitrogen, sulphur and different heavy metals and gives rise to the problems of 'acid rain'.

water type See classification of lakes

weed-killer (herbicide) Weed killing pesticide.

welfare sylviculture Sylviculture which, in addition to the cultivation of the greatest possible quantity and value of wood and other products, i.e. the economic development of forests, simultaneously, secures the preservation, use for leisure activities and possibly the enrichment of intangible assets of the forest, especially, those of its long-term interests.

WFPA World Federation for the Protection of Animals. Its seat is in Zurich.

WHO World Health Organization, a special organization of the UNO, established in 1948, which now has 151 members. It deals with health, medical and epidemiological problems and with environmental control (the impact of water and air pollution on the human organism). Its seat is in Geneva.

WLUS World Land Use Survey. Its seat is in Zurich.

WMO World Meteorological Organization. A special organization of the UNO founded in 1951. Its main function is to co-ordinate work in the field of meteorology and hydrology and to promote research in related activities, e.g. it co-ordinates the study of global air pollution.

WWF World Wildlife Fund. It was founded in 1962 as an affiliated organization of IUCN. It deals with nature and environmental protection, and environmental control and educational activities. Its seat is in Gland (Switzerland).

ZEG Zero Economic Growth. *See* global equilibrium

ZPG Zero Population Growth.

zooplankton See plankton

Subject index